L.F.

DEVELOPMENT OF FISHES
OF THE CHESAPEAKE BAY REGION

AN ATLAS OF EGG, LARVAL, AND JUVENILE STAGES

Part I.

Alice J. Mansueti

Jerry D. Hardy, Jr.

Edited by

Earl E. Deubler, Jr.

STURGEON GAR BOWFIN TARPON BONEFISH HERRINGS ANCHOVIES MUD-MINNOW PIKES LIZARDFISHES MINNOWS SUCKERS SEA CATFISHES CATFISHES

Published by

Natural Resources Institute

University of Maryland

Supported by:

NATURAL RESOURCES INSTITUTE, University of Maryland

NATIONAL SCIENCE FOUNDATION, Grant No. GB2948

INSTITUTE OF MARINE SCIENCES, University of North Carolina

SPORT FISHING INSTITUTE

Printed in United States by Port City Press, Baltimore, Maryland

DEDICATION

This volume is dedicated to Dr. Romeo J. Mansueti who conceived the idea of a compilation of illustrations and descriptions of early developmental stages of fishes of the Chesapeake Bay region and initiated the project. His enthusiastic encouragement and magnetic interest led to active participation of both authors and, after his untimely death, generated their determination to complete this work.

ACKNOWLEDGMENTS

This project would not have been possible without the help and encouragement of many. The authors and editor are particularly grateful to William Massmann of the United States Bureau of Sport Fisheries and Wildlife for his assistance in the critical period following Dr. Mansueti's death, for his help in evolving the format and taxonomic list, and his loan of larval specimens of *Synodus foetens*. William W. Anderson, Frederick H. Berry and Jack Gehringer of the United States Bureau of Commercial Fisheries gave advice on terminology and taxonomy as we began this project, provided encouragement throughout, and, finally, reviewed manuscripts on sturgeon, gar, tarpons, bonefish, herrings, anchovies and lizardfishes. Special thanks go to those others who reviewed separate groups of species: Edward C. Raney, of Cornell University, for reviewing minnows, carps and suckers; E. J. Crossman, of the Royal Ontario Museum, for reviewing pickerels; William Ralph Taylor, of the United States National Museum, for reviewing catfishes; and H. C. Boyar, John E. Watson and Joseph Graham, of the United States Bureau of Commercial Fisheries, for reviewing the *Clupea harengus* manuscript. We appreciate the photographic assistance of Grover Butz, formerly of Chesapeake Biological Laboratory, and the professional advice of August Selckmann, Technical Information Section, Fort Detrick, Maryland. We thank the many individuals on the staff of the Chesapeake Biological Laboratory who willingly answered our innumerable questions, offered helpful suggestions, and contributed original data; in particular, William Dovel, Frank J. Schwartz, and Caldwell D. Meyers. Our summer student aides, Eben Oldmixon and Ellen Kennedy, provided cheerful assistance as did our secretary, Alice Lee Parks, who patiently typed third and fourth drafts of the same manuscripts. We are indebted to L. Eugene Cronin and Ted S. Y. Koo of the Chesapeake Biological Laboratory, and A. F. Chestnut of the Institute of Marine Sciences, University of North Carolina, for their administrative support. Finally, our thanks are extended to all the authors who so kindly gave permission for use of their illustrations; to Oscar E. Sette, for allowing us to use his unpublished notes from the United States Bureau of Commercial Fisheries Laboratory at Woods Hole; to Robert and Nancy Smith who supplied drawings and descriptions of young stages of *Anchoa mitchilli* and *Hybognathus nuchalis;* to personnel of the United States Bureau of Commercial Fisheries Laboratory, Beaufort, North Carolina for specimens of young *Brevoortia tyrannus;* and to personnel of the National Science Foundation and United States National Museum for their helpful suggestions and encouragement.

CONTENTS

INTRODUCTION

Knowledge of early developmental stages of fishes is obviously fundamental to proper understanding of many aspects of fishery biology and ichthyology. It is paradoxical, then, that eggs, larvae, and juveniles of many species of fishes remain completely or essentially unknown and undescribed.

Recognizing this, the late Dr. Romeo J. Mansueti became intimately involved in early life history studies of fishes in the Chesapeake Bay estuary approximately twelve years ago. As his work progressed, he became increasingly aware, not only of lack of good descriptions and illustrations of early developmental stages for many species, but also of a number of other problems associated with such studies: An intensive literature search was often involved in establishing known information on certain wide ranging species; highly important references were often unavailable except through elaborate and, often, time consuming interlibrary loans; existing illustrations were frequently of poor quality; errors of identification existed in the literature; and terminology used to describe the developmental sequence or morphological features of early stages of fishes was inconsistent.

To help alleviate these problems, Dr. Mansueti developed the concept of an atlas of egg, larval, and juvenile stages of fishes of the Chesapeake Bay region. The most pertinent information would be compiled from a wide variety of published sources and supplemented with unpublished, original data wherever available. Accordingly, an exhaustive survey of the literature and accumulation of all available data and illustrations was begun. Much of this preliminary work had been accomplished before Dr. Mansueti's death in 1963. The authors have relied heavily upon Dr. Mansueti's file, although they have made some modifications in his original format.

While pursuing the literature survey, the great geographic and temporal diversity of the literature and historical trends of development of life history studies as a specialized discipline of ichthyology were emphasized. Generally, major works on early developmental stages of fishes began to appear with greater regularity both in Europe and in North America during the last half of the nineteenth century and the first years of the twentieth century. In this period, studies on fish eggs and larvae were directed primarily toward anadromous and fresh water species, presumable because of greater ease in collecting specimens. These works include the first important contributions on the sturgeon, *Acipenser oxyrhynchus* (Agassiz, 1879; Balfour and Parker, 1881, 1882;

Dean, 1895a and Ryder, 1888); the goldfish, *Carassius auratus,* (Ryder, 1887; and Watase, 1887); the carp, *Cyprinus carpio,* (Ehrenbaum, 1909): the mudminnow, *Umbra pygmaea,* (Carbonnier, 1874); the white catfish, *Ictalurus catus,* (Ryder, 1883, 1887) and a number of clupeid fishes (Ryder, 1882a, 1887; and Price, 1907).

Early life histories of marine species were generally not as well documented during this period, although some excellent papers on commercially important species such as the sea herring, *Clupea harengus,* were available (Brooks, 1885, 1886b; Kupffer, 1878) as were some well-illustrated monographs on early development of a number of teleosts from the English Channel (Cunningham, 1889) and the North Sea (Ehrenbaum, 1909). Many of these papers demonstrate the importance of early European studies towards the knowledge of North American species.

It is interesting that a large number of classic monographs and shorter papers of this period dealt exclusively with development of two of the most primitive fish in this volume; the bowfin, *Amia calva,* and the longnose gar, *Lepisosteus osseus.* A perusal of their reference citations show over twenty-five major papers published in these years: In England (Dean, 1896; Balfour and Parker, 1881; and Parker, 1882); in Germany (Fullerborn, 1894; Eycleshymer, 1899; Sobotta, 1896; Allis, 1899; Heronimus, 1911, and Brachet, 1912); in Italy (Lanzi, 1909); and in North America (Agassiz, 1879; Allis, 1889; Beckwith, 1907; Dean, 1895a, 1895b, 1899; Eycleshymer and Wilson, 1909; Hay, 1895; Phelps, 1900; Reighard, 1900, 1903; and Whitman and Eycleshymer, 1897). Some were well illustrated broad studies of the morphology and histology of all phases of development; others detailed investigations on some circumscribed aspect of development such as osteology. The net result of this concentrated effort was that these two species were among the first to have well documented early life histories.

During the last fifty years, United States biologists have continued to accumulate knowledge of early life history stages of both fresh water and marine species. An excellent review of early life histories of a number of fresh water species was presented by Adams and Hankinson in 1928; however, this paper dealt primarily with behavior and ecology. Descriptive morphologic studies of eggs, larvae, and young of fresh-water species were greatly advanced in 1932 when Marie Poland Fish presented descriptions of at least some early developmental stages of sixty-two species from Lake Erie. Since then

1

individual accounts of a number of other fresh water species have become available.

Similarly, work progressed on estuarine and marine species of Atlantic coastal waters with such major contributions as Kuntz (1914) and Kuntz and Radcliffe (1917) describing early life history stages of fourteen species of fish collected along the coast of North Carolina, Hildebrand and Cable (1934) decribing early development of fourteen more species of this same area, and Pearson (1941) presenting information on young stages of thirty-one species of lower Chesapeake Bay.

More recently, others have contributed important studies based on data and specimens accumulated in Atlantic coastal waters. This extensive list includes the work of Alexander (1961) on the bonefish, *Albula vulpes;* Harrington (1958) and Wade (1962) on the tarpon, *Megalops atlantica;* Gibbs (1954) on the lizardfishes, Synodontidae; and Mansueti (1962) on the hickory shad, *Alosa mediocris.*

In addition, recent literature published in foreign countries, primarily sea-oriented nations such as Russia, Scotland, Canada, Japan and Italy, has contributed greatly to our understanding of commercially important species such as the herring (Blaxter, 1956, 1957, 1962; Harder, 1952, 1953, 1954; Hempel, 1953; Krevanovski, 1956a, 1956b; and Parrish, et.al., 1959) and the goldfish (Kajishima, 1958, 1960; Okada, 1960; and Khan, 1929) while adding valuable new information to other less significant species such as the ladyfish, *Elops saurus,* (Alikunhi and Rao, 1951), and the bonefish, *Albula vulpes,* (Uchida, 1958).

It is evident, then, that ichthyologists throughout the world are becoming increasingly aware of the importance of detailed descriptions of early development of fishes and vigorous efforts are being made by both marine and fresh-water fisheries personnel to expand our present fund of knowledge. Despite this current worldwide effort, early life histories of many species are still completely unknown and much work remains.

OBJECTIVES

We have attempted primarily to present a well-illustrated work manual for use of biologists in identifying early developmental stages of fishes. We have also tried to supplement published descriptions with new information on early life histories whenever possible, to indicate areas where further investigation is needed, to define and standardize terms directly applicable to young stages of fish, and to present a comprehensive bibliography covering works on life history problems of the species included.

METHODS

The present volume summarizes information on early development of forty-five species of fishes from fourteen families arranged in phylogenetic order (Acipenseridae through Ictaluridae). A species is represented if any or all of its life history stages occur in the Chesapeake Bay or its tributaries to and including tidal-fresh water, or in estuarine and coastal waters of New Jersey, Delaware, Maryland and Virginia (Fig. 1). We have excluded rare and poorly known species such as the shortnosed sturgeon, *Acipenser brevirostris;* species recorded only from extreme northern or southern limits of the region and unknown in the Chesapeake Bay, such as the American smelt, *Osmerus mordax;* and certain strictly oceanic deep-sea forms, typified, perhaps, by some of the Myctophidae, which may occasionally undertake shoreward excursions over the continental shelf.

The phylogenetic sequence and nomenclature employed essentially agree with that set forth in "A List of Common and Scientific Names of Fishes from the United States and Canada" (American Fisheries Society, 1960). We digress from this list in recognizing the Atlantic and Pacific herring as distinct species (see Berry 1964), and in substitution of the name *Etrumeus teres* for *Etrumeus sadina* as suggested by Whitehead (1963, 1965). We have confined ourselves to the species level except for the redfin pickerel, *Esox americanus americanus* in which, in nonintergrade areas, there are apparently definite and easily recognized differences between it and the subspecies *vermiculatus,* particularly in pigmentation of juveniles (see Crossman 1966).

SOURCES OF MATERIAL

Species accounts summarize information accumulated from an extensive survey of world literature, from unpublished manuscripts and illustrations resulting from projects at the Chesapeake Biological Laboratory, and from similar unpublished material made available through various contributors. The original source of all published information is indicated by superscript numbers corresponding to appropriately numbered reference listings at the end of each species account. Original, unpublished contributions are indicated by the initials of the contributor as follows:

AJM   Alice Jane Mansueti, Chesapeake Biological Laboratory, Solomons, Maryland.

ECR   Edward C. Raney, Cornell University, Ithaca, New York.

EJC   E. J. Crossman, Royal Ontario Museum, Toronto, Canada.

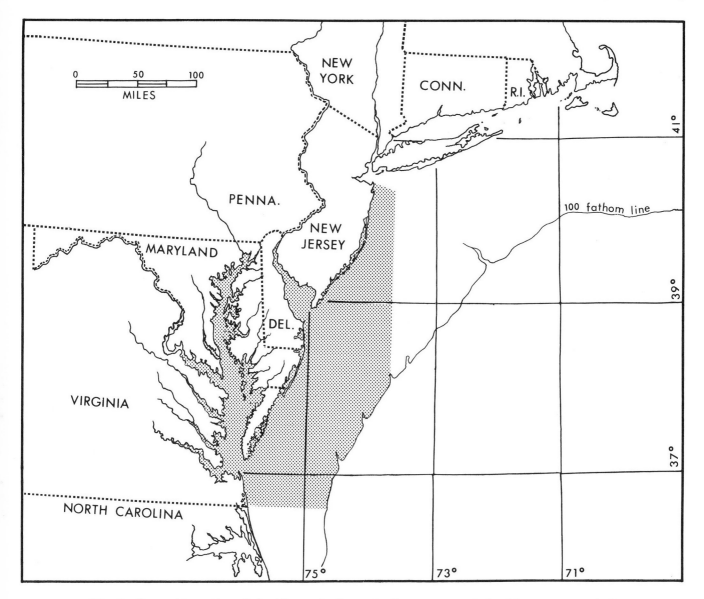

Fig. 1. Geographic position of the Chesapeake Bay and adjacent region of the Atlantic Ocean. Shading delineates the area considered as the *Chesapeake Bay Region.*

FHB Frederick H. Berry, United States Bureau of Commercial Fisheries, Biological Laboratory, Miami, Florida.

FJS Frank J. Schwartz, Chesapeake Biological Laboratory, Solomons, Maryland.

HCB H. C. Boyar, United States Bureau of Commercial Fisheries, Biological Laboratory, Boothbay Harbor, Maine.

JDH Jerry D. Hardy, Jr., Chesapeake Biological Laboratory, Solomons, Maryland.

NSS Nancy S. Smith, 7322 Eisenhower Court, Camp Springs, Maryland.

ORS Oscar R. Sette, United States Bureau of Commercial Fisheries, Biological Laboratory, Stanford, California.

RJM Romeo J. Mansueti, late of Chesapeake Biological Laboratory, Solomons, Maryland.

WLD William L. Dovel, Chesapeake Biological Laboratory, Solomons, Maryland.

WHM William H. Massmann, United States Bureau of Commercial Fisheries, Washington, D. C.

WRT W. Ralph Taylor, United States National Museum, Washington, D. C.

All statements are annotated by either a number(s) or initials.

Some species accounts include additional references which, although not used directly in the text, give supplementary information on some aspect of the life history.

Because we wanted to present as much illustrative material as possible, we have, in the case of certain species with a limited selection of illustrations available, made the decision that a poor illustration is sometimes better than none. We feel that this decision is justified in that it serves to emphasize the need for further study of these species while presenting the best illustrations currently available. Occasionally halftone illustrations have been replaced with line tracings and original line drawings have been modified slightly to emphasize details or correct obvious errors. All such modifications are noted in the appropriate figure legend.

TERMINOLOGY

Terms used in published sources have been converted to conform with our standards wherever this was necessary and could be done with impunity. If specific definitions have not been provided, it is assumed that they follow the most widely accepted interpretations. Generally our usage of names of anatomical features and methods of counting and measuring follow those of Hubs and Lagler (1958). However, their terms, which apply more specifically to adult forms, must frequently be modified or replaced by different terms in describing early developmental stages.

In Fig. 2, the typical anatomy and development of a teleostean egg, a yolk-sac larva and a larva are illustrated. All major anatomical features clearly recognizable at various stages have been included, although structures and organs illustrated will not necessarily be evident in all specimens. Anatomical and developmental terms in the figure are defined in the glossary. Measurements in Fig. 2 and counts and measurements used in the text which are either modified from or excluded by Hubbs and Lagler (1958) are defined as follows:

Total Length: Straight-line distance from the most anterior part of head to tip of tail. All length measurements given in older reference before the adoption of standard length are assumed to be total length.

Standard Length: In larval forms prior to completion of the hypural complex, the straight-line distance from the most anterior part of head to tip of urostyle or notochord; after completion of the hypural complex, the straight-line distance from most anterior part of head to end of hypural plate.

Head Length: Before development of the operculum, the distance from the most anterior part of head to most posterior part of auditory vesicle; following operculum formation, the distance from the most anterior part of head to the most posterior part of opercular membranes (excluding spines).

Snout to Vent Length: Distance from the most anterior aspect of snout to posterior margin of anus. The precise method of measuring is often not stated.

Egg Diameter: In essentially spherical eggs, the greatest diameter of the egg capsule. In obviously elliptical eggs, two measurements are given: The length of the longest axis, the *Greatest Diameter* or *Major Axis;* the length of the shortest axis, the *Least Diameter* or *Minor Axis.*

Yolk Diameter: Greatest diameter of the yolk. This measurement is taken most accurately prior to embryo formation when margins of the yolk are clearly defined.

Oil Globule Diameter: Greatest diameter of oil globule.

Width of Perivitelline Space: Distance between egg capsule and yolk, expressed in our account as the ratio of width of perivitelline space to radius of egg capsule.

Hatching Length: Standard or total length at time of hatching; sometimes stated as mean or average length and so indicated.

Length at end of Stage: The longest recorded specimen that can be considered within a certain stage.

Size Range of Stage: The smallest and largest recorded individuals that can be considered within a particular stage.

Preanal Myomeres: The number of myomeres between the most anterior myoseptum and a vertical line drawn from posterior margin of anus. This excludes the triangular area behind the auditory vesicle and anterior to first myoseptum.

Postanal Myomeres: The number of myomeres between a vertical line drawn from posterior margin of anus and the most posterior myoseptum. Last myoseptums in yolk-sac larva and early larva are frequently obscured, resulting in a low count.

Total Myomeres: The sum of preanal and postanal myomeres.

INFORMATION PRESENTED

Although the present volume emphasizes morphological descriptions of early developmental stages of fishes, we feel that other aspects of the biology of species involved are of direct or potential value in the collection and identification of eggs, larvae, and juveniles. For this reason we have elected to include adult descriptions and comments on distribution, ecology, and spawning.

Adult descriptions are limited to brief summaries of extremes of meristic and morphometric data, and general comments on significant morphological features, pigmentation, and maximum size. Such descriptions are critical

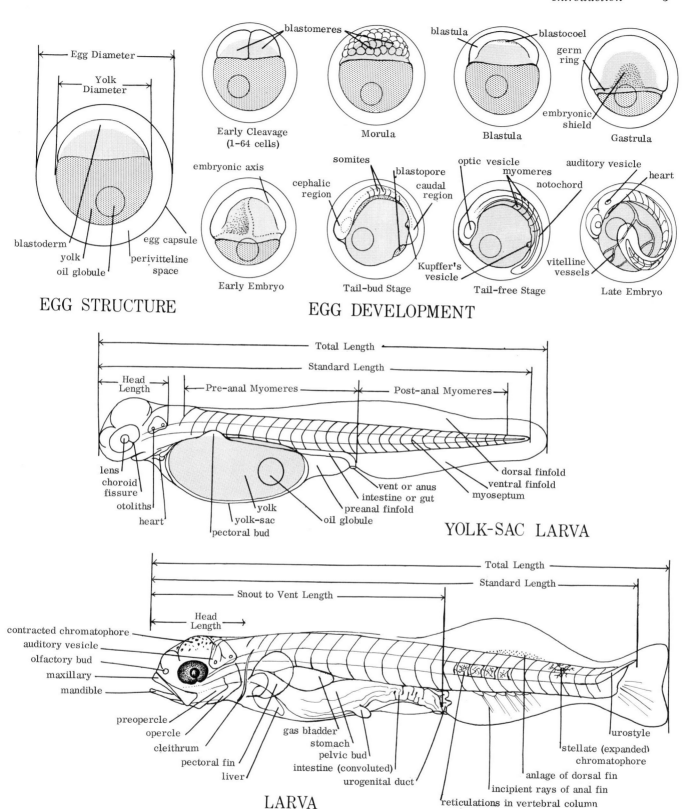

EGG STRUCTURE

EGG DEVELOPMENT

YOLK-SAC LARVA

LARVA

Fig. 2. Diagrammatic representation of morphology and development of egg and larval stages of a typical teleost.

in identifying prejuveniles and juveniles in which adult meristic counts and morphometric relationships have or are becoming established and major details of adult pigmentation are developing. They are also of considerable value in identification of larvae of some species, especially where indications of adult morphometry are evident early in development. Further, they serve to emphasize peculiarities in development as, for example, in *Megalops atlantica* and *Amia calva* in which certain adult fin ray counts are notably lower than the counts of developing or definitive rays in juveniles of the same species.

Both total and regional distribution of each species are delineated, and summaries of available information on habitat, movements, and environmental limits of both adults and early life history stages are presented. Specific details of regional distribution are given only for those species which have scant documentation, are of unusual occurrence, or are limited to certain areas within the Chesapeake Bay region.

Location, season, and time of spawning are briefly reviewed as are temperatures, salinities, and depths which limit spawning activity. In some cases the spawning area has been deduced from the presence of eggs and/or yolk-sac larvae rather than from observations of actual spawning activity. This deduction can be quite valid, particularly in species with short incubation periods which do not allow enough time for extensive movement away from spawning grounds.

We have attempted to present complete descriptions of all developmental stages from ripe ovarian eggs to juveniles. Detailed data on meristic, morphometric, and pigmentary characteristics of early developmental stages are presented wherever possible. Identifications should ideally be based on a combination of these diverse characters in order to offset the influence of genetic or environmentally induced variations which frequently occur. Such variations are particularly evident with pigmentation patterns.

Early post-hatching stages are described in the literature in terms of both length and age, depending on individual authors. Because of variability of growth in young fish, we have elected to emphasize length rather than age since, in a given species, morphologic development of equal-size specimens will be approximately the same, while specimens of identical age may show distinct meristic and morphological variations resulting from their developing in different environments.

To facilitate a logical and consistent discussion of all species within the same framework we have established our own definitions of stages within the developmental sequence. Terminology of various authors has been adapted to these definitions, although we recognize that

such decisions can be quite arbitrary when existing illustrations and morphologic data represent a limited number of specimens. It must be emphasized also that transition from one stage to another is seldom dramatic but, rather, is characterized by almost imperceptible changes that occur over a relatively long period.

Developmental stages recognized and discussed in the present volume are as follows:

Egg: The egg stage is characterized by presence of an egg capsule and includes all stages from time of capsular formation within the ovary to hatching. The section on eggs describes basic morphology of the egg as well as subsequent morphological changes during embryonic development. It includes also information pertaining to ecology of the egg and length of incubation period relative to developmental temperature.

Immediately after hatching, most fishes pass through a larval period having two distinct phases distinguished by presence or absence of a yolk sac. Hubbs (1943) proposed the terms *prolarvae* and *postlarvae* for these stages, defining them, respectively, as larvae "still bearing yolk," and larvae "following the time of absorption of yolk; applied only when the structure and form continues to be strikingly unlike that of the juvenile." Although our categories are essentially similar, we have elected to use the terms *yolk-sac larva* and *larva* in place of prolarva and postlarva.

Yolk-sac larva: The yolk-sac larva stage begins at time of hatching and continues until the yolk sac is no longer visible. Specimens in this stage are essentially dependent upon yolk for nourishment, but gradually begin feeding by mouth prior to disappearance of the yolk sac.

Larva: The larva stage begins with disappearance of the yolk sac, although vestiges of the yolk may remain in the gut region during the early parts of the stage. Termination of this stage has been variously described by a number of authors (Ahlstrom and Counts, 1955; Berry, 1959; Caldwell, 1962; and Gehringer, 1959a). From their comments and our own observations, we equate termination of the larval stage with acquisition of the adult fin-ray complement. These counts are frequently attained before the rays are fully ossified. We have retained use of such specific terms as leptocephalus, but they are discussed as unique forms within the larval stage.

Prejuvenile: The prejuvenile stage is the intermediate stage between larval and juvenile forms which begins with acquisition of the adult fin-ray complement and continues, with rapid metamorphosis, until the more adult-like form of a juvenile is attained. Hubbs (1958) first proposed the use of the word "prejuvenile" "to cover a diversity of more or less strikingly- often bizarrely-modified pelagic life history stages, of various marine fishes, that are not appropriately termed either post larval or juvenile." We have broadened his concept of prejuvenile stages to include the intermediate period between the larval and typically juvenile form of any species in which it occurs. Fishes in this stage are characterized by an opaque body, inception and often completion of scale formation, differentiation of developing rays into soft-rays and spines, and rapid acquisition of pigmentation, frequently with pigment patterns that are apparent only during this relatively brief phase of development. Various commonly used terms such as "young," "fry," "trans-forming young," "recently formed juveniles," "fingerling," and "early juveniles," may all be applicable to the pre-juvenile stage as we have defined it. In some species a distinct prejuvenile stage cannot be recognized at the end of the larval period since along with acquisition of adult fin-ray counts, other adult meristic counts are complete, and body configuration and proportions are much like the adult.

Juvenile: The juvenile stage begins when the body form closely approximates that of the adult and terminates with attainment of sexual maturity.

GLOSSARY

A. Abbreviation for anal fin.

abbreviate heterocercal. Condition in which the urostyle is prominently flexed upward, only partly invading upper lobe of caudal fin.

adherent. Attached or joined together, at least at one point.

adhesive egg. An egg which adheres on contact to substrate material or other eggs; adhesiveness of entire egg capsule may or may not persist after attachment.

adhesive organ. Specialized attachment structure on snouts of certain larvae; the suctorial disc.

adipose fin. Fleshy, rayless fin on dorsal ridge between dorsal and caudal fins.

adnate. Congenitally united; conjoined.

anadromous. Designating fish which ascend rivers from the sea to spawn.

anal. That which pertains to the anus or vent.

anal fin. The unpaired median fin immediately behind anus or vent.

anal origin. The anterior-most point at which the anal fin attaches to the body.

anlage. Rudimentary form of an anatomical structure; primordium.

anus. External orifice of the intestine; vent.

auditory vesicle. Sensory primordium from which the ear develops; clearly evident during early development.

axillary process. Enlarged, accessory scale attached to the upper or anterior base of pectoral or pelvic fins in certain fishes.

barbel. A fleshy, tactile, elongated process or filament, usually located on lips, chin, or nose of certain fishes.

blastocoel. The cavity of the blastula; segmentation cavity.

blastoderm. Strictly defined as early embryonic tissue composed of blastomeres; generally used to designate embryonic tissue until formation of embryonic axis.

blastodisc. Embryo-forming site of the egg prior to cleavage.

blastomeres. Individual cells formed during cleavage.

blastopore. Opening formed and bordered by the germ ring as it extends over the yolk.

blastula. Stage in embryonic development which represents the final product of cleavage stages, characterized by formation of the blastocoel.

branched ray. Soft ray with two or more branches distally.

branchial arches. Bony or cartilaginous structures, located on each side of the pharynx, that support the gills.

branchiostegals. Elongated bones arranged fan-wise within the branchiostegal membrane; branchiostegal rays.

buoyant egg. An egg that floats freely within the water column; pelagic.

C. Abbreviation for caudal fin.

caudal fin. Tail fin of fishes.

caudal peduncle. Area of a fish between posterior end of anal-fin base and base of caudal fin.

cheek. Lateral surface of head between eye and opercle, usually excluding preopercle.

choroid fissure. Line of juncture of invaginating borders of optic cup; apparent in young fish as a trough-like area below lens.

chromatophores. Pigment-bearing cells; frequently capable of expansions and contractions which change their size, shape, and color.

cleavage stages. Initial stages in embryonic development where division of blastomeres is clearly marked; usually includes 1st through 6th cleavages (2–64 cells).

cleithrum. Prominent bone of pectoral girdle, clearly visible in many fish larvae.

D. Abbreviation for dorsal fin.

demersal egg. An egg which remains on the bottom, either free or attached to substrate material.

dorsal fin(s). Unpaired, rayed, median fin(s) located on the back.

dorsal origin. Point where first dorsal ray or spine attaches to body.

early embryo. Stage in embryonic development characterized by formation of embryonic axis.

egg capsule. Outermost encapsulating structure of the egg, consisting of one or more membranes; the protective shell.

9

emarginate. Notched but not definitely forked, as in the shallowly notched caudal fin of some fishes.

embryonic axis. Primitive differentiation of the embryo; an elongate thickening of blastodermal tissue.

embryonic shield. Thickened shield-like area of the blastoderm at caudal edge of the germ ring.

erythrophores. Red or orange chromatophores.

esophagus. Alimentary tract between pharynx and stomach.

falcate. Deeply concave, as a fin with middle rays much shorter than anterior and posterior rays.

finfold. Median fold of integument which extends along body of developing fishes and from which median fins arise.

FL. Abbreviation for fork length.

ganoid scales. Diamond- or rhombic-shaped scales consisting of bone covered with enamel.

gas bladder. Membranous, gas-filled organ located between the kidneys and alimentary canal in teleosts; air bladder or swim bladder.

gastrula. Stage in embryonic development between blastula and embryonic axis.

germ ring. The thickened rim of the blastoderm evident during late blastula and gastrula stages.

germinal disc. The blastodisc.

gill arch. The branchial skeleton supporting the gill rakers and filaments.

gill rakers. Variously shaped bony projections on anterior edge of the gill arches.

granular yolk. Yolk consisting of discrete units of finely to coarsely granular material.

guanophores. White chromatophores; characterized by presence of iridescent crystals of guanine.

gular fold. Transverse membrane across throat.

gular plate. Bony plate between anterior third of lower jaws, as in *Amia calva.*

heterocercal. Tail in which the urostyle is flexed upward and extends nearly to tip of upper lobe of caudal fin.

HL. Abbreviation for head length.

holoblastic. Type of cleavage in which the entire egg, including the yolk, undergoes division.

hypochord. A transitional rod of cells which develops under the notochord in the trunk region of some embryos.

hypurals. Expanded, fused, haemal spines of last few vertebrae which support caudal fin.

incubation period. Time from fertilization of egg to hatching.

inferior mouth. A mouth located near or on ventral side of head with snout usually overhanging upper lip.

insertion of fin. Line along which a fin is attached to body.

interorbital. Space between eyes over top of head.

iridocytes. Crystals of guanine having reflective and iridescent qualities.

isthmus. The narrow area of flesh in the jugular region between gill cavities.

jugular. Pertaining to the throat.

juvenile. Young fish after attainment of full adult counts and before sexual maturation.

keeled. With a ridge or ridges.

Kupffer's vesicle. A small, vesicular, ventro-caudal pocketing which forms as blastopore narrows.

larva. Young fish between time of hatching and attainment of adult fin-ray compliments.

late embryo. Stage prior to hatching in which the embryo has developed external characteristics of its hatching stage.

lateral line. Series of sensory pores and tubes extending backward from head; complete when line extends to caudal base, incomplete when it does not.

mandible. Lower jaw.

maxillary. Upper jaw.

Meckel's cartilage. Embryonic cartilaginous axis of the lower jaw in bony fishes.

melanophores. Black and brown chromatophores.

meroblastic. Type of cleavage in which only the blastodisc undergoes division.

micropyle. Opening in egg capsule through which spermatozoa enter.

morula. Stage in development of egg in which blastomeres form a mulberry-like cluster.

myomeres. Serial muscle segments of the body of a fish.

myoseptum. Line of connective tissue separating myomeres.

nape. Area on back of fish from occipital region to insertion of dorsal fin in spiny-rayed fish and back to about same length as occiput in soft-rayed fish.

nasal. Pertaining to region of the nostrils.

notochord. Longitudinal supporting axis of body which is eventually replaced by the vertebral column in teleostean fishes.

occipital region. Area on dorsal surface of head of fishes, beginning above or immediately behind eyes and extending backwards to end of head.

oil globule(s). Discrete sphere(s) of fatty material within the yolk.

olfactory buds. Incipient olfactory organs.

optic vesicles. Embryonic vesicular structures which give rise to the eyes.

otoliths. Small, calcareous, secreted bodies within the inner ear.

P. Abbreviation for pectoral fins.

palatine teeth. Teeth on the paired palatine bones in the roof of the mouths of some fishes.

pectoral bud. Swelling at site of future pectoral fin; anlage of pectoral fin.

pectoral fins. Paired fins behind head, articulating with pectoral girdle.

pelvic bud. Swelling at site of future ventral (pelvic) fins; anlage of ventral fin.

pelvic fins. Paired fins articulating with pelvic girdle; ventral fins.

periblast. A layer of tissue between the yolk and cells of blastoderm which is observed as a thin border around blastula.

peritoneum. Membranous lining of abdominal cavity.

perivitelline space. Fluid filled space between egg proper and egg capsule.

pharyngeal teeth. Teeth attached to pharyngeal bones.

predorsal scales. Scales along dorsal ridge between occiput and origin of dorsal fin.

prejuvenile. Young fish in an intermittent stage between a larvae and a juvenile.

primordium. Rudimentary form of an anatomical structure; anlage.

principal ray. Branched or unbranched ray which is not rudimentary.

pronephric ducts. Ducts of pronephric kidney of early stages of fishes.

quadrate. Squarish.

reticulated. Having a network of lines.

scute. Horny or bony plate, often spiny or keeled.

sigmoid heart. The S-shaped heart which develops from the primitive heart tube.

SL. Abbreviation for standard length.

somites. Primitive, segmented, mesodermal tissue along each side of notochord.

stomodeum. Primitive invagination of the ectoderm which will eventually give rise to the mouth.

suctorial disc. Adhesive organ.

tail-bud stage. Stage of embryonic development characterized by a prominent caudal bulge and marked development of cephalic region.

tail-free stage. Stage of embryonic development characterized by separation of the tail from the yolk.

TL. Abbreviation for total length.

urostyle. Elongate last centrum of vertebral column.

V. Abbreviation for the ventral or pelvic fins.

vent. Anus.

ventral fins. Paired fins articulating with the pelvic girdle; pelvic fins.

vitelline vessels. Arteries and veins of yolk region.

villi. Thread-like processes extending from surface of egg capsule of certain fishes.

water-hardening. Expansion and toughening of egg capsule due to absorption of water into the perivitelline space.

xanthophores. Yellow chromatophores.

yolk. Food reserve of embryonic and early larval stages, usually seen as a yellowish sphere diminishing in size as development proceeds.

yolk plug. Yolk within the blastopore.

yolk sac. A bag-like ventral extension of the primitive gut containing the yolk.

yolk-sac larva. A larval fish characterized by the presence of a yolk-sac.

Acipenser oxyrhynchus

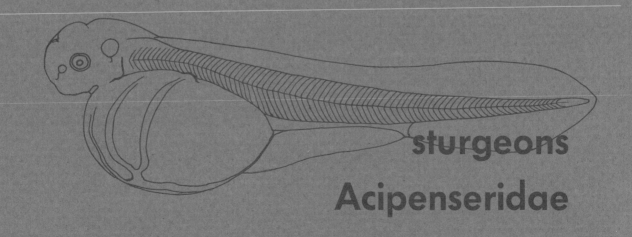

sturgeons

Acipenseridae

ACCOUNTS OF SPECIES

ORDER ACIPENSERIFORMES
Acipenseridae—sturgeons

Atlantic sturgeon   *Acipenser oxyrhynchus* **Mitchill**

ADULT (Fig. 3 A)

D. 30 [4]–46; [8] A. 22–32; P. 40–41; V. 28–29; [14] gill rakers 7–13+9–14 (may include some prejuveniles); dorsal shields 7 [2]–16; [4] lateral shields 24 [2]–36. Body depth 7–10 in length.

Body elongate; [4] more or less pentagonal; [2] head flattened above; eyes small, oval; mouth inferior, sucker-like, lacking teeth; 2 pairs of short, slender barbels in transverse line midway between end of snout and anterior edge of mouth. [4] Successive bucklers in dorsal series touching or overlapping; [6] preanal and post-dorsal shields in double row. [2]

Olive-green, bluish-gray, or brownish above, pale below; iris pale golden; peritoneum nearly white.

Maximum length 4,267 mm [2] to possibly 5,486 mm. [6]

DISTRIBUTION AND ECOLOGY

Range: Nominate subspecies from Atlantic coast of Labrador and Gulf of St. Lawrence to eastern Florida; represented in Gulf of Mexico, Bermuda, and French Guiana by *Acipenser o. desotoi* Vladykov.

Area distribution: Delaware, Virginia, and Maryland seaside; [2] formerly tributaries throughout Chesapeake Bay region, presently restricted to lower part of Bay. [4]

Habitat and movements: Adults—a bottom species closely associated with estuaries but sometimes wandering across continental shelf eastward at least to offshore fishing banks; anadromous, moving toward freshwater in spring, returning to salt water in fall. Maximum depth, 25 fathoms. [6]

Juveniles—may remain in fresh or brackish water until 760–915 mm long, [2,6] sometimes make oceanic excursions of at least 900 miles. [1] Maximum depth at least to 60 feet. [2]

SPAWNING

Location: Brackish or fresh water, [7] possibly preferring brackish, [5] over hard bottom of clay, rubble, gravel or shell [2,7,10] in shallow running water [10] or water up to 5 fathoms deep; possibly in pools below waterfalls. [2,3] Earliest arrivals are said to spawn furthest upstream. [12]

Season: Migrations begin in February in Georgia, April in Chesapeake Bay, May and June in Gulf of Maine. [2] Spawning recorded north of Chesapeake Bay from May to early July depending on locality, with peak activity in late May in Delaware Bay. [3,13]

EGGS (Fig. 3 B,C)

Description: Demersal; adhesive, attached to weeds, stones, shells, sticks, etc.; [2,9] sometimes in stringy clusters or ribbons. [5]

Ripe ovarian eggs—2.6 mm in diameter. [15]

Freshly deposited, unfertilized eggs—globular; light to dark brown; [3] germinal disc evident; [12] 3–9 micropyles. [9]

Fertilized eggs—diameter 2.0 [14]–2.9 mm; [2,9] initially globular, becoming oval as development proceeds; [11] slate-gray [9] or light to dark brown, [2,3,9] with distinct cross- or star-shaped pigment patch at animal pole; egg capsule distinctly 2-layered [9] with outer layer comprised of a viscous substance; strongly adhesive, and firmly attached to substrate within 20 minutes. [10]

Cleavage, modified holoblastic. [16]

Development: At mean temperature 20 C.

1 hour—first cleavage.
1 hour and 15 minutes—second cleavage.
2 hours and 20 minutes—third cleavage.
19 hours—early gastrula.
33 hours—embryo around 90° of egg circumference.
42 hours—pronephric ducts formed.
43 hours—central nervous system formed.
46 hours—optic vesicles formed.
58 hours—blastopore closed.
76 hours—embryo around ca. 320° of circumference.
82 hours—first movement.

Incubation: 92 hours at unspecified temperature; [10] 94 hours at ca. 20 C; [9] ca. 168 hours at 17.8 C. [2]

13

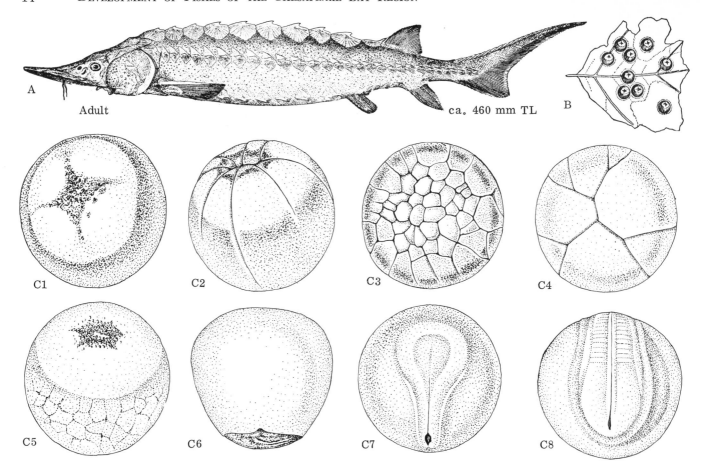

Fig. 3. *Acipenser oxyrhynchus,* Atlantic sturgeon. A. Adult, ca. 460 mm TL. B. Eggs attached to leaf. C. Development of egg at 20 C. Capsule diameter 2.5–2.9 mm; yolk diameter ca. 2.2 mm; egg capsule removed; cleavage modified holoblastic. C1. Egg just before fertilization. C2. Third cleavage, lateral view; second furrow traverses yolk. C3. Sixth cleavage, 4 hours. C4. Sixth cleavage, lower pole. C5. Late blastula, 16 hours. C6. Gastrula, 28 1/2 hours. Dorsal lip of blastopore with indentation. C7. Early embryo, 43 hours. Blastopore still open; early neurenteric canal formed; 8 somites present but indistinguishable in surface view. C8. Early embryo, 48 hours. View of tail region; 20 somites present. (A, *Goode, et al., 1884: pl. 243.* B, *Dean, 1895b: fig. 194.* C, *redrawn after Dean, 1895a: pl. 3.*)

YOLK-SAC LARVAE (Fig. 4 A)

Hatching length ca. 11 mm TL. Duration of stage ca. 6 days.[2]

Yolk sac large, oval, vascular; head not deflected over yolk; mouth formed; eye relatively small; auditory vesicles round, equal to eye; branchial arches concealed by opercular folds; barbels lacking; pectoral buds present; origin of dorsal finfold in occipital region.[3]

Head and tail darkly pigmented, yolk dirty yellow.[11]

LARVAE

Undescribed, except for comment that this species is toothless "except in larval stages." [6]

JUVENILES (Fig. 4 B)

Minimum size tentatively included 60 mm TL.[2]

Head pointed up to ca. 915–2,220 mm TL;[4] snout longer than post-orbital distance in individuals up to 950 mm; interorbital width rather narrow, 22.4–28.4% HL at 60–490 mm.

Age and size at maturity: Females probably at minimum age of 10 years; males at minimum weight of 70 pounds or length of ca. 1,753 mm TL.[2]

LITERATURE CITED

1. Magnin, E., and G. Beaulieu, 1960:251.
2. Vladykov, V. D., and J. R. Greeley, 1963:46–58.
3. Ryder, J. A., 1890:260, 267–8, Pl. 42.

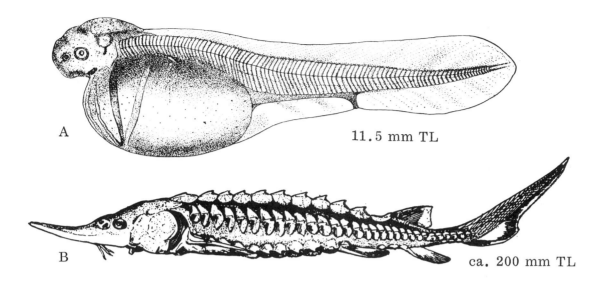

A   11.5 mm TL

B   ca. 200 mm TL

Fig. 4. Acipenser oxyrhynchus, Atlantic sturgeon. A. Yolk-sac larva, 11.5 mm TL, just hatched. B. Juvenile, ca. 200 mm TL, 12 months. (A, *Ryder, 1890: pl. 42, fig. 18.* B, *Dean, 1895b: fig. 302.*)

4. Hildebrand, S. F., and W. C. Schroeder, 1928:72–3, 76.
5. Dean, B., 1893b:71–74.
6. Bigelow, H. B., and W. C. Schroeder. 1953:81–3.
7. Dees, L. T., 1961:4–5.
8. Moore, G. A., 1957:52.
9. Dean, B., 1895a:12, 14.
10. Dean, B., 1893a:473–5.
11. Ryder, J. A., 1888:659–60.
12. Dean, B., 1894:339.
13. Migdalski, E. C., 1962:98–9.
14. Slastenenko, E. P., 1958:27–8.
15. Borodin, N., 1925:186.
16. Lagler, K. F., J. E. Bardach, and R. R. Miller, 1962: 305.

ADDITIONAL REFERENCES

Brice, J. J., 1898; Kirsch, P. H., and M. W. Fordice, 1890.

ORDER SEMIONOTIFORMES
Lepisosteidae—gars

Longnose gar

ADULT (Fig. 5 A)

D. 6–9; A. 8–10; C. 11–14; P. 10–13; V. 6; lateral line scales 57–63; predorsal scales 47–55; transverse scale rows between pelvic and dorsal origins 31–35; gill rakers 14–31. Snout long (67.4–73.8% HL), very narrow (least width, 3.1–4.5% HL).[4] Distance from posterior edge of eye to posterior edge of opercular membrane 3.5 times in HL in fish more than ca. 100 mm long.[5]

Teeth numerous, present on jaws, vomer, and palatines.[1]

Generally olivaceous brown above, white below; vertical fins and body usually with dark spots.[4]

Maximum recorded size 1,524 mm,[4] possibly to ca. 1,830 mm.[1]

DISTRIBUTION AND ECOLOGY

Range: Quebec to Florida, excluding eastern parts of New England states, in the east; Great Lakes region to northern Mexico in the west.[4]

Area distribution: Fresh and brackish tributaries of Chesapeake Bay in Maryland and Virginia;[1,2] Delaware;[20] New Jersey.[19]

Habitat and movements: Adults—clear, low or basic gradient streams;[5] shallow, grassy areas in rivers and lakes;[6] in more or less stagnant water over both muddy and sandy bottoms;[11] shallow mud flats as well as mid-channel areas of streams;[10] sometimes in moderately swift current.[5] Maximum salinity, taken in water which varies from 13–25 o/oo.[9] Apparently migratory during spawning season in rivers, and often runs up smaller streams tributary to Lake Erie.[12]

Larvae—recently hatched larvae attached by adhesive organ to aquatic vegetation both near surface and at bottom; free swimming after yolk absorption.[15,16]

Juveniles—close inshore among weed beds, at least in Lake Erie.[12]

SPAWNING

Location: Shallow water, usually in grassy or weedy areas, also around stone piles[11] and over naked granite.[16]

Season: May or June in Maryland,[3] up to July in New York.[14]

Time: Usually during daylight hours,[13] possibly with peak activity between 12 noon and 3:00 p.m.[14]

Temperature: Ca. 19–21 C in New York.[13]

Fecundity: Ca. 1,110–77,156.[10]

EGGS (Figs. 5 B-C)

Description: Demersal;[6] adhesive, attached singly or in irregularly arranged groups[16] to stones, sticks, and weeds, but becoming detached from slime-covered rocks in 2 or 3 days. Diameter 3.3[13] to ca. 5.0 mm.[16] Egg capsule distinctly two-layered;[15] micropyle single.[13] Color variable; green prior to spawning,[8] slate-gray at time of extrusion, 3 hours later cream-yellow, 2 days later dull greenish-brown;[13] also described as having yellowish-green outer envelope and whitish-blue yolk.[16]

Development: At mean temperature of 17.8 C.

  1 hour—first cleavage.
  2 hours—second cleavage.
  3 hours—third cleavage.
  37 hours—early gastrula; pigment noticeable in yolk region.
  46 hours—closure of blastopore.
  70 hours—central nervous system outlined; pronephric ducts apparent.
  80 hours—optic vesicles distinct; notochord, blood vessels, 4 somites developed.
  90 hours—7 somites.
  ca. 140 hours—embryo around ca. 200° of egg circumference.
  149 hours—first movement.
  160 hours—embryo around 320° of egg circumference.

Incubation: Ca. 72 hours at unspecified temperature,[22] 200–220 hours at 16.7–22.2 C.[13]

YOLK-SAC LARVAE (Fig. 6 A-E)

Hatching length 8.0[16]–10 mm TL;[21] duration of stage up to 3 weeks.[4]

Mouth open, more or less rhomboidal, and preceded by papillate suctorial disc at 11 mm, becoming narrow slit accompanied by elongation of pre-oral region into short snout with terminal, suctorial disc at 15 mm. At

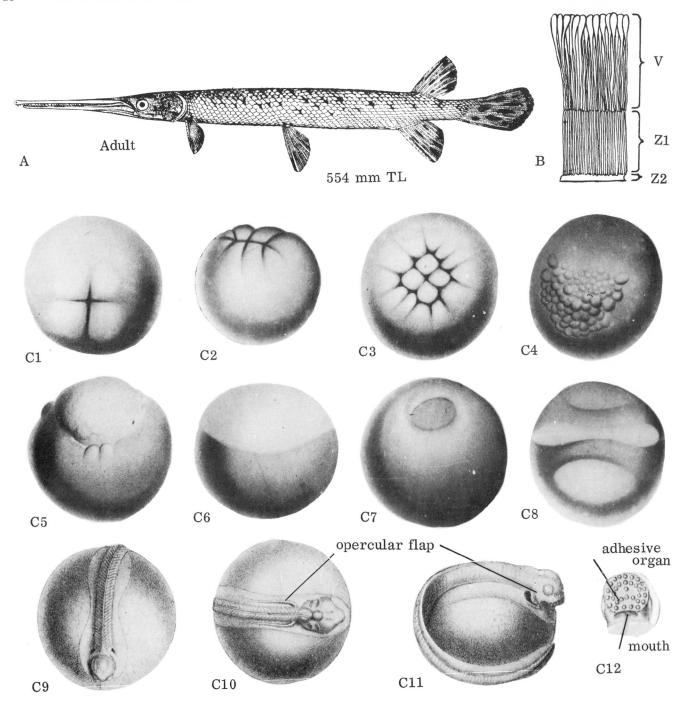

Fig. 5. Lepisosteus osseus, longnose gar. A. Adult, 554 mm TL. B. Enlarged view of capsule of recently deposited egg; outer, villous layer (V), inner, two-layered zona radiata (Z1 and Z2). C. Development of egg at ca. 17.8 C; diameter ca. 2.4 mm with egg capsule removed. C1. Four-cell stage, 2 hours. C2. Eight-cell stage, 3 hours. C3. Sixteen-cell stage, 3 3/4 hours. C4. Early morula, 8 hours. C5. Late morula, 25 hours. C6. Early gastrula, 32 hours. C7. Late gastrula with blastopore, 44 hours. C8. Early embryo with notochord, 90 hours. C9. Embryo, 6 days. Myomeres and gill region well developed. C10. Embryo, 7 days. Rudimentary opercular flaps present. C11. Embryo just before hatching, ca. 10 mm TL, 11 days. Mouth, gill region, and suctorial disk well developed; complete myomere count. C12. Ventral view of head of 11-day embryo with details of mouth and adhesive organ. (A, *Suttkus, 1963: fig. 13.* B, *redrawn from Balfour and Parker, 1882: pl. 21.* C1-C8, *Dean, 1895a: pl. 1.* C9-C12, *Balfour and Parker, 1882: pl. 21.*)

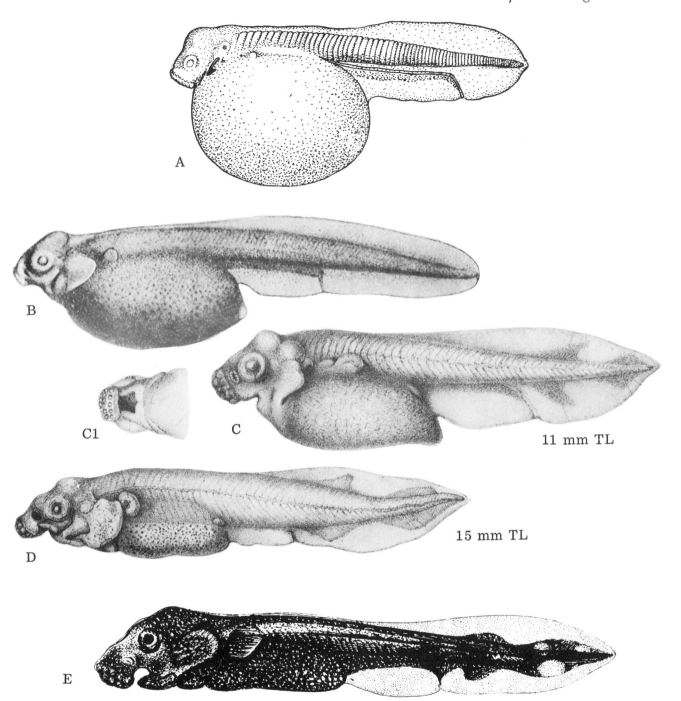

Fig. 6. Lepisosteus osseus, longnose gar. A. Yolk-sac larva. Newly hatched, with prominent adhesive organ. B. Yolk-sac larva. Yolk half absorbed; opercular flaps prominent. C. Yolk-sac larva, 11 mm TL. Olfactory pit formed; darkening in areas of dorsal, anal, and caudal fins. C1. Ventral view of head with details of adhesive organ and mouth. D. Yolk-sac larva, 15 mm TL, 5–6 days. E. Yolk-sac larva, 11 days. (A, *redrawn after Kerr, 1919: fig. 198.* B, *reprinted from* Textbook of Embryology, *by S. Graham Kerr, fig. 198. Copyright © 1919 by Macmillan & Co. Ltd. Used by permission of the publisher.* C–D, *Balfour and Parker, 1882: pl. 21.* E, *Agassiz, 1879: pl. III, fig. 19.*)

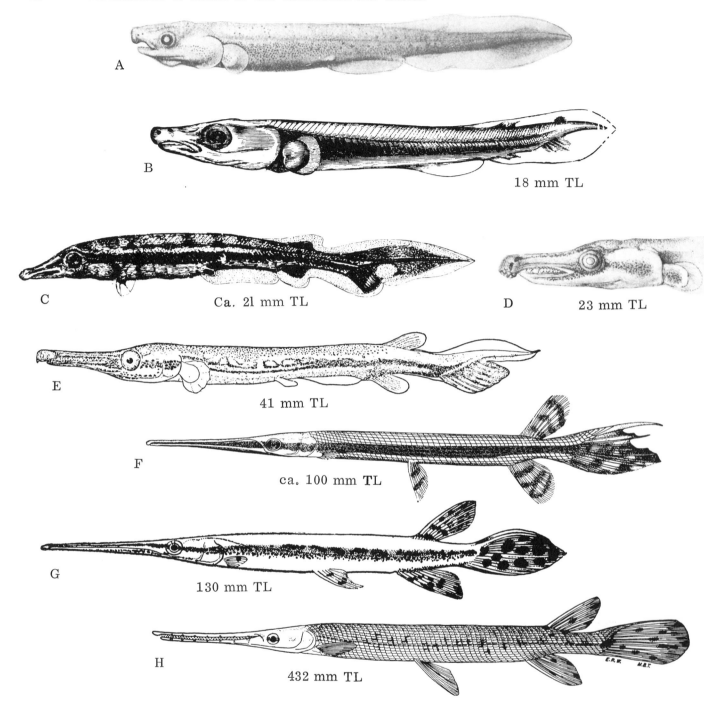

Fig. 7. *Lepisosteus osseus*, longnose gar. A. Larva. Lower jaw and ventral buds developed. B. Putative larva, 18 mm TL. Snout more elongate. C. Larva, ca. 21 mm TL. Marked heterocercal tail. D. Head of larva, 23 mm TL. End of snout markedly bulbous; adhesive organ still evident; teeth present. E. Larva, 41 mm TL. Adhesive organ still apparent; tail heterocercal. F. Juvenile, ca. 100 mm TL. Ventral lobe of caudal enlarged; dorsal lobe reduced; lateral band pronounced. G. Juvenile, 130 mm TL. Lateral band persists; snout attaining adult proportions; tail abbreviate-heterocercal with pointed tip. H. Juvenile, 432 mm TL, 365 mm SL. Tail adult-like. (A, *reprinted from* TEXTBOOK OF EMBRYOLOGY, *by J. Graham Kerr, fig. 198. Copyright © 1919 by Macmillan & Co. Ltd. Used by permission of the publisher.* B, Wilder, 1877: fig. 9. C, Agassiz, 1879: pl. IV, fig. 38. D, Balfour and Parker, 1882: pl. 21. E, Fish, 1932: fig. 2. F, Fowler, 1945: Fig. 6. G, Fowler, 1935: fig. 1. H, *reprinted from* THE FISHES OF OHIO, *by Milton B. Trautman. Copyright © 1957 by the Ohio State University Press. Used by permission of the author and the publisher.*)

21 mm, snout increased greatly in length, and lower jaw elongated.[21] Eye poorly developed at hatching,[16] choroid fissure retained to at least 11 mm.[21]

Dorsal, anal, and caudal indicated by dense pigment in finfold at 11 mm, becoming even more dense at 15 mm; pectorals forming as prominent, vertically projecting, longitudinal ridges on surface of yolk sac at 11 mm; pectoral insertions oriented more or less horizontally with body and covered by large opercular flap at 15 mm; ventrals visible as small longitudinal projections near posterior end of yolk sac at 15 mm;[21] urostyle oblique by 2nd day.

Pigmentation: Body colorless, transparent; yolk sac opaque bluish-gray at hatching. "Somewhat later" upper edge of yolk sac and surface of alimentary canal with small melanophores; at 3 days, body with numerous, small melanophores toward head region and on sides; by 5th day, entire body with melanophores except yellowish-gray venter. By 11th day, melanophores most numerous above eye, in dorsal region, in dark band from upper margin of yolk to tail, and in region of future vertical fins; white areas, completely enclosed in black, developed dorsally and ventrally in caudal region; fleshy lobes of pectorals and outer edge of gill cover bluish.[16]

LARVAE (Fig. 7 A-D)

Specimens described 20 [16]–41 mm TL.

D. 7; A. 7.[12]

At ca. 20 mm, suctorial disc reduced to a swelling on extremity of elongate upper jaw; teeth evident.

Incipient rays of dorsal, anal, pectorals, and caudal evident by ca. 20 mm; ventral rays evident at ca. 23–24 mm,[16,21] although ventrals may develop before pectorals in some cases.[4] Notochord produced posteriorly into an elongate fleshy filament above caudal at ca. 23 mm.[21] Preanal finfold still evident at 41 mm.[12]

Pigmentation: At ca. 20 mm, dorsal region mottled with broad, irregular patches of brown and heavy black line extends from back of eye to tip of tail.[16] At 41 mm, various shades of brown banded irregularly on sides with white.[12]

JUVENILES (Fig. 7 E-H)

Smallest specimen tentatively included 55.0 mm.[17]

Distance from posterior edge of eye to posterior edge of opercular membrane contained 3.0–3.5 times in HL in specimens 50–100 mm long.[5]

Scale outlines visible on posterior part of body at 108 mm.[18] Caudal filament adnate to lower portion of caudal fin at 247–301 mm.[7] Vertebral constrictions visible in notochord at 55 mm.[17]

Pigmentation: Young less than ca. 75 mm long with black or chocolate-brown bellies, a light yellow ventrolateral band, and dusky lateral band; young ca. 75–375 mm long with dusky lateral band and midline of belly white, bordered on each side with band of chocolate.[5]

Size at maturity: Males average 660–686 mm; females average 838 mm.

Age at maturity: Males ca. 3–4 years, females ca. 6 years.[8]

LITERATURE CITED

1. Hildebrand, S. F., and W. C. Schroeder, 1928:77–8.
2. Uhler, P. R., and O. Lugger, 1876:154.
3. Schwartz, F. J., 1962a:22.
4. Suttkus, R. D., 1963:66, 77–8.
5. Trautman, M. B., 1957:166–168.
6. Williamson, R. F., 1951:4, 5.
7. Riggs, C. D., and G. A. Moore, 1960:46.
8. Netsch, N. F., and A. Witt, Jr., 1962:251, 257–8.
9. Jean, Y., 1946:100.
10. Holloway, A. D., 1954:443, 446.
11. Forbes, S. A., and R. E. Richardson, 1920:32–3.
12. Fish, M. P., 1932:305–6.
13. Dean, B., 1895a:3–14, 26–8
14. Beard, J., 1889:111, 113–4.
15. Mark, E. L., 1890:5–6, 29.
16. Agassiz, A., 1879:66, 68–76, Pl. 1, Pl. 3.
17. Balfour, F. M., and W. K. Parker, 1881:115.
18. Wilder, B. G., 1877a:13.
19. Fowler, H. W., 1906:89.
20. Fowler, H. W., 1911:6.
21. Balfour, F. M., and W. K. Parker, 1882:372–74, Pl. 21.
22. Eycleshymer, A. C., 1903:263.

ADDITIONAL REFERENCES

Agassiz, A., 1878a, 1878b; Allen, B. M., 1909; Beard, J., 1896; Eycleshymer, A. C., 1899, 1903; Fülleborn, F., 1894; Landacre, F. L., 1912; Landacre, F. L., and A. C. Conger, 1913; Lanzi, L., 1909; Parker, W. K., 1882, 1883; Putman, E. W., 1866; Roach, L. S., 1941; Schreiner, K. E., 1902; Trembley, F. J., 1930; Wilder, B. G., 1876; Wright, E. P., 1878, 1879.

Amia calva

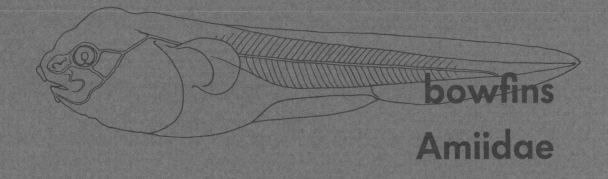

bowfins

Amiidae

ORDER AMIIFORMES
Amiidae—bowfins

Bowfin

Amia calva Linnaeus

ADULT (Fig. 8 A)

D. 42–53;[24] A. 9[8]–12; scales in lateral line 62–70, in transverse series 18–20;[24] vertebrae 90.[13] Depth 4.6–6.2 in length.[8]

Body long, robust; head conic; jaws with strong, conical teeth;[24] anterior nostrils at end of short barbels;[25] large gular plate between anterior halves of lower jaw; scales cycloid.

Dark olive above, lighter on sides, cream or greenish below; dorsal dark green with 2 broken, longitudinal, olive bars; lower fins vivid green; adult males with prominent, orange-bordered, black spot at upper caudal base.[7,8]

Maximum length ca. 914 mm.[24]

DISTRIBUTION AND ECOLOGY

Range: Minnesota, Quebec, Vermont,[12] and Great Lakes region;[11] south to Florida and Texas; north on Atlantic coastal plain to Susquehanna River;[12] probably introduced in Hudson River (ECR) and in Connecticut.[11]

Area distribution: Tidal tributaries of Chesapeake Bay in Virginia;[9,10] probably extinct in Maryland although formerly present in some rivers (RJM).

Habitat and movements: Adults—clear water in lakes, low or basic gradient portions of streams, oxbows, marshes, and harbors among aquatic vegetation;[7] occasionally in slightly brackish water (RJM); apparently somewhat migratory during spawning season.[15,21]

Larvae—in nest, remaining attached to roots or lying on bottom until adhesive organ is absorbed, thereafter in tight "swarm" guarded by male parent outside nest.[14]

Juveniles—with male until ca. 100 mm long, but with schools becoming smaller, loosely aggregated, and not well guarded after 35 mm;[2] specimens 25–60 mm long among weeds in water as shallow as 6 inches.[5]

SPAWNING

Location: Shallow, sluggish, or stagnant water[1,24] up to 4 feet deep or deeper[3] among thick vegetation in hollowed-out, more or less circular[1] or elliptical[6] depressions 18–30 inches in greatest diameter,[4] and with bottoms of fibrous roots, water-soaked leaves, or gravel; also under stumps, logs, and bushes.[15] Number of eggs per nest 2,000–5,000.[5]

Season: Last week of March to June.[17,33]

Time: Usually at night, occasionally by day,[8,17] with spawning lasting 1–3 hours.

Temperature: 16–19 C.

Fecundity: 23,600–64,000.[26]

EGGS (Fig 8 C)

Description: Adhesive, attached to decaying vegetation and upright reeds[6] by thread-like extensions of egg surface;[28] cleavage intermediate between holoblastic and meroblastic;[27] micropyle apparently single.[21]

Fertilized eggs—oval,[17] becoming nearly spherical following blastodisc formation; greatest diameter 2.16[28]–3.0 mm;[17] least diameter 2.14[28]–2.5 mm,[17] but with egg capsule becoming progressively distended with jelly-like fluid until dimensions are about twice original size. Color variable, with white[28] to yellowish-brown animal pole[17] and charcoal-grey[28] to dark, greyish-brown[17] yolk; egg possibly becoming darker with age[15] or varying in color with locality.[2]

Development: At 16–17 C.[28]

9 hours—30–40 cleavage furrows present.[30]
26 hours—late cleavage.
36 hours—blastoderm distinctly 2-layered.
40 hours—3 primary germ layers established; blastoderm over 230° of egg.
58 hours—neural cord established.
73 hours—tail bud, 4–5 pairs of somites formed.
124 hours—choroid fissure and ca. 25 somites (10–12 in trunk) formed; heart sigmoid in shape and beating.
129 hours—adhesive organs developed as pair of crescent-shaped protuberances; lens and anlagen of pectoral fins formed; liver developing; hypochord greatly reduced; cilia developed over entire body; ca. 43 somites; melanophores beginning to develop.
141 hours—sensory canal system established; gas bladder developing; ca. 53 somites; melanophores concentrated in cephalic region, but found over entire area dorsal to yolk sac.

Incubation: At 16–17 C, ca. 6 days (141–150 hours);[28] at unspecified temperatures, 4[21]–14 days.[17]

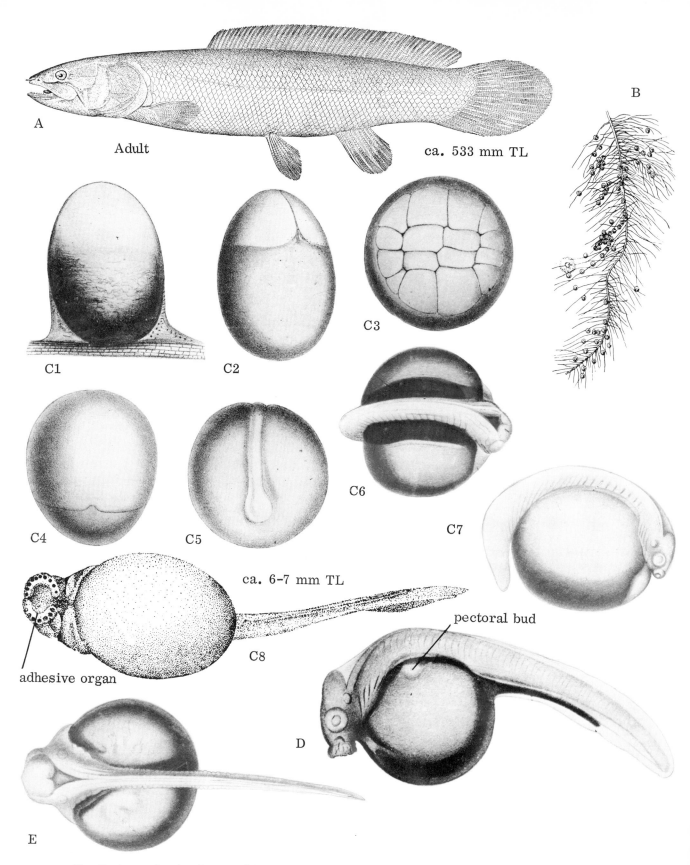

Fig. 8. *Amia calva*, bowfin. A. Adult, ca. 533 mm TL. B. Eggs attached to bulrush. C. Development of egg. Major axis 2.2–3.0 mm; minor axis 2.0–2.5 mm; membrane removed from all but C1. C1. Blastodisc forming, 1/2 hour. C2. Two-cell stage. C3. Sixteen-cell stage, 3 hours. C4. Gastrula, 54 hrs. C5. Early embryo, 4 days. Head undeveloped; 2 somites; embryo encircles 195° of egg circumference. C6. Embryo, 5 days. Eyes, adhesive organ, and auditory vesicles formed. C7. Late embryo, 6 days. Head free from yolk. C8. Ventral view of straightened embryo just before hatching, ca. 6–7 mm TL. D. Yolk-sac larva, recently hatched. Pectoral buds on dorsal surface of yolk. E. Yolk-sac larva, recently hatched, dorsal view. (A, *Goode, et al., 1884: pl. 241*. B, C1–C5, *Dean, 1895c: fig. 1, pl. 30*. C6, C7, D, *Dean, 1896: pl. 9*. C8, *Reighard and Phelps, 1908: pl. 1, fig. 4*.)

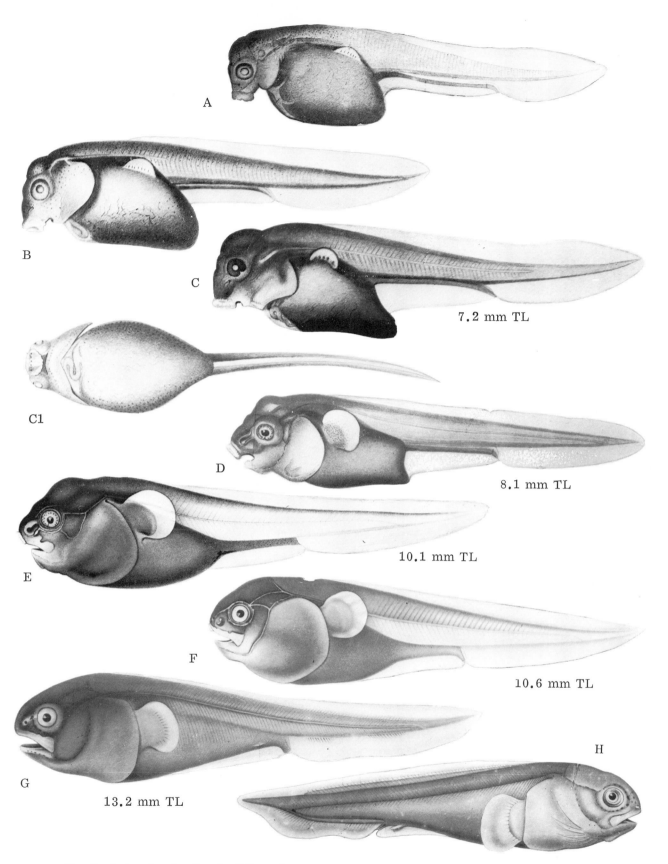

Fig. 9. Amia calva, bowfin. A. Yolk-sac larva, ca. 1 day. B. Yolk-sac larva, 3 days. C. Yolk-sac larva, 7.2 mm TL, 4 days. C1. Ventral view. Opercular flaps continuous; gular plate not yet developed. D. Yolk-sac larva, 8.1 mm. TL, 5 days. E. Yolk-sac larva, 10.1 mm TL, 6 days. F. Yolk-sac larva, 10.6 mm TL, 8 days. Adhesive organ reduced and non-functional; gular plate forming. G. Larva, 13.2 mm TL, 10 days. H. Larva, 15 days. (Dean, *1896: pl. 9, 10.*)

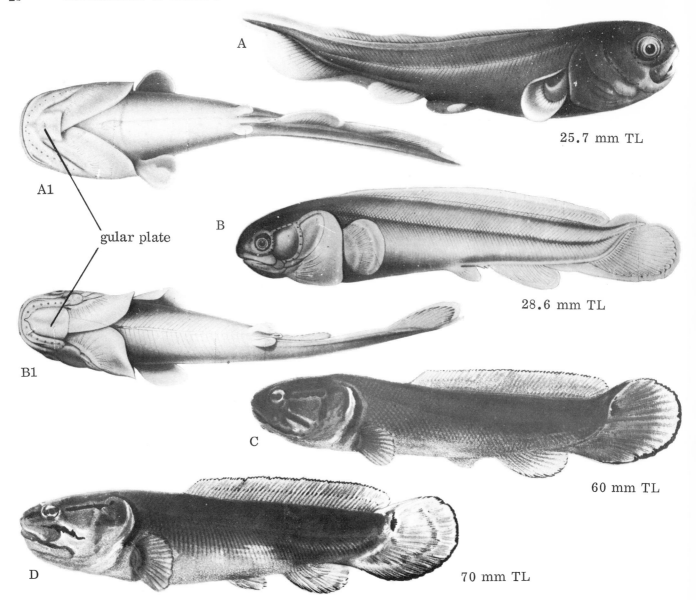

Fig. 10. *Amia calva*, bowfin. A. Larva, 25.7 mm. TL, 22 days. A1. Ventral view. B. Larva, 28.6 mm TL, 35 days. B1. Ventral view. C. Juvenile, 60 mm TL. D. Juvenile, 70 mm TL. (A,B, *Dean, 1896: pl. 11.* C,D, *Reighard, 1903: pl. 7, fig. 1, 2.*)

YOLK-SAC LARVAE (Fig. 8 D,E; Fig. 9 A-F)

Length at hatching ca. 3.0 [32]–7.0 mm TL; [2] length at end of stage ca. 9 [17]–13 mm.

Total myomeres ca. 60.[28] By ca. 10 mm, incipient rays as follows: D. 47; A. 9; C. 16; P. 14.[19]

Body "tadpole-like," [17] flexed at hatching, straightened by 2nd day. Yolk initially spherical and with prominent vitelline vessels; [19] egg-shaped at 1 day; [18] posterior end distinctly pointed, ventral surface concave, and anterior part covered by opercular flap by ca. 7.0 mm; greatly reduced by 10.5 mm.

Mandible distinct by ca. 9.0 mm. At ca. 10.0 mm, adhesive organ reduced to small, nonfunctional tubercle; gular plate visible; maxillary and premaxillary established.[19] Mouth functional by 11.0 mm.[2] Eye oval at hatching; [29] choroid fissure still evident at ca. 7.2 mm.[19]

Pectorals oblique in specimens 6–8 mm long, vertical at 9–10 mm,[17] and with ossified support elements at 11.0 mm.[31] Origin of dorsal finfold over pectorals at 10 mm,[18] further back at earlier stages.[19] Lateral line evident anteriorly at 1 day.[18]

Pigmentation: At hatching, body pale, flesh-colored; yolk sac deep sepia [17] or pale slate; eye with traces of pigment.[19] At 6–8 mm, pigment developed on head.[17] At 12 mm, body dark greenish-black, greenish-brown, or black above, dirty white below; iris metallic-golden.[2]

LARVAE (Fig. 9 G-H; Fig. 10 A-B)

Sizes described ca. 9 [17]–29 mm.

D. 47 (a count of 70 rays by 35th day is questioned); A. 10–13; C. 20–21; P. 17–22.[19]

Body tadpole-like; [17] lower jaw shorter than upper.[18] Adhesive disc evident as small, median opening at apex of upper jaw at 17-18 mm; [22] no longer visible, except histologically,[16] at 20 mm.[22] Skull cartilagenous at 15–16 mm; [23] gular plate 4-lobed at ca. 13 mm; [19] nasal openings fully established by 10th day (ca 13 mm), developing as tube-like outgrowths by ca. 15th day.

Ventrals first evident at 10–11 mm; [28] preanal finfold lost by ca. 29 mm. Scales first evident by ca. 26 mm, entire trunk region scaled at ca. 29 mm; [19] lateral line complete at ca. 11 mm.[18,20] Urostyle tipped slightly upward at 21 mm,[18] conspicuously upturned and extended into dorsal lobe of caudal at ca. 25 mm.[20]

Pigmentation: At 9–11 mm, body deeply pigmented with brown; [17] at 12–30 mm, back and sides black and acquiring a greenish hue.[2]

JUVENILES (Fig. 10 C,D)

Estimated minimum size ca. 30 mm.

Gular plate complete by 78 mm; teeth present on both jaws at 136 mm; [18] scales fully formed at 30–32 mm.

Pigmentation: Predominately black to at least 30–40 mm. At 40 mm, top of head, back, and sides dark green; sides of head olive-green with 3 black stripes, the 2 uppermost bordered with orange. At 50 mm, a small black spot at caudal base.[2] At 60 mm, upper parts olive-green or nearly black; lower parts silvery; ventrolateral aspects of head greenish-white; ocular and subocular stripes bordered with yellow; caudal spot bordered with orange; fins and opercle bordered with black; sometimes a black stripe lengthwise through middle of dorsal. At 70 mm, a vertical black band on caudal; yellow stripes on opercle. At 170 mm, fins green rather than yellow; black pigment increased in dorsal and caudal; males with reticulated pattern.[3]

Size at maturity: Minimum ca. 380 mm.[7]

LITERATURE CITED

1. Adams, C. C., and T. L. Hankinson, 1928:294.
2. Reighard, J., 1903:86, 91–2, 99.
3. Dean, B., 1899: 94, 250.
4. Evermann, B. W., and H. W. Clark, 1920:318.
5. Richardson, R. E., 1913b:407.
6. Doan, K. H., 1938:204.
7. Trautman, M. B., 1957:169–171.
8. Forbes, S. A., and R. E. Richardson, 1908:38–40.
9. Raney, E. C., and W. H. Massmann, 1953:427.
10. Massmann, W. H., 1958:3.
11. Hubbs, C. L., and K. F. Lagler, 1958:41.
12. Moore, G. A., 1957:54.
13. Shufeldt, R. W., 1885:84.
14. Reighard, J., 1902a:80–1.
15. Reighard, J., 1900:133–4, 136.
16. Phelps, J., 1900:139.
17. Whitman, C. O., and A. C. Eycleshymer, 1897:315–6, 326–7, 330.
18. Allis, E. P., 1889: Pls. 30–36.
19. Dean, B., 1896:644–50, 652, 654–5, Pl. 9.
20. Jungersen, H. F. E., 1894:246.
21. Dean, B., 1895c:416, 421.
22. Reighard, J., and J. Phelps, 1908:470.
23. Eycleshymer, A. C., and B. M. Davis, 1897:54.
24. Smith, H. M., 1907;60–1.
25. Legendre, V., 1954:24.
26. Carlander, K. D., 1953:20.
27. Lagler, K. F., J. E. Bardach, and R. R. Miller, 1962: 305.
28. Pierson, E. C., 1953:7–37, 137–9, 174–6.
29. Beckwith, C. J., 1907: Pl. 3.
30. Eycleshymer, A. C., and J. M. Wilson, 1906:134.
31. Heronimus, C. 1911:195–6, 200.
32. Allen, B. M., 1911:14–15, 25.
33. Goode, G. B., 1884:659–60.
34. Fülleborn, F., 1894:1062.

ADDITIONAL REFERENCES

Allen, B. M., 1909; Allis, E. P., Jr., 1899; Bade, E., 1898, 1902; Brachet, A., 1912; deBeer, G. R., 1924; DeBruine, H., 1937; Desrochers, J. E., 1904; Forbes, S. A., 1878; Franklin, D., 1914; Hay, O. P., 1895b; Hesdörffer, M., 1901; Lanzi, L., 1909; Maison, E., 1897a, 1897b; Pehrson, T., 1922; Piper, H., 1902a, 1902b, 1903; Prather, J. M., 1900; Reighard, J., 1902b; Reighard, J., and S. O. Mast, 1908; Robeson, J. M., Jr., 1932; Robinson, W. E., 1875; Schreiner, K. E., 1902; Sobotta, J., 1896; Sprenger, W., 1901; Stauffer, J., 1879; Virchow, H., 1896; Wilder, B. G., 1876, 1877a, 1877b.

Elops saurus

Megalops atlantica

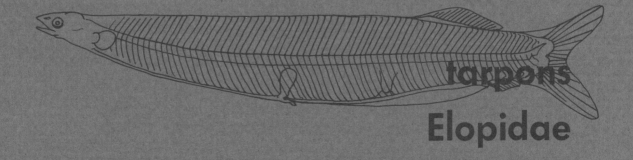

tarpons

Elopidae

ORDER CLUPEIFORMES
Elopidae—tarpons

Ladyfish   *Elops saurus* **Linnaeus**

ADULT (Fig. 11 A)

D. 25–29; A. 16–19 (dorsal and anal counts include rudimentary rays); P. 17–18; V. 14–15;[7] scales 103–120; vertebrae 73[1]–85;[7] gill rakers on first arch 5[8]–8+10–15 (excluding rudiments);[1] branchiostegals 26[1]–33.[7] Proportions expressed as percent of SL (based in part on immature specimens): Body depth 14.5–19.3; head length 25.0–31.0; eye diameter 5.0–6.3.

Body very slender, moderately compressed; snout rather long, usually somewhat longer than eye; mouth large, nearly horizontal; maxillary extending beyond rear edge of eye; gular plate present; scales small, thin; lateral line nearly straight, extending onto caudal base; axillary scale of pectoral reaching to about mid-length of fin.[1]

Bluish above, sides silvery, venter yellowish; dorsal and caudal dusky and yellowish; ventrals and pectorals yellowish with dusky punctations;[2] eye greenish-gold and silver with black pupil.[7]

Maximum length ca. 915 mm TL.[3]

DISTRIBUTION AND ECOLOGY

Range: Cape Cod[1] and possibly Gulf of Maine[5] to Brazil; also West Indies and Bermuda;[1] possibly Pacific and Indian Oceans and Red Sea.[12,13]

Area distribution: "Large rivers" in Chesapeake Bay region;[6] also Cape Charles and Lynnhaven Roads, Virginia.[2]

Habitat and movements: Adults—often in schools; usually in shallow, salt or brackish water; sometimes encountered several miles offshore[11] or up rivers to nearly fresh water;[9] inshore from June to October in South Carolina;[10] occurring sporadically north of Chesapeake Bay in autumn.[1] Minimum salinity 0.17–0.18 o/oo.[9]

Stage I larvae (leptocephali)—offshore in water of 20–100 fathoms or deeper.
Stage II larvae (shrinking)—primarily along beaches; also tidal marshes.
Stage III larvae—in brackish to nearly fresh-water pools and ponds in marshes.[7,8]

SPAWNING

Area: Unknown, probably at sea,[7] although nearly ripe females have been taken in Gatun Locks, Panama.[4]

Season: Prolonged, either concentrated in the fall, or continuing throughout year.[8]

Fecundity: Unknown.

EGGS

Undescribed, probably pelagic.[2]

YOLK-SAC LARVAE

Undescribed.

LARVAE

Development is represented by profound changes in body form accompanied by 2 periods of length increase (Stages I and III), interspaced by a period of length decrease (Stage II).

STAGE I, LEPTOCEPHALUS (Fig. 11 B-E; Fig. 12 A-B)
Specimens described 5.1–43.3 mm SL; size at end of stage ca. 40–45 mm.

C. 1+19+2 with 6 principal rays branched in each lobe at 43.3 mm SL; total myomeres 74–82 (usually more than 75); preanal myomeres 70 at 5.3 mm, 65–72 at 17.3–43.3 mm; predorsal myomeres 59–65 at 14.3–43.3 mm; hypurals 4 at 10 mm, 8–9 at 15 mm. Four teeth in single row on each side of jaw at 5.3 mm, the anterior two in upper jaw the longest, fang-like, uniform throughout their length, and beveled at tips; at 10.0 mm, 6 teeth on each side of each jaw; at ca. 40–45 mm, ca. 10–11 teeth in upper jaw, 12–14 in lower, all approximately same size.

Body ribbon-like, long, thin, deep. Head at 5.3 mm broader and slightly deeper than body; at ca. 10 mm triangular in dorsal aspect, less deep than body;[7] at 34.5–36.5 mm strongly depressed;[1] at end of stage relatively smaller than at any other stage of development.

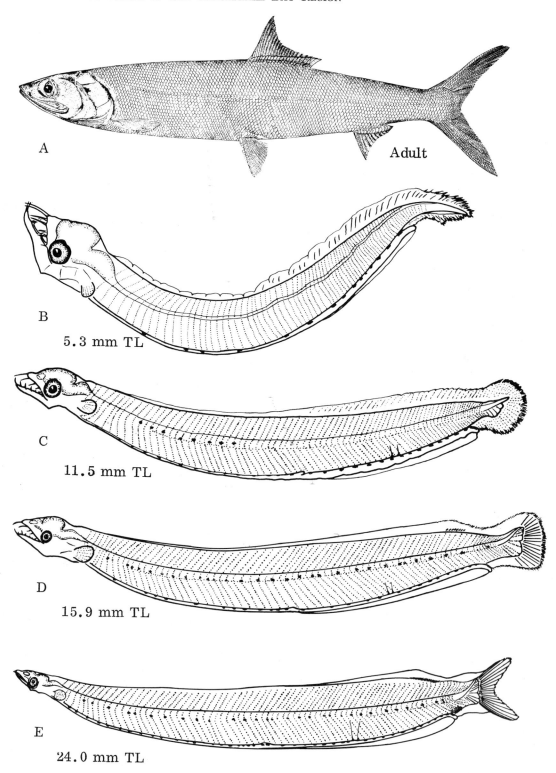

Fig. 11. *Elops saurus*, ladyfish. A. Adult, 450 mm TL. B. Stage I larva, leptocephalus, 5.3 mm TL, 5.3 mm SL. Four teeth on each side of upper and lower jaws. C. Stage I larva, leptocephalus, 11.5 mm TL, 11.2 mm SL. Caudal fin forming; number of upper teeth increased to 6 on each side; blood vessels of kidney visible as dark parallel lines at myomeres 51 and 52; gas bladder discernible at myomeres 35–36. D. Stage I larva, leptocephalus, 15.9 mm TL, 15.2 mm SL. Dorsal ray bases, hypurals, and caudal rays present. E. Stage I larva, leptocephalus, 24.0 mm TL, 22.4 mm SL. Anal ray bases present. (A, *Goode, et al.* 1884: *pl.* 218. B-E, *Gehringer, 1959a: fig. 2–5.*)

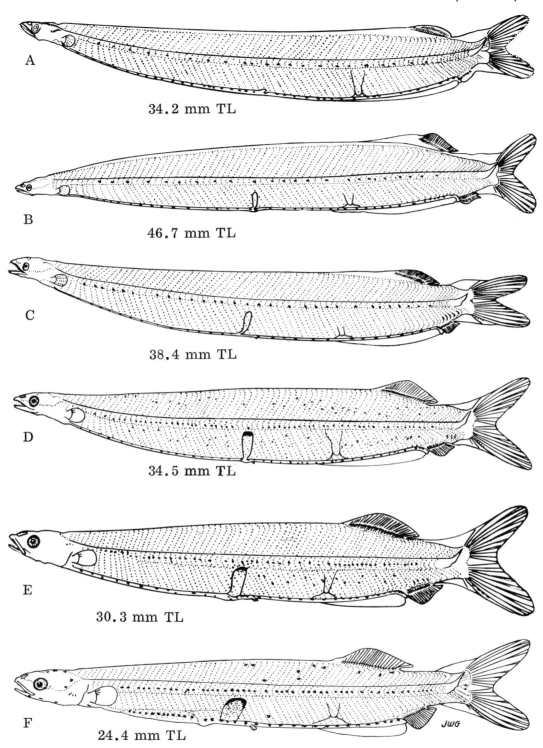

Fig. 12. *Elops saurus*, ladyfish. A. Stage I larva, leptocephalus, 34.2 mm TL, 31.3 mm SL. Dorsal rays present. B. Stage I larva, leptocephalus, 46.7 mm TL, 43.3 mm SL. Anal rays present; caudal rays branching; upper teeth increased to 11 on each side; gas bladder cylindrical, directed dorsally; pigment on dorsal surface of eye. C. Stage II larva, 38.4 mm TL, 34.0 mm SL. Ventral fin buds evident. D. Stage II larva, 34.5 mm TL, 30.9 mm SL. Pectoral rays forming; dorsal surface of gas bladder pigmented. E. Stage II larva, 30.3 mm TL, 26.6 mm SL. Branching of caudal rays complete. F. Putative stage II larva, 24.4 mm TL, 21.5 mm SL. Ventrals with 5 rays, gas bladder more pigmented and thickening. (*Gehringer, 1959a: fig. 6–11.*)

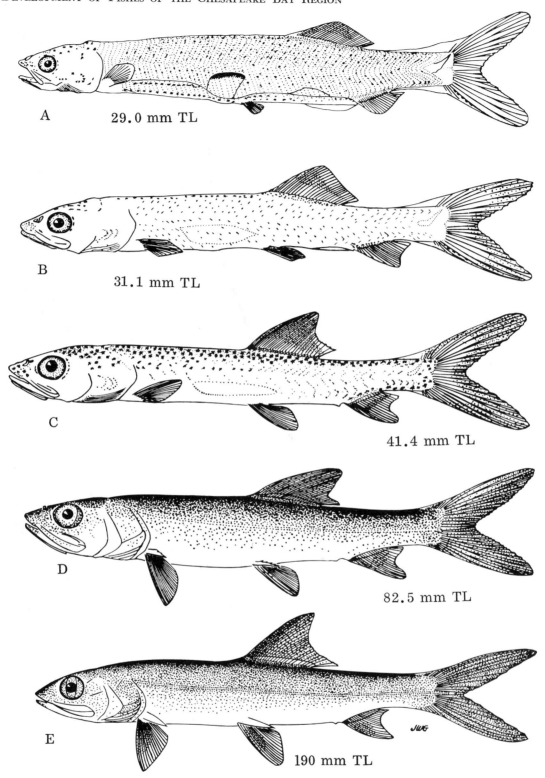

Fig. 13. Elops saurus, ladyfish. A. Stage III larva, 29.0 mm TL, 24.7 mm SL. Dorsal and anal shifted anteriorly; dorsal with distinct pigment pattern. B. Stage III larva, 31.1 mm TL, 25.9 mm SL. Remnants of preanal finfold present; elongate gas bladder visible through body wall. C. Juvenile, 41.4 mm TL, 34.2 mm SL. Gas bladder visible, pigmentation dense over back. D. Juvenile, 82.5 mm TL, 67.5 mm SL. Lateral line formed; scalation complete although not illustrated; axillary scales with scalloped margins; adipose eyelid formed; fins punctuate. E. Juvenile, 190 mm TL, 152 mm SL. Axillary scales smooth. (*Gehringer 1959a:* fig. 12–16.)

At 5.3 mm, dorsal finfold originating immediately behind head; preanal finfold from anus to point 1/3 distance to head; by ca. 11.0 mm, dorsal finfold reduced anteriorly; at 31.3 mm, dorsal and ventral finfolds diminished except in region of developing vertical fins. Dorsal ray bases discernible at ca. 15 mm; incipient rays at ca. 31 mm,[7] although sometimes not developed at 37 mm.[1] Anal ray bases at ca. 17 mm; incipient rays first evident at 34.5–43.3 mm. Posterior margin of caudal somewhat truncate at 15 mm, forked and with 1 secondary ray at ca. 20 mm. Pectoral a rounded bud throughout stage. Urostyle tipped slightly upward at ca. 10.0 mm.

Rudimentary gas bladder visible as slight bulge in dorsal wall of digestive tract at ca. 35–36th myomere in a 11.2 mm specimen; at 43.3 mm, gas bladder a long, cylindrical, blind sac directed dorsally from digestive tract at 34th myomere.

Two large renal blood vessels at myomeres 51 and 52 at 11.2 mm; at ca. 20 mm, a mass of renal tissue along dorsal wall of digestive tract.

Pigmentation: At 5.3 mm, body translucent; few melanophores along dorsum of digestive tract; eye silvery, pupil black; by end of stage, melanophores increased along digestive tract, developed on myoseptums, along mid-lateral line of body, on caudal fin, between anal ray bases, and on dorsal surface of eye.[7]

STAGE II (Fig. 12 C-F)
Specimens described 34.0–21.5 mm SL; size range from ca. 40–45 mm SL down to ca. 18–20 mm.

A. 12–15.

Body thicker, shorter; ribbon-like appearance lost. Head no longer triangular in dorsal aspect by end of stage.

Incipient rays of pectorals first evident in dorsal portion of fin at ca. 30 mm; ventral buds opposite 36th myomere at 34.0 mm.[7]

Gut loosely attached to abdomen;[1] gas bladder extended to and flattened against vertebral column at ca. 30 mm.

Pigmentation: Melanophores increased in number and size; gas bladder densely pigmented.[7]

STAGE III (Fig. 13 A-B)
Specimens described 24.7 and 25.9 mm SL, size range of stage from ca. 18–30 mm SL.

Gill rakers first evident at 20–25 mm; at 25 mm, 3 palatine teeth in a row on each side of mouth, teeth on vomer, and in bands on ventral surfaces of maxillae.

Finfold partially retained to ca. 25–30 mm.

Gas bladder elongate and occupying a considerable portion of body cavity at ca. 26 mm. Kidney between myomeres 48 and 54 at ca. 25 mm.[7]

Pigmentation: Silvery color may develop on body at ca. 20 mm[8] while leptocephalid pigmentation may be retained in specimens up to ca. 32 mm.[7]

JUVENILES (Fig. 13 C-E)

Minimum size ca. 35 mm SL.

Branchiostegals ca. 30 at ca. 35 mm, usually with more on left side than right; gill rakers on first arch 5–7 + 12–15 in specimens exceeding 30 mm; teeth present on tongue at ca. 35 mm; pterygoid teeth developed in juveniles of unspecified size.

At ca. 50 mm, adipose eyelid evident at anterior and posterior margin of eye; lateral line,[7] scales on body,[8] and axillary scales developed.[7] Scalation, including sheaths of scales at dorsal and anal bases, complete at ca. 60–65 mm.[1,7] Gas bladder long and thin at ca. 35 mm.

Pigmentation: By ca. 35 mm, pattern on dorsal surface of head and body denser; pigment on dorsal and caudal fin extended, and developed on anal. At 50–60 mm, dorsum dense greenish-black, grading to silvery below; dorsal and caudal fins with uniform pepper-spots; pectoral, ventrals, and anal with few scattered spots.[7]

Age and size at maturity: Unknown.

LITERATURE CITED

1. Hildebrand, S. F., 1963c:124–31.
2. Hildebrand, S. F., and W. C. Schroeder, 1928:78–9.
3. Jordan, D. S., and B. W. Evermann, 1896:410.
4. Hildebrand, S. F., 1939:25.
5. Bigelow, H. B., and W. C. Schroeder, 1940:139.
6. Uhler, P. R., and O. Lugger, 1876:132.
7. Gehringer, J. W., 1959a:619–47.
8. Hildebrand, S. F., 1943b:91–3.
9. Gunter, G., 1942:313.
10. Holbrook, J. E., 1860:183.
11. Migdalski, E. C., 1958:314.
12. Okada, Y., 1959–60:291.
13. Whitehead, P. J. P., 1962:321.

ADDITIONAL REFERENCES

Alikunhi, K. H., and S. N. Rao, 1951; Fowler, H. W., 1931; Gopinath, D., 1946; Indian Council of Agricultural Research, 1951; Nair, R. V., 1952; Regan, C. T., 1909; Smith, H. M., 1907.

ADULT (Fig. 14 A)

D. 13–15; A. 22–25; P. 13–14; vertebrae 53–57; gill rakers 19 [1]–22 [2]+36–40; lateral line scales 41–48 (counts based in part on juvenile specimens). Proportions expressed as percent SL (based in part on juveniles): Body depth 23.5–29.0; head length 25.0–31.0; snout length 4.5–6.2; eye diameter 5.3–9.5.

Body moderately deep, rather strongly compressed; mouth large, oblique; maxillary extended far beyond eye in large individuals; elongate gular plate between rami of lower jaw; mandible projecting prominently; scales very large, firm, with crenulate membranous border; lateral line complete, decurved anteriorly.

Silvery, darker above.[1]

Maximum length 2,489 mm.[3]

DISTRIBUTION AND ECOLOGY

Range: Nova Scotia to Brazil;[2] also to Pacific terminus of Panama Canal;[13,14] Bermuda; in the eastern Atlantic from French West Africa to the Belgian Congo.[2]

Area distribution: Chesapeake Bay,[4] north to Anne Arundel County, Maryland (FJS); New Jersey;[5] Virginia.[6]

Habitat and movements: Adults—primarily coastal waters, seldom more than few miles from land; also estuaries and freshwater lakes and streams; some individuals northward along coast of United States during summer.[1]

Yolk-sac larvae (putative)—float inverted at surface.[9]

Leptocephali—known only from warm, offshore, epipelagic waters of North Atlantic[2] as far out as 150 miles.[7]

Stage III larvae—euryhaline; along beaches in lagoons, rivers, canals,[2] potholes, and ponds;[8] rarely as far north as North Carolina.[12]

Prejuveniles—rarely in clear freshwater; typically restricted to shallow, brackish, dark-colored pools which are usually foul and connected to sea only during high water.[2]

Juveniles—apparently ascending rivers; specimens 305–487 mm long are common in headwaters of brackish and freshwater streams.[1]

SPAWNING

Location: Unknown; possibly in shallow water between coastal islands[9] or close to shore in salty or brackish water;[1] also possibly offshore.[2] Some populations may complete life cycle in freshwater; e.g., Lake Nicaragua in Central America,[1] and Deep Lake, Florida.[10]

Season: Estimated from May to July in Florida,[9] probably during summer months throughout range.[10]

Fecundity: Ca. 12,202,000 in a specimen 2,032 mm long.[15]

PUTATIVE EGGS (Fig. 14 B)

Normally demersal, buoyant in high salinity water; non-adhesive; average diameter 1.8 mm. Egg capsule thick, ca. 1/4 egg radius; yolk coarsely granular with single small oil globule.[9]

PUTATIVE YOLK-SAC LARVAE (Fig. 14 C,D)

Specimens described 3.0–3.9 mm TL.

Yolk mass oval, ca. 1/3 TL, ca. 2/3 absorbed in 24 hours; pectoral buds present; pigment lacking.[9]

LARVAE

Larval development is divided into 3 stages modified from Wade:[2] Stage I, a period of initial length increase ending with a fully formed leptocephalus; Stage II, a period of marked shrinkage during which the larva loses its leptocephalous form; Stage III, a second period of length increase which terminates with the onset of the juvenile stage.

STAGE I, PUTATIVE LARVAE (Fig. 14 E,F)
Maximum size attained under laboratory conditions, 3.45 mm SL in 48 hours.[10] Other specimens attained a TL of 2.9 mm in 43 hours but shrank to 1.9 mm TL by 72 hours. The normalcy of shrinking at this size is not established and is not emphasized.

At 2.9 mm, body elongate; head deep; finfold continuous from occiput to anus; preanal finfold extending to jugular region, as deep as dorsal. At 1.9 mm, gape conspicuously increased; auditory vesicles evident; incipient rays in caudal.

Eye pigmented throughout stage; chromatophores anteriorly above and posteriorly below gut at 1.9 mm TL.[9]

STAGE I, LEPTOCEPHALUS (Fig. 15 A-C)
Sizes described 11.0–21.3 mm SL; maximum length unknown.

D. 12; A. 20 at 21.3 mm; C. 17 at 11.7 mm, 19 at 17.5 mm, remaining constant at larger sizes. Total myomeres ca. 54–56; predorsal myomeres ca. 37–41; preanal myomeres 41 to ca. 44. Teeth (one side) $\frac{1+5}{5}$ at 11.0; $\frac{1+5}{6}$ at 17.5 mm[2] (reported elsewhere as $\frac{1+4}{5}$);[7] $\frac{1+6}{7}$ at 18.1–21.3 mm. Hypural plates 7 at 17.5 mm.

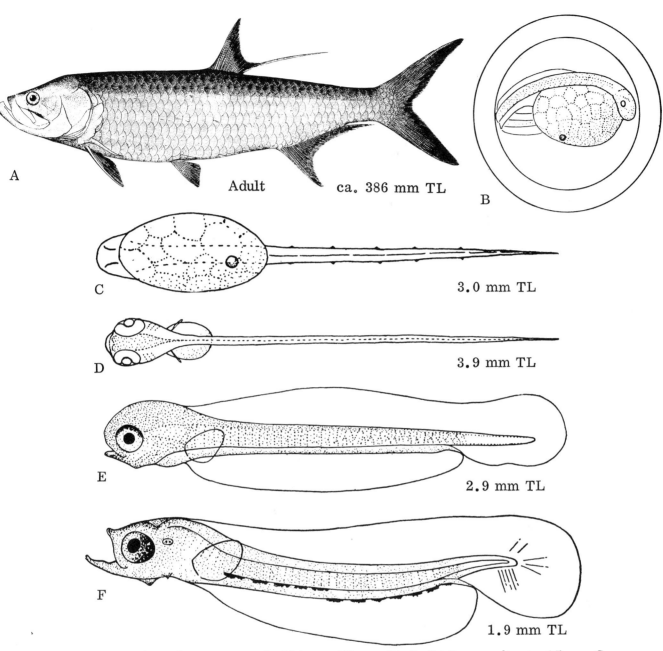

Fig. 14. *Megalops atlantica*, tarpon. A. Adult, ca. 386 mm TL. B. Putative egg, diameter 1.7 mm. C. Putative yolk-sac larva, 3.0 mm TL, just hatched. Ventral view. D. Putative yolk-sac larva, 3.9 mm TL, one day. Dorsal view. E. Stage I putative larva, 2.9 mm TL, 43 hours. Mouth functional. F. Putative Stage I larva, 1.9 mm TL, 72 hours. (A, *Goode, et al., 1884: pl. 217B.* B-F, *Breder, 1944b: 227, fig. 2.*)

Proportions as percent SL: Body depth at pectoral 5.6–7.8; head length 9.3–14.5; preventral length (at 21.3 mm) 55.9; predorsal length 73.0–80.1; preanal length 81.7–84.6.

Proportions as percent HL: Snout length 24.4–31.3; eye diameter 17.7–23.5.

Body ribbon-like, elongate, thin, and deep. Head triangular in dorsal aspect and wider than body, at least to 17.5 mm; mouth large, oblique; lower jaw protruding

at 11.7 mm, jaws equal at 17.5 mm; nostrils first visible as shallow depressions at 17.5 mm, apparently not bifurcate. First tooth in upper jaw fang-like followed by needle-like teeth of uniform diameter in single row extending to angle of gape; teeth in lower jaw thicker with anterior pair apparently not set in jaw. Eye nearly round at 11.7 mm, oval at 17.7 mm.

Gut tubular, extending more than 3/4 length of body at

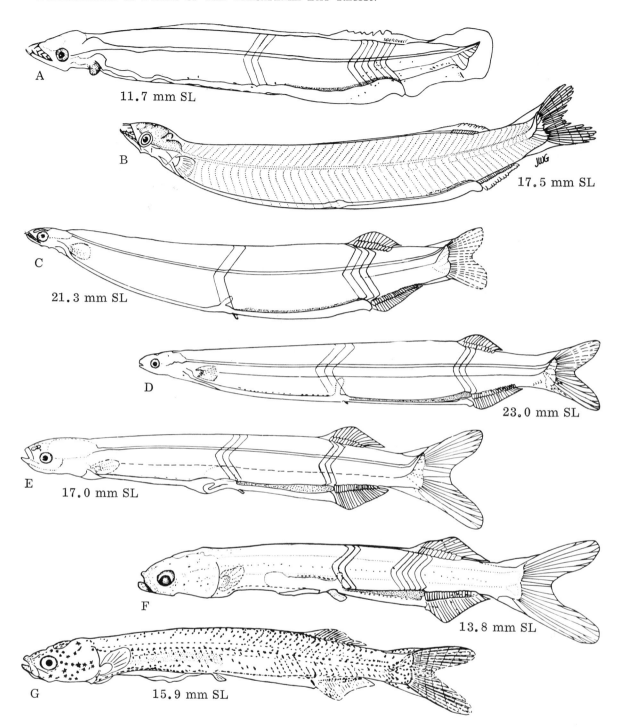

Fig. 15. Megalops atlantica, tarpon. A. Stage I larva, leptocephalus, 11.7 mm SL. Kidney shown as shaded area above posterior gut; incipient rays in dorsal. B. Stage I larva, leptocephalus, 17.5 mm SL, total myomeres 57, 12 dorsal and 21 anal ray bases. Gas bladder at 23rd myomere. C. Stage I larva, leptocephalus, 21.3 mm SL. Dorsal rays 12; anal rays 20; ventral buds at 23rd myomere; kidney extends anteriorly to 24th myomere; gas bladder a cylindrical sac extending dorsally. D. Stage II larva, 23.0 mm SL. Head shape changing, body thick. E. Stage II larva, 17.0 mm SL. Dorsal and anal have moved anteriorly; area of gular plate swelling. F. Stage III larva, 13.8 mm SL. Dorsal and anal continue to move anteriorly; gas bladder extends forward to 12th myomere; pigmentation increased over snout and opercle. G. Stage III larva, 15.9 mm SL. Pigmentation increased over whole body, particularly between myomeres; dark band over gas bladder. (A, C-F, *Wade, 1962: fig. 2, 3.* B, *Gehringer, 1959b: fig. 1.* G, *Harrington, 1958: fig. 5.*)

11.7 mm, terminating at anus opposite myomeres 45–47. Gas bladder evident at 11.7 mm at myomeres 22–23, gradually expanding and by 21.3 mm appears as short cylindrical sac arising from digestive tract at myomeres 23–24, extends dorso-caudally about 1/3 distance to central nerve cord. Kidney dorsad to gut between myomeres 35 and 41 at 17.5 mm.

Origin of dorsal finfold ca. 2/3 body length behind head; caudal finfold truncate, its margin invaginated dorsally and ventrally anterior to urostyle at 11.7 mm. Finfold reduced to small remnants anterior to caudal fin at 21.3 mm. At 11.7 mm, 8 probable ray bases in dorsal finfold opposite myomeres 41–45; opaque area in post-anal region of median finfold which may indicate developing anal fin. Dorsal and anal with rays at 21.3 mm. Urostyle prominent, tipped up slightly at 11.7 mm, more sharply at 17.5 mm. Caudal fin forked and with un-branched rays at 17.5 mm. Pectoral a rounded bud at 11.7 mm, slightly larger at 21.3 mm. Ventral fin buds present at 20.0 mm. Vertebrae developing and visible at 11.7 mm.

Pigmentation: At 11.7 mm, a few scattered melanophores on posterior part of gut and dorsally to central nerve cord; also 3 chromatophores on ventral surface of opercle, 6 on dorsal border of gut anterior to gas bladder, and 1 on air bladder. At 21.3 mm, body somewhat more opaque.[2]

STAGE II (Fig. 15 D,E)
Sizes described 24.5–17.0 mm SL; minimum size attained at end of stage unknown.

D. 9–12 (12th ray split at 23.0 mm SL); A. 16–21. Total myomeres ca. 53–57; predorsal myomeres 39–43; preanal myomeres 41–45; prepelvic myomeres 22–25. Gill arches 4 at 23.0 mm; hypurals ca. 6 at 17.0 mm.

Proportions as percent SL: Body depth at pectoral 6.5–8.8; head length 10.2–14.7; preventral length 50.6–53.6; preanal length 79.1–83.7; predorsal length 76.5–79.2. Proportions expressed as percent HL: Eye diameter 16.5–23.2; snout length 22.0–29.2.

At 23.0 mm, body laterally compressed, but thicker along entire length and no longer ribbon-like; depth at pectorals increased slightly; mid-section depth unchanged; depth of peduncle decreased. At 17.0 mm, depth at pectorals increased considerably eliminating bottleneck-like appearance of previous stage.

Head at 23.0 mm "bullet-shape" rather than "eel-like," slightly broader than body in dorsal aspect but not triangular and width nearly uniform except for slight bulge at eyes; snout rounded. At 17.0 mm, head increased

greatly in relative size; a slight swelling visible between developing mandibles in region of future gular plate.

Eye nearly round at 23.0 mm, more so at 17.0 mm. Mouth oblique, small; gape much shorter than in previous stages; lower jaw slightly exceeding upper at 17.0 mm; maxillary and mandible developing cartilage at 23.0 mm; teeth absent. Gill filaments fairly well formed at 23.0 mm; gill rakers lacking. At 23.0 mm, gas bladder a blind, upright sac extending about 2/3 distance to central nerve cord, its base increased in size and extending from myomeres 23–25; at 17.0 mm, more inflated and extending forward to myomere 21. At 23 mm, kidney enlarged, extending from myomeres 35 to 45 and separated from posterior end of digestive tract.

Twelfth dorsal ray split, its posterior half slightly elongate; caudal rays beginning to branch; fleshy base of pectorals enlarged and fins more rigid; ventral fin buds at 24th myomere. At 17.0 mm, dorsal and anal increased in height and length with origins located at myomeres 40 and 42 respectively; caudal fin with some branched rays; pectorals larger, more pointed, their fleshy bases reduced.

Pigmentation: At 23.0 mm, a line of thin brown dashes along dorsal surface of digestive tract and kidney; a few spots on anal ray bases; scattered spots on ventral half of last 4 myomeres and on caudal fin. At 17.0 mm, pigment apparently limited to a few brown dashes on dorsal surface of intestine; however, lack of pigment in this specimen is thought to be an artifact of preservation.[2]

STAGE III (Fig. 15 F,G; Fig. 16 A,B)
Sizes described 12.6 to ca. 25 mm SL.

D.12[2]–17;[8] A. 19[2]–25[8] (including rays which consolidate as growth continues).[8,9] Predorsal myomeres 37–39; preanal myomeres 38–41. Upper teeth 0–6, lower teeth 0–8. Gill rakers 1+7 at 13.1 mm, 2+13 at 13.8 mm, 5+14 at 15.9 mm, 8+21 at 20.2 mm. Branchiostegal rays 7–15 at 13.1–15.9 mm.

Proportions as percent SL at sizes less than 17.1 mm: Body depth at pectoral 9.9–17.0; head length 20.7–28.6; preventral length 48.2–54.0; predorsal length 61.8–76.0; preanal length 70.2–78.6.

Proportions as percent HL: Eye diameter 21.4–29.3; snout length 17.3–26.2.

Body depth at pectorals increased in relation to SL at 13.8 mm, but decreased just behind this region. Head somewhat irregular in outline at 15.9 mm; mandible oblique, extending to point in vertical alignment with pupil; posterior end of mandible distinctly flared. Teeth on lower jaw throughout stage, developing on upper

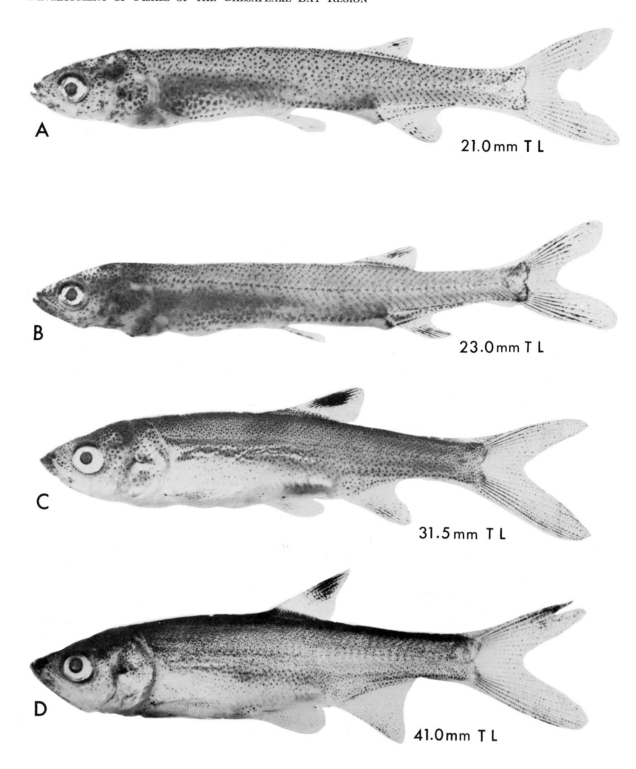

Fig. 16. *Megalops atlantica,* tarpon. A. Stage III larva, 21.0 mm TL, 17.5 mm SL. Pigmentation concentrated between myomeres; pigmented dorsal surface of gas bladder visible through body wall. B. Stage III larva, 23.0 mm TL, 19.6 mm SL. Spots developing on dorsal and anal. C. Juvenile, 31.5 mm TL, 25.5 mm SL. Spot on dorsal fin distinct; body pigmentation more profuse. D. Juvenile, 41.0 mm TL, 36.8 mm SL. Scales forming along lateral line. (*Harrington, 1958: pl. I, II.*)

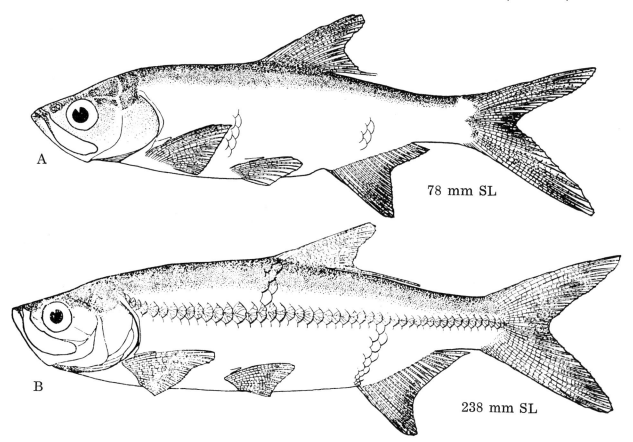

Fig. 17. Megalops atlantica, tarpon. A. Juvenile, 78 mm SL. Last dorsal ray elongating; scalation, including axillaries, complete. B. Juvenile, 238 mm SL. Last dorsal ray filamentous; pattern on individual scales formed. (*Hollister, 1939: fig. 10, 11.*)

jaw from 13.9–14.1 mm. Eye compressed dorso-ventrally at 12.6 mm; nares bifucating. Gular plate forming at 15.9 mm. At 13.8 mm, gas bladder enlarged anteriorly extending to myomere 12 and having a dorsal finger-like projection from posterior region to mid-lateral line.

Dorsal origin at 37th myomere, anal origin at 39th myomere; depth of anal greater than dorsal; last anal ray split; fleshy base of pectoral reduced; ventrals with incipient rays.

Pigmentation: At 13.8 mm, chromatophores on head and body concentrated on snout, opercle, over brain, and in area below midline. Pigment also on dorsal fin ray bases and anterior dorsal and posterior anal rays, on dorsal surface of gas bladder and gut, and in region separating gut and kidney. At 15.9 mm, chromatophores outline myomeres and are developed on body above midline.[2]

JUVENILES (Fig. 16 C,D; Fig. 17 A,B)

Minimum size described 25.2 mm SL.[2]

D. 14–18; A. 24–28 in specimens up to 59.9 mm, with

anal and dorsal counts lowered by consolidation of rudimentary rays as growth continues.[8] Gill rakers 9+24 at 25.2 mm, 16+34 at 35.0 mm, 17+34–22+40 at 51–271 mm. Branchiostegals 22–25 at 51–271 mm.

At 25.2 mm, body torpedo-like; at 51.0 mm, body deepened. At 25.2 mm, mouth large; lower jaw projecting; maxillary broad, reaching posterior margin of eye. At 194.1 mm, maxillary extending beyond eye; snout obtusely conical; villiform teeth on jaws, tongue, vomer, palatines, pterygoids, and sphenoid.[2] Incipient scales first evident along lateral line at ca. 30–34 mm; 4 rows of scales, 1 above, 2 below the lateral line at 36.8 mm;[8] lateral line pores visible at 51.0 mm;[2] axial scales formed at least by 78 mm SL.[11]

At 25.2 mm, 4th dorsal and 5th anal ray longest; anal falcate, its origin slightly posterior to dorsal insertion; pectorals broad, the central rays almost to origin of pelvics; ventrals about midway from snout to hypural plate.[2] By at least 140 mm two specialized ray scales cover uppermost and lowest caudal rays.[11] At 194.1 mm, filamentous ray of dorsal grooved on underside; anal with scaly sheath and last ray produced; caudal scaly.

Pigmentation: At 25.2 mm, body opaque, internal organs no longer visible, pigment mostly above the lateral line; gular plate heavily pigmented; opercles silvery; pigment on tip of mandible, snout, and occiput.[2] Juveniles become darker dorsally with age.[8]

Age and size at maturity: End of 6th or 7th winter, ca. 1,220 mm.[9]

LITERATURE CITED

1. Hildebrand, S. F., 1963c:113–21.
2. Wade, R. A., 1962:548, 554–67, 616.
3. Bigelow, H. B., and W. C. Schroeder, 1953:87.
4. Hildebrand, S. F., and W. C. Schroeder, 1928:80.
5. Fowler, H. W., 1929:608.
6. Shreves, M. L., 1959:1–5.
7. Gehringer, J. W., 1959b:235.
8. Harrington, R. W., Jr., 1958:7, 8.
9. Breder, C. M., Jr., 1944b:218–29, 251.
10. Ellis, R. W., 1956:5, 7.
11. Hollister, G., 1939:459, 467.
12. Hildebrand, S. F., 1934:45.
13. Hildebrand, S. F., 1939:20.
14. Swanson, P. L., 1946:175.
15. Babcock, L. L., 1936:41.

ADDITIONAL REFERENCES

Beebe, W., 1927; Breder, C. M., Jr., 1933a, 1939b; Coker, R. E., 1921; Erdman, D. S., 1960b; Gill, T., 1907c; Harrington, R. W., Jr., and E. S. Harrington, 1960; Shlaifer, A., 1941; Simpson, D. G., 1954; Storey, M., and L. M. Perry, 1933.

Albula vulpes

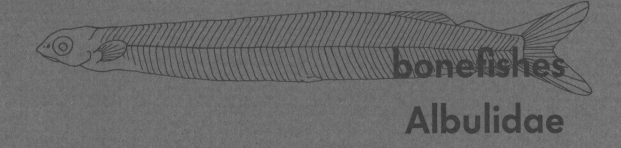

bonefishes

Albulidae

Bonefish

Albula vulpes (Linnaeus)

ADULT (Fig. 18 A)

D. 17 [20]–19; A. 8–9; P. 15–17; lateral line scales 65 [1]–75; [20] total vertebrae 69–74; preanal vertebrae 42–47; [3] gill rakers on first arch 7–8 + 9–10.

Proportions expressed as percent SL: Body depth at origin of dorsal 14.0–23.0; head length 27.5–32.0; eye diameter 5.5–8.0; snout length 8.5–13.6; length of maxillary 9.1–12.7.

Body slender, dorsal profile more convex than ventral; head flat above; snout conical; [1] roundish teeth on tongue, roof and floor of mouth; [7] gular plate much reduced, not visible externally; [15] maxillary not quite reaching eye.[1] Silvery-white [16] to bluish above with dark streaks between scale rows.[1]

Maximum length ca. 1,054 mm.[17]

DISTRIBUTION AND ECOLOGY

Range: Virtually all warm seas; in the western Atlantic from Woods Hole, Massachusetts and possibly Bay of Fundy to Rio de Janeiro, Brazil; also the West Indies and Bermuda.[1]

Area distribution: Known from a single specimen from off Seaford, Virginia in the Chesapeake Bay.[5]

Habitat: Adult—in schools or singly over mud and sand flats,[10] usually in comparatively shallow water.[1]

Leptocephali—sometimes in shallow tide pools [1] but mainly offshore where bottom depth may reach 4,000 meters.

Stage I larvae—usually in first 100 meters with greatest concentration at 33 meters.

Stage II larvae—in shallow bay areas and around piers,[10] dropping to sand bottom as metamorphosis begins.[6]

Juveniles—among islands in Panama; in shallow tide pools; [1] over bottoms of hard sand and shell at Great South Bay, New York.[14]

"Young" ca. 70 mm long and still transparent—300 yards offshore on bottom in water 4–5.5 fathoms deep.[20]

SPAWNING

Location: Unknown, probably at sea.

Season: Possibly throughout the year; [10] however, ripe specimens reported only from November through January in the West Indies.[14]

EGGS

Undescribed, probably pelagic.[10]

LARVAE

Larval development is represented by profound changes in body form accompanied by two periods of length increase (Stage I and III) interspaced by a period of length decrease (Stage II), as with the tarpon and ladyfish.

STAGE I, LEPTOCEPHALUS (Fig. 18 B-F; Fig. 19 D-G)

Size range described 7.8 mm SL [10] to ca. 87 mm.[2]

D. 3–12 at 38–40 mm, 10–16 at 47–49 mm, 16 at 50–52 mm and beyond; A. 4–7 at 44–52 mm, 7 at 53 mm and beyond; C. 10/9 at 29-31 mm, 11/11 at 32 mm and beyond. Total myomeres 65–72; preanal myomeres 62–72; preventral myomeres 31–34; predorsal myomeres 40–60.

Proportions expressed as percent SL: Head length 6.0–10.1; predorsal length 79.9–85.0; prepectoral length 6.8–12.2; preanal length 96.7–98.2.

Depth greatest at 30th myomere at 7.8 mm.[10] Head narrow, eel-like; snout small, conical.[10,12] At 7.8 mm, upper jaw with 2 protuberant incisors and 3 smaller teeth posteriorly; lower jaw remarkable longer than upper, with ca. 4 teeth. At 17.8 mm, teeth reduced in size; both jaws equal. At 29.1 mm, teeth smaller and more numerous. At 43.5 mm, snout slightly hooked. At 64.2 mm, small numerous teeth on both jaws; snout sharply hooked; upper jaw distinctly overlapping lower.[10] Mouth reaching to below eye at 58 mm TL; [9] nostril divided and bony opercle scarcely visible at 64.2 mm.

Origin of dorsal finfold at about 30th myomere at 7.8 mm SL. Incipient dorsal rays at 20–22 mm; dorsal ray count nearly complete but rays unsegmented at 43.5 mm; [10] origin of dorsal over 50th myomere at 48 mm TL.[9] Anal with incipient rays at ca. 26–28 mm. Incipient caudal

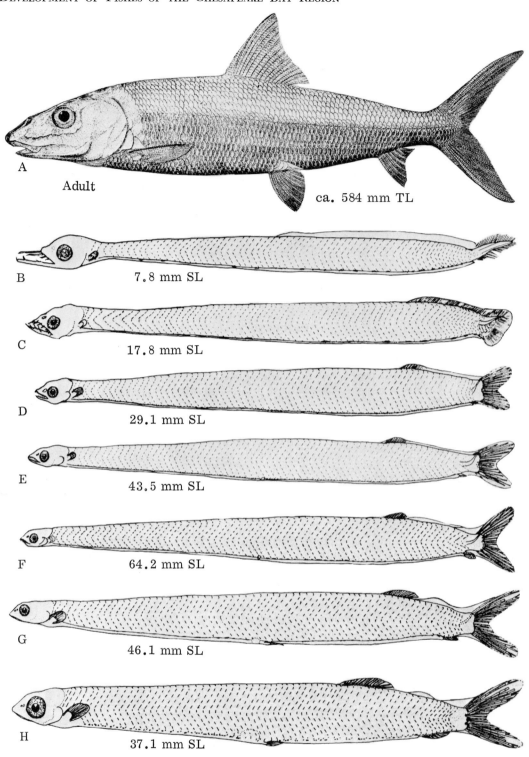

Fig. 18. Albula vulpes, bonefish. **A.** Adult, ca. 584 mm TL. **B.** Stage I larva, leptocephalus, 7.8 mm SL. Anus at base of caudal. **C.** Stage I larva, leptocephalus, 17.8 mm SL. Myomeres 68; gas bladder forming at myomere 32 but not illustrated. **D.** Stage I larva, leptocephalus, 29.1 mm SL. D. 5, gas bladder forming at myomere 31. **E.** Stage I larva, leptocephalus, 43.5 mm SL. Gas bladder at myomere 30; ventral buds at myomere 33; rays in all fins except ventrals. **F.** Stage I larva, leptocephalus, 64.2 mm SL. A. 7; gas bladder a slight protuberance. **G.** Stage II larva, 46.1 mm SL. Total myomeres 67; dorsal and anal more anterior; gas bladder inflated; anus at myomere 63. **H.** Stage II larva, 37.1 mm SL. Anal at myomere 60; dorsal at myomere 47. (A, *Goode, et al., 1884: pl. 218.* B-H, *Alexander, 1961: fig. 2.*)

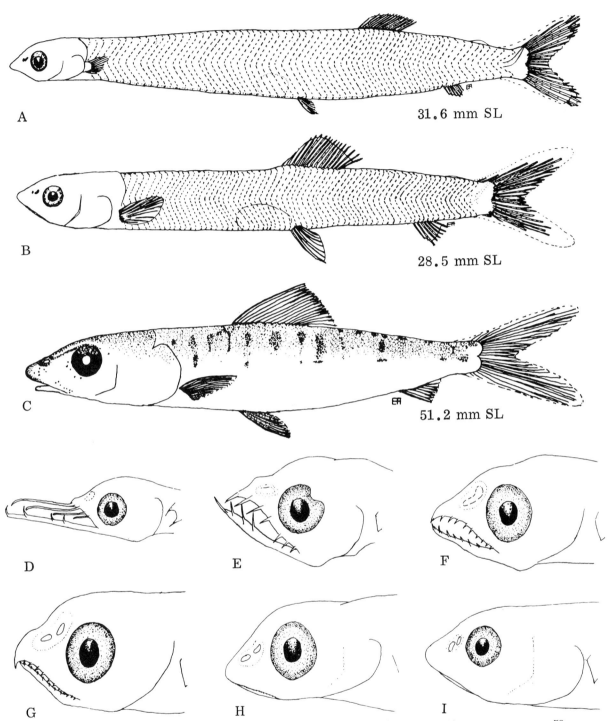

Fig. 19. Albula vulpes, bonefish. A. Stage II larva, 31.6 mm SL. Total myomeres 69; anus at myomere 59; dorsal at myomere 42; anal at myomere 60. B. Stage II larva, 28.5 mm SL. Anus at myomere 56; anal at myomere 57. C. Juvenile, 51.2 mm SL. Scales present. D. Head of Stage I larva, leptocephalus, 7.8 mm SL. Exact number of teeth not illustrated. E. Head of Stage I larva, leptocephalus, 17.8 mm SL. Snout longer, teeth shorter. F. Head of Stage I larva, leptocephalus, 43.5 mm SL. Upper jaw slightly hooked. G. Head of Stage I larva, leptocephalus, 64.2 mm SL. Snout hooked; upper jaw overlaps lower; numerous teeth barely visible. H. Head of Stage II larva, 41.6 mm SL. Teeth barely perceptible. I. Head of Stage II larva, 25.5 mm SL. (*Alexander, 1961: fig. 2, 3.*)

rays visible at 7.8 mm; caudal rays segmented at 26–28 mm, beginning to branch at 64.2 mm; caudal forked at 29.1 mm. Ventrals first evident at 35–37 mm SL.

Notochord with 72 visible divisions at 7.8 mm; urostyle turned upward and hypural plate developing at 17.8 mm, nearly complete at 64.2 mm.[10] Anus below 61st myomere at 58 mm.[9] Gas bladder present at 30th myomere at 7.8 mm (although not indicated in illustration of this stage).

Pigmentation: At 7.8 mm, small dark brown spots along dorsal edge of gut changing to series of thin red-brown dashes at 43.5 mm; pigment formed on posterior edge of caudal and cephalic region becoming opaque by end of stage.[10]

STAGE II (Fig. 18 G,H; Fig. 19 A,B, H,I)
Size range of specimens described ca. 60–65 mm SL [10] to ca. 20 mm TL.[3,4]

D. 16 [10] (a count of 18 has been recorded for larvae 55–65 mm long);[21] A. 7; C. 11/11. Total myomeres 65–70 or more;[18] preanal myomeres 55–68; predorsal myomeres 29–55; preventral myomeres 28–35.

Proportions expressed as percent SL: Prepectoral length 6.38–21.0; predorsal length 80.99–55.44; preanal length 96.46–82.46.

Horizontal diameter of eye as percent HL, 35.01–24.54.

Body deeper than in previous stage, much thicker and more "fish-like" by 31.6 mm SL. Head bullet-shaped becoming proportionately larger as stage progresses; mouth inferior at 31.6 mm SL; [10] teeth minute, projecting somewhat forward at 57 mm SL; [1] crushing palate forming at 28.5 mm SL.[10] Auditory vesicles about equal to eye at 58 mm; [8] opercle prominent at 46.1 mm SL; bifurcate nostrils surrounded by prominent ridges of cartilage at 31.6 mm SL.

Remnant of dorsal finfold present at 37.1 mm SL, sometimes absent at 31.6 mm SL. Dorsal fin migrating forward from 55th to 29th myomere, anal from 66th to 57th myomere during stage; pectoral rays becoming pointed at 37.1 mm SL, fleshy base absent at 28.5 mm SL.[10]

Vertebrae present at 22 mm.[3] Anus located at 56th myomere at 28.5 mm SL; gas bladder inflated at 46.1 mm SL, extended to midline of body at 28.5 mm SL.[10]

Pigmentation: Initially with dusky blotches mixed with yellow, becoming dusky silver as stage progresses.[4] At 57 mm SL, 2 rows of chromatophores along intestinal tract from pectoral fins to vent; vertical series of dark dots on caudal base; eyes dark; body transparent.[1] At 45 mm

SL, few pigment spots on dorsal and ventral contours.[7] At 39 mm SL, as in earlier stages but with few chromatophores on head and a broken, dark line of pigment on upper and lower lobe of caudal.[1] At 28.5 mm SL, no visible pigment.[10] Three days after capture, in specimens of unspecified size, 7 small spots along dorsal surface each surrounded by an opaque area; 2 opaque spots on caudal peduncle; whitish areas along lateral surface. On 5th day after capture, xanthophores prominent over brain, around spinal cord, on dorsal and ventral surfaces, and around snout.[11]

STAGE III
Size range described ca. 20–36 mm SL.

P. ca. 12; V. ca. 8 at 28.5 mm.[10] Depth at dorsal origin 6.5 times in SL, eye 5.05 times in head length at 28.0 mm TL.

Gape extending to anterior margin of pupil; dorsal origin equidistant between base of caudal and tip of snout at 28.0 mm. Scales first evident at ca. 35 mm.[1]

Pigmentation: At 25 mm, body transparent; dark spots along, above, and below lateral line; 5 dark saddles over back.[13] At 28 mm, 2 dark lines along sides of intestine; 2 rows of dark spots on back; few elongate dark spots along sides; some pigment at base of anal and ventrally on caudal peduncle.[1] Living specimens of unknown size 8 days after capture, melanophores on caudal; 5 clusters of melanophores along line of junction of dorsal and ventral myomeres; iridocytes over brain; large clumps of iridocytes over dorsal surface interspaced by melanophores and xanthophores.[11]

JUVENILES (Fig. 19 C)

Minimum size described ca. 36 mm SL.[7]

Proportions as percent SL in "juvenile" 51.2 mm SL: Head length 31.3; predorsal length 57.60; prepectoral length 31.30; preanal length 82.68. At 51.2 mm SL, head bullet-shaped, snout conical, mouth inferior, teeth quite small, crushing palate formed.[10]

At 40–45 mm, pectorals more than halfway to ventrals, not yet falcate; scalation complete except, perhaps, on belly; lateral line formed; anus in advance of anal fin by a distance nearly equal to length of snout.[1] Branching in all fins at 51.2 mm SL.[10]

Pigmentation: About 12 crossbands on back extending to lateral line [10] and persisting to ca. 75 mm.[1] At 51.2 mm, pigment developed on snout and above eye; chromatophores on dorsal and caudal fins.[10]

Age and size at maturity: Unknown.

LITERATURE CITED

1. Hildebrand, S. F., 1963d:134–41.
2. Gill, T., 1907c:42.
3. Hollister, G., 1936a:268, 274–5.
4. Hollister, G., 1936b:109.
5. Massmann, W. H., 1957:156.
6. Breder, C. M., Jr., 1962:565.
7. Fitch, J. E., 1950:4–5.
8. Delsman, H. C., 1926:406.
9. Whitney, G. P., 1937:7.
10. Alexander, E. C., 1961:3–46.
11. Rasquin, P., 1955:81.
12. Hildebrand, S. F., 1943b:93.
13. Longley, W. H., and S. F. Hildebrand, 1941:5.
14. Alparin, I. M., and R. M. Shaefer, 1964:5–6.
15. Nybelin, O., 1960:78.
16. Migdalski, E. C., 1958:207.
17. International Game Fish Association; 1962:1.
18. Uchida, K., 1958:2.
19. Meek, S. E., and S. F. Hildebrand, 1923:178.
20. Thompson, W. F., 1919:158.
21. Gopinath, K., 1946:15.

ADDITIONAL REFERENCES

Beebe, W., and G. Hollister, 1935; Beebe, W., and J. Tee-Van, 1928; Erdman, D. S., 1960a; Gehringer, J. W., 1959a; Jordan, D. S., 1905a; Longley, W. H., and S. F. Hildebrand, 1941; Meek, A., 1916; Meek, S. E., and S. F. Hildebrand, 1923.

Alosa aestivalis

Alosa mediocris

Alosa pseudoharengus

Alosa sapidissima

Brevoortia tyrannus

Clupea harengus

Dorosoma cepedianum

Etrumeus teres

Opisthonema oglinum

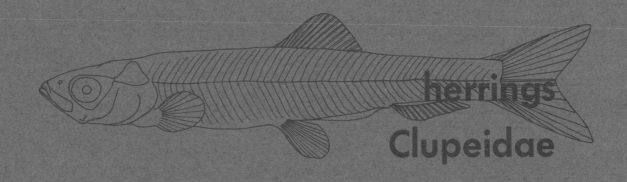

herrings
Clupeidae

Blueback herring   *Alosa aestivalis* **(Mitchill)**

ADULT (Fig. 20 A)

D. 15–20; A. 16–21; P. 14–16; V. 9; [1] vertebrae 47(FHB)–53; scale rows between gill openings and base of caudal 46–54; ventral scutes 31–36 (18–21 in advance of V.); gill rakers 41–52. Body moderately compressed, depth 3.0 to 4.6 times in SL.

Eye small, equal to or shorter than snout; mouth oblique; upper jaw with definite median notch; lower jaw not extending into dorsal profile. Teeth lacking on premaxil-laries, sometimes evident on posterior maxillary; mandibular teeth present anteriorly but lacking free points; narrow band of granular teeth on tongue. Scales moderately adherent with crenulate membranous edges preceded by scarcely visible striae.

Bluish above, sides silvery. Upper scale rows with more or less distinct longitudinal lines. A single dark shoulder spot usually present. Fins plain, greenish or yellowish. Peritoneum generally dark.

Maximum length ca. 380 mm.[1]

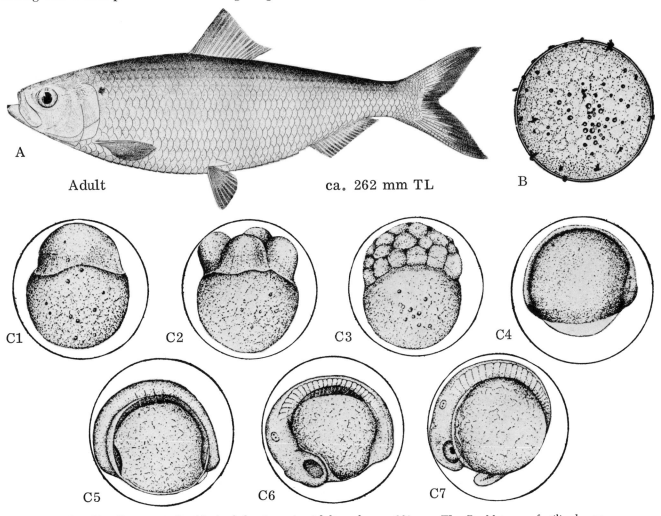

A   Adult   ca. 262 mm TL   B

C1   C2   C3   C4

C5   C6   C7

Fig. 20. Alosa aestivalis, blueback herring. A. Adult, male, ca. 262 mm TL. B. Mature unfertilized egg, diameter ca. 1.0 mm. Water-hardened; debris sticking to adhesive egg capsule. C. Development of egg. Diameter ca. 1.0 mm. C1. Blastodisc; yolk granular with small oil globules. C2. Four-cell stage. C3. Sixty-four cell stage. C4. Early embryo; germ ring darker area at edge of blastoderm. C5. Early embryo; 3 somites; blastopore open. C6. Embryo; 24–26 somites. C7. Tail-free embryo. (A, *Goode, et al., 1884: pl. 209.* B-C, *Kuntz and Radcliffe, 1917: fig. 87, 88, 90, 91, 93–6.*)

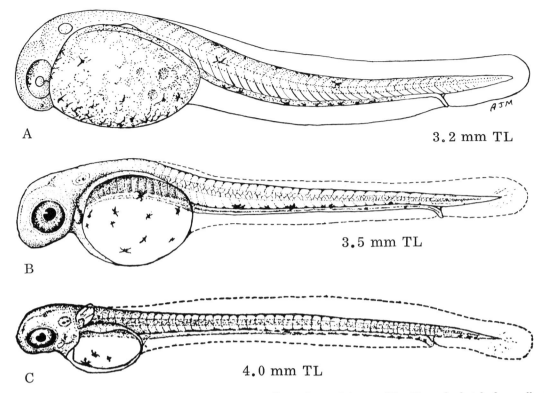

A   3.2 mm TL

B   3.5 mm TL

C   4.0 mm TL

Fig. 21. Alosa aestivalis, blueback herring. A. Yolk-sac larva, 3.2 mm TL. Recently hatched; small oil glubules still visiblc in yolk. B. Yolk-sac larva, 3 5 mm TL. Recently hatched. C. Yolk-sac larva, 4.0 mm TL. One day. (A, *Original drawing, A. J. Mansueti.* B, C, *Kuntz and Radcliffe, 1917: fig. 97, 98.*)

DISTRIBUTION AND ECOLOGY

Range: Nova Scotia to St. Johns River, Florida.[1]

Area distribution: Chesapeake Bay and "virtually all streams tributary to the Bay",[2] Delaware River,[3] and off-shore waters of New Jersey.

Habitat and movements: Adults—an anadromous, schooling species typically inhabiting a narrow band of coastal water, but entering fresh and brackish water during spawning season and apparently moving to offshore, bottom water during winter.

Larvae—fresh and brackish rivers.

Juveniles—leave fresh and brackish nursery grounds during late summer and fall, with some lingering in lower Chesapeake Bay during their first and possibly second winters.[1,2,4]

SPAWNING

Location: Fresh and brackish water rivers and tributaries, apparently never far above tidewater; also ponds having an outlet to the sea.[1,5]

Season: Last half of April through first half of May in Potomac River; later in more northern localities.[1]

Temperature: Optimum ca. 21–24 C.[4]

Fecundity: Similar to that of *Alosa pseudoharengus*, i.e., an average of 100,000.[6]

EGGS (Fig. 20 B,C)

Description: Demersal, somewhat adhesive, semi-transparent, yellowish. Average diameter 1.0 mm.

Fertilized egg—perivitelline space ca. 1/4 egg radius. Capsule relatively thick with inner surface appearing finely corrugated. Yolk granular; oil globules small, unequal, scattered.

Development: At "laboratory temperature." Fully differentiated blastodisc relatively thick, cap-like. Early blastomeres large and tending to be spherical. Peripheral growth of blastoderm apparent before periblast is well differentiated, but greatly increased following periblast formation and covers more than half the yolk at completion of germ ring and early differentiation of embryonic shield. Embryonic shield long, narrow; embryonic axis, when clearly differentiated, extending more than halfway around circumference of yolk. Three somites visible just prior to closure of blastopore within 16 hours after fertilization. With 24–26 somites present, embryo extends slightly more than 2/3 around yolk; optic and auditory vesicles developed. Just prior to hatching, length of

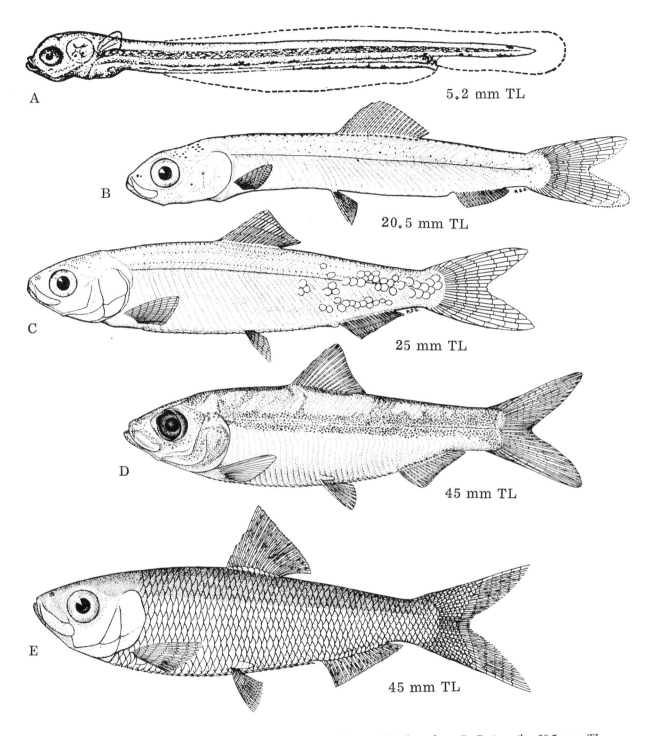

Fig. 22. Alosa aestivalis, blueback herring. A. Larva, 5.2 mm TL, four days. B. Prejuvenile, 20.5 mm TL, 16.5 mm SL. C. Prejuvenile, 25.0 mm TL, 20.0 mm SL. D. Juvenile, 45.0 mm TL, 36.5 mm SL. Irregular band of pigment along side variable. E. Juvenile, 45.0 mm TL. Scalation complete. (A, *Kuntz and Radcliffe, 1917: fig. 99. B, C, E, Hildebrand, 1963a: fig. 81. D, original drawing, A. J. Mansueti.)*

embryo exceeds yolk circumference. Embryo relatively opaque; slightly pigmented.[7]

Incubation: Ca. 50 hours at 22 C.[4]

YOLK-SAC LARVAE (Fig. 21 A-C)

Hatching length ca. 3.5 mm TL; longest specimen described 4.0 mm TL (1 day old).

Body elongate, relatively slender. Head moderately deflected at hatching, not deflected at 4.0 mm. Yolk mass initially sub-spherical, greatest length less than 1/4 TL; markedly reduced at end of first day; completely absorbed around fourth day. Anus ca. 1/6 TL from tip of caudal finfold.

Incipient caudal rays apparently formed at hatching. Pectorals initially absent; conspicuous and possibly rayed at 4.0 mm. Origin of dorsal finfold relatively far back on body at hatching; dorsal finfold apparently somewhat more narrow at hatching than at 4.0 mm.

Pigmentation: Chromatophores initially over yolk mass and in a series along intestine; at 4.0 mm, additional chromatophores developed at base of ventral finfold posterior to vent; intestinal chromatophores more conspicuous.[7]

LARVAE (Fig. 22 A)

One specimen described 5.2 mm TL (4 days old).

Mouth open, protuberant; auditory vesicles greatly enlarged; ventral finfold deep.

Pigment essentially as in yolk-sac larvae.[7]

PREJUVENILES (Fig. 22 B,C)

Specimens described 20.5 and 25.0 mm TL.

Body initially very slender, its depth increasing with age, 7.5 times in SL at 16.5 mm SL, 5.0 times in SL at 20.0 mm SL. At 20.5 mm TL, eye longer than snout; maxillary nearly to pupil.

Hickory Shad

ADULT (Fig. 23 A)

D. 15–20; A. 19–23; P. 15–16; V. 9. Scale rows between upper angle of gill opening and base of caudal 48–57; ventral scutes 33–38;[1] vertebrae 53 (FHB)–55; gill rakers 18–23.

Ventrals inserted under origin of dorsal at 20.5 mm TL, considerably further back at 25.0 mm TL. Scales developed posteriorly and scutes evident at 25.0 mm TL.

Pigmentation: Large chromatophores scattered over head, dorsum, and upper sides at 20.5 mm TL; those of upper sides apparently arranged in definite rows at 25.0 mm TL.[1]

JUVENILES (Fig. 22 D,E)

Smallest specimen tentatively included in this stage, 30 mm SL. Two specimens, each 45.0 mm TL, are described in detail and indicate wide variability at this stage [1] (AJM).

Gill rakers on lower limb 28–36 at 30–49 mm SL; 30–39 at 50–69 mm SL; 35–41 at 70–89 mm SL; 38–44 at 90–109 mm SL; 42–48 at 110–129 mm SL; and 42–50 at 130–149 mm SL.

Minute teeth on premaxillary; teeth on free rim of maxillary rather prominent; mandibular teeth with free points.[1] Nictitating membrane present. One 45 mm specimen with well developed axial scales and ventral scutes (AJM), another fully scaled.

Pigmentation: Tongue pigmentation along margin when present. Peritoneum usually black.[1] Least developed of two 45 mm specimens with broad mid-lateral band of chromatophores from which irregular blotches extend dorsally; chromatophores also present on head, opercle, and caudal fin (AJM).

Age and size at maturity: Ca. 4 years; 250 mm or less.[1]

LITERATURE CITED

1. Hildebrand, S. F., 1963a:314, 325–9, 331.
2. Hildebrand, S. F., and W. C. Schroeder, 1928:88–9.
3. Fowler, H. W., 1948:6.
4. Bigelow, H. B., and W. C. Schroeder, 1953:107.
5. Raney, E. C., and W. H. Massmann, 1953:427.
6. Smith, H. M., 1907:124.
7. Kuntz, A., and L. Radcliffe, 1917:92, 123–6.

Alosa mediocris (Mitchill)

Body elliptical, compressed, depth 3.0 to 3.75 in SL. Mouth oblique; upper jaw with median notch; lower jaw strongly projecting and extending into dorsal profile; upper margin of mandible with no pronounced angle. Teeth absent in upper jaw, very small on lower jaw and

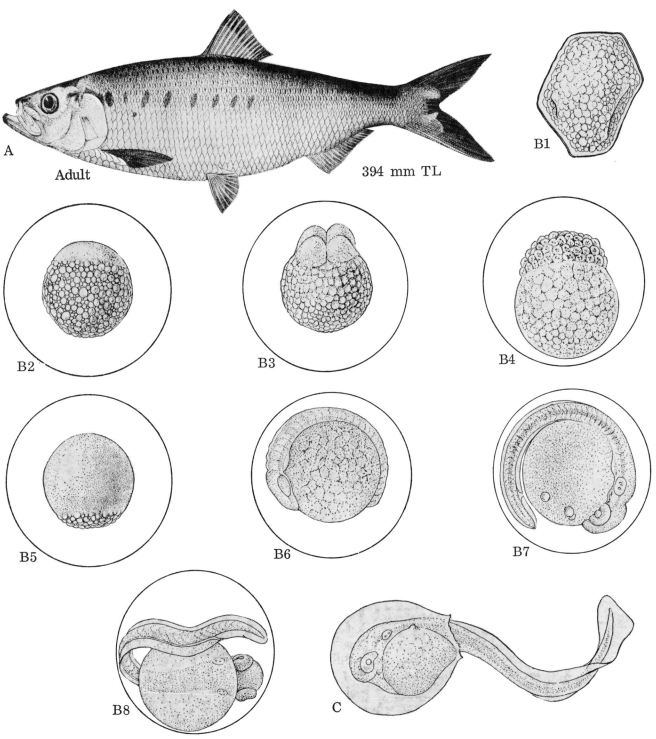

Fig. 23. Alosa mediocris, hickory shad. A. Adult, 394 mm TL. B. Development of egg at ca. 16–21 C. Average diameter 1.5 mm. B1. Ripe unfertilized egg; diameter 1.1 mm. Asymmetrical appearance typical. B2. Blastodisc formed, 1 hour. B3. Four-cell stage, 2 hours. B4. Morula, 4 hours. B5. Gastrula, blastopore open, 16 hours. B6. Embryo with 30 somites and optic vesicles, 24 hours. B7. Tail-free embryo, 36 hours. Auditory vesicles, anus, and pectoral buds formed; small oil droplets in yolk. B8. Pre-hatching embryo, 48 hours. C. Hatching larva, 6.1 mm TL, 48 hours. (A, *Goode, et al., 1884: pl. 216a.* B, C, *Mansueti, 1962b: fig. 3, 4.)*

tongue. Scales moderately adherent with longitudinal striae and crenulate, membranous borders.

Grayish-green above; sides iridescent silver. Nape green; side of head brassy; tip of lower jaw dusky. Caudal, dorsal, and pectoral dusky; ventral and anal plain. Narrow, dark lines along upper sides. Shoulder spot commonly followed by several obscure, dark spots. Peritoneum pale with scattered punctations.

Maximum length 600 mm.[1]

DISTRIBUTION AND ECOLOGY

Range: Bay of Fundy to Florida.[3]

Area distribution: Throughout Chesapeake Bay;[2] also recorded from New Jersey and Virginia.[1]

Habitat and movements: Adults—marine waters probably never far from land; also estuaries, tidal rivers and tributaries during late spring and early summer. A schooling, anadromous species whose oceanic movements are unknown. Well-defined "runs" of adults enter estuaries during spring and, to a lesser degree, during fall in Chesapeake Bay;[2] apparently return to ocean shortly after spawning.

Juveniles—tend to leave nursery areas during early summer; however specimens in age group I found sporadically throughout most of year in Chesapeake Bay and tributaries.[3]

SPAWNING

Location: Tidal freshwater.

Season: Late April through early June.

Time: Possibly dusk to midnight.[3]

Fecundity: Unknown.

EGGS (Fig. 23 B,C)

Description: Apparently broadcast at random; typically demersal although tending to be buoyant under turbulent conditions; slightly adhesive, but easily dislodged by currents.

Unfertilized eggs—asymmetrical; average diameter 1.12 mm (range 0.98–1.19 mm); average yolk diameter 0.98 (range 0.88–1.08 mm); egg capsule relatively thick, surface appearing finely corrugated; micropyle single.

Fertilized and water-hardened eggs—transparent, spherical, diameter 0.96 to 1.65 mm, perivitelline space ca. 1/2 egg radius. Yolk, in life, light amber-yellow and densely granular; in preservative, dark amber or whitish-yellow, diameter 0.83–1.16 mm; few small oil globules.

Development: Temperature at time of fertilization 14.4 C; rearing temperature from 2nd hour 18 to 21 C.

1 hour—predominately blastodiscs; few 2-cell stages; blastomeres with fine oil globules.

2 hours—predominately 2- and 4-cell stages.

4 hours—2- to 64-cell stages.

8 hours—16-cell stage to blastula.

16 hours—blastula to headfold stage; about 5 somites present in most advanced embryos.

24 hours—embryonic axis through early embryo; head, trunk, tail, spinal cord, gut, heart, pectoral buds, and ca. 30 somites evident in early embryos.

36 hours—some embryos with tail attached, others tail-free; somites 28–38; notochord and otoliths well developed; eyes colorless; body pigmentation absent; yolk sometimes with several small oil globules; yolk membrane vascular.

Incubation: 48–70 hours at ca. 16 to 31 C.[3]

YOLK-SAC LARVAE (Fig. 24 A,B)

Average size at hatching 6.1 mm TL (range 5.2–6.5 mm).

Preanal myomeres 37–40 at 1 day, 36–44 at 2 days; 5 branchial arches.

Proportions as percent SL: Depth ca. 13–16; snout-vent distance ca. 80–86; head length ca. 9–10.

Eye diameter ca. 40–47% head length. Yolk large, restricted to anterior 1/4 of body and characterized by granular appearance. Eye large, unpigmented at hatching; hyomandibular, Meckel's cartilage, auditory vesicles present; mouth open, but lacking esophageal connection; cleithrum and gill clefts formed or forming by 2nd day. Pectoral buds prominent at hatching, leaf-like at 1 day.

Pigmentation: Initially limited to few chromatophores along gut. At 1 day, abdomen with small melanophores; 18–20 elongate melanophores along ventral surface of gut between yolk and anus; few dots on dorsal surface; eye darkly pigmented. At 3 days, single line of 18–25 melanophores on upper surface of intestine, bifurcating at yolk and extending to region below origin of pectoral fin; few melanophores posterior to anus and on caudal finfold.[3]

PUTATIVE LARVAE (Fig. 24 C-D)

Size range ca. 6.5–18.0 mm TL.

Anus 80% back along body. Average preanal myomeres 39 at 6.5–7.0 mm, increasing to 44 by 7.0–7.5 mm, and decreasing to 38 by end of stage.

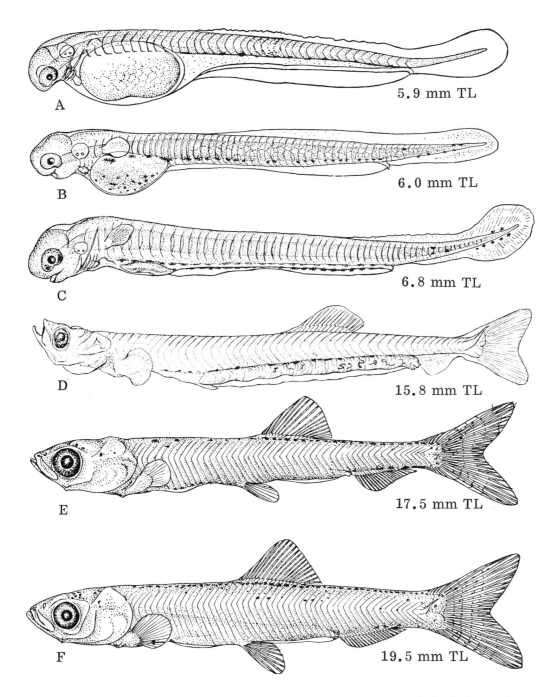

Fig. 24. *Alosa mediocris*, hickory shad. A. Yolk-sac larva, 5.9 mm TL. Recently hatched; irregular margin of dorsal finfold typical. B. Yolk-sac larva, 6.0 mm TL, 1 day. Pectoral buds flattened. C. Larva, 6.8 mm TL, 3 days. Incipient rays in caudal and pectoral. D. Larva, 15.8 mm TL. Angle of lower jaw acute; intestine with marked convolutions along entire length. E. Prejuvenile, 17.5 mm TL. Preanal finfold present. F. Prejuvenile, 19.5 mm TL. Preanal finfold present. (*Mansueti, 1962b: fig. 5, 6, 8.*)

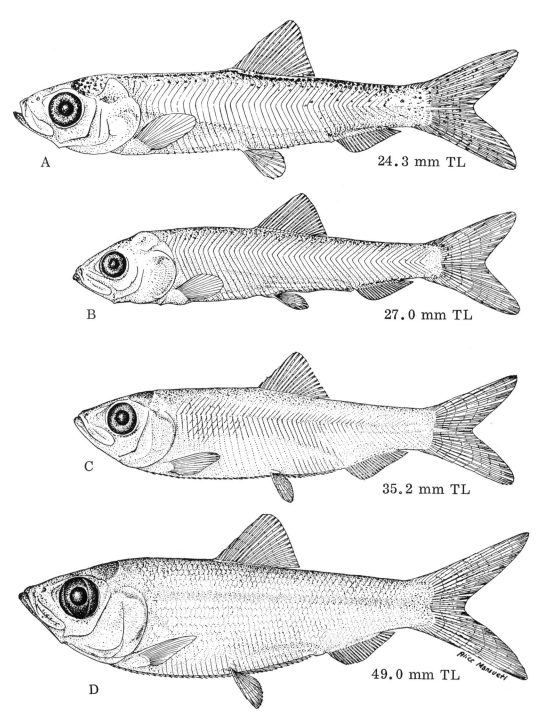

Fig. 25. *Alosa mediocris,* hickory shad. A. Prejuvenile, 24.3 mm TL. Scutes formed. B. Prejuvenile, 27.0 mm TL. Pigmentation over back more regular; gill rakers visible through operculum. C. Juvenile, 35.2 mm TL. Scales in pectoral region; axial scale formed; myomeres visible. D. Juvenile 49.0 mm TL. Scalation almost complete; nictitating membrane formed; light, lateral band of pigmentation present. (*Mansueti, 1962b: fig. 8, 9.*)

Body elongate. Dorsal fin first evident at ca. 9.0 mm, anal at 14.0 mm, and ventrals at 13.0 mm.

Pigmentation: Initially as in yolk-sac larvae; by end of stage, melanophores on ventral part of body from gular region to area above anal fin.[3]

PREJUVENILES (Fig. 24 E,F; Fig. 25 A,B)

Size range ca. 18.0–33.0 mm TL.

Gill rakers on lower limb of first arch 11–20. Total myomeres 50–54; predorsal myomeres ca. 17–26; preanal myomeres 36–42.

Proportions as percent SL: Greatest depth 10.9–20.8; snout-vent distance 74.5–81.8; head length ca. 22–30.

Proportions as percent HL: Eye diameter ça. 20.0–30.6; mandibular length ca. 42.6–51.6.

Preanal finfold retained to ca. 20.0 mm; scutes evident at 24 mm.

Pigmentation: An ill-defined double row of melanophores along dorsum; caudal fin with melanophores.

By end of stage, dorsum with numerous melanophores; a conspicuous U-shaped blotch behind eyes.[3]

JUVENILES (Fig. 25 C,D)

Minimum size ca. 35 mm TL.

Body shape similar to adult. Scales first evident at ca. 35 mm, originating in pectoral region; pelvic axial scales present or absent. Nictitating membrane evident at ca. 49 mm.

Size at maturity: Males 287 mm; females 320 mm TL.[3]

LITERATURE CITED

1. Hildebrand, S. F., 1963a:319–21.
2. Hildebrand, S. F., and W. C. Schroeder, 1928:84–5.
3. Mansueti, R. J., 1962b:173–205.

ADDITIONAL REFERENCES

Mansueti, R. J., 1958; Massmann, W. H., E. C. Ladd, and H. H. McCutcheon, 1952.

Alewife

Alosa pseudoharengus (Wilson)

ADULT (Fig. 26 A)

D. 15–19;[2] A. 15[12]–21; P. 13–16; scales in lateral series 42[2]–54;[12] longitudinal scale rows between base of ventrals and base of dorsal 14; vertebrae 46–50; gill rakers on lower limb of first arch 38–44; preventral scutes 18–21; postpelvic scutes 12–16.

Proportions as percent SL (based in part on juvenile specimens): Body depth 23.5–35.5; head length 22.6–34.8; eye diameter 5.0–12.0.

Body compressed; mouth oblique; eye large, longer than snout.

Grayish-green above; sides silvery; upper scale rows sometimes with more or less definite dusky lines; a dark shoulder spot; fins pale, yellowish, or green; peritoneum pale or silvery, often with dark punctations.

Maximum length 380 mm.[2]

DISTRIBUTION AND ECOLOGY

Range: Coastal populations from Gulf of St. Lawrence and Nova Scotia[8] to South Carolina;[14] also landlocked populations in the Great Lakes, Finger Lakes in New York,[2] and other freshwater lakes.[8]

Area distribution: Virtually all streams tributary to Chesapeake Bay;[7] Virginia,[9] Delaware,[20] New Jersey.[10]

Habitat and movements: Adults—a schooling species whose oceanic movements are apparently restricted to coastal areas proximal to natal estuaries; maximum depth 60–80 fathoms; maximum distance from land ca. 80 miles;[8] sometimes in coastal ponds.[5] In Lake Ontario, confined to deep water from about September to March; inshore movement begins during April and lasts until late July, with fish appearing first in shallow water during daylight hours, but later mainly at dusk and after dark.[15] Anadromous, arriving in Chesapeake Bay in late February or early March, returning to sea after spawning.

Larvae—remain in vicinity of spawning grounds.

Juveniles—pass slowly down Chesapeake drainage system until fall when main seaward migration occurs (WLD); some spend first winter in deeper parts of Bay, most go directly to sea.[2] In Gulf of Maine, apparently leave nursery grounds throughout summer; tend to remain near surface for their first year or so in saltwater.[8]

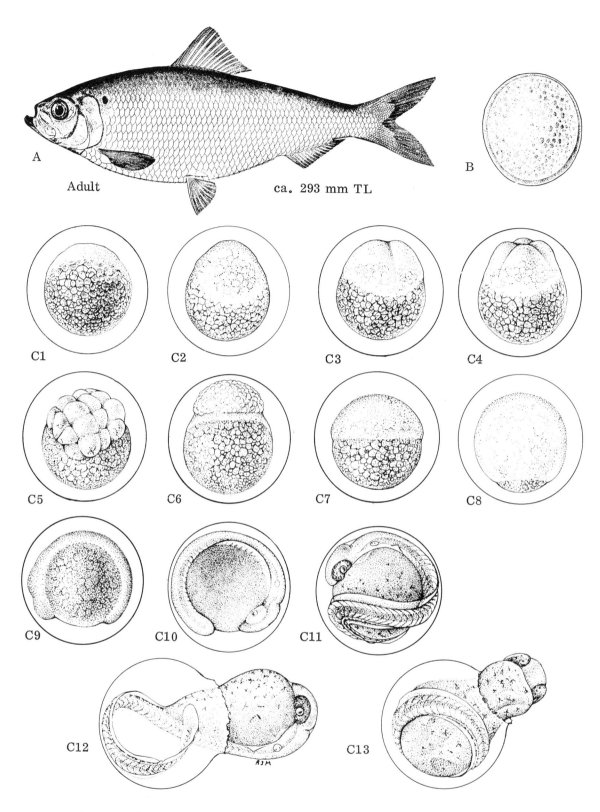

Fig. 26. Alosa pseudoharengus, alewife. A. Adult, female, ca. 293 mm. B. Unripe, unfertilized egg; diameter 0.9 mm. C. Development of egg at average temperature of 20 C. Diameter ca. 1.0 mm. C1. Blastodisc, ca. 45 minutes. C2. Blastodisc, oblique view. C3. Two-cell stage, ca. 1 hour. C4. Four-cell stage, ca. 1 hour. C5. Sixteen-cell stage, 3 hours. C6. Morula, 4 1/2 hours. C7. Early gastrula, ca. 11 hours. C8. Late gastrula, 12–15 hours. C9. Early embryo, one day. Blastopore closed; brain folds developed. C10. Tail-free embryo, 3 days. Total myomeres 28. C11. Late embryo, 5 days. Pigmentation over eyes and yolk. C12. Hatching embryo, ca. 3.5 mm TL, 5 days. C13. Hatching embryo, ca. 3.5 mm TL, 5 days. (A, *Goode, et al., 1884: pl. 207.* B-C, *original drawings, A. J. Mansueti.*)

SPAWNING

Location: Large rivers;[8,16] streams only a few feet wide;[1,16] small ponds, including barrier beach ponds;[5] sometimes in rapid flowing water ca. 2 feet deep over coarse stones, sand, and gravel;[3] usually in sluggish water often only a few inches deep;[8,13] sometimes in water as deep as 10 feet.[17]

Season: Late March through April in Maryland (AJM) with spawning lasting only a few days for each spawning group;[8] April and May in New England;[11] late May to mid-August in Finger Lakes, New York.[6]

Time: Observed both diurnally[3,17] and nocturnally,[17] but apparently with greatest activity at night.[15,17]

Temperature: Running ripe of both sexes observed at 4.2–16.7 C in Chesapeake Bay area (AJM).

Fecundity: Variously estimated, 2,180–10,011;[13] 60,000–100,000;[8] average of 102,800.[1]

EGGS (Fig. 26 B,C)

Description: Broadcast at random; demersal; possibly somewhat adhesive immediately after extrusion, although recent investigations indicate that they are essentially non-adhesive (AJM).[16]

Green, unfertilized eggs—uneven spheres with thin transparent capsules; diameter 0.80–0.95 (average 0.90 mm); yolk diameter 0.70–0.85 (average 0.80 mm); yolk dark amber, opaque, granular, although not as much so as in fertilized eggs.

Fertilized eggs—diameter 0.94–1.25 mm; capsule slightly rippled at high magnification; yolk granular, bright translucent amber, lacking oil globules.

Development: At average temperature of 20° C.

45 minutes—blastodiscs.
1 to 3 hours—2- and 4-cell stages.
3 hours—16- and 32-cell stages.

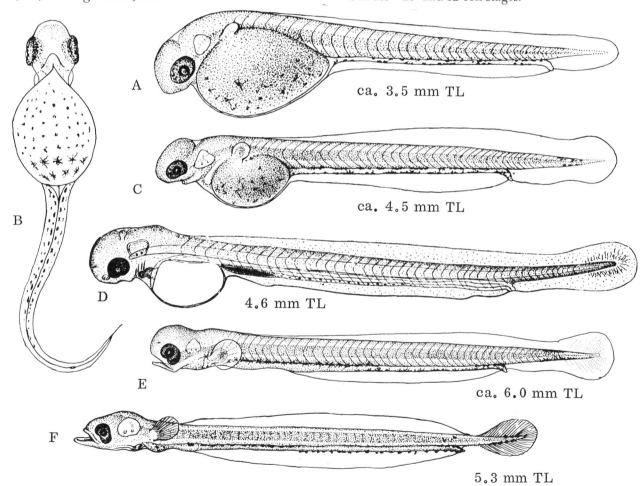

Fig. 27. *Alosa pseudoharengus*, alewife. A. Yolk-sac larva, ca. 3.5 mm TL, recently hatched. Notochord reticulated. B. Yolk-sac larva, recently hatched. Typical ventral chromatophore pattern. C. Yolk-sac larva, ca. 4.5 mm TL, one day. D. Yolk-sac larva, ca. 4.6 mm TL. E. Larva, ca. 6.0 mm TL. F. Larva, 5.30 mm TL, 5.05 mm SL. 5 days. Preanal myomeres 39. (A-C, E, F, *original drawings, A. J. Mansueti.* D, *Ryder, 1887: pl. 2, fig. 8.*)

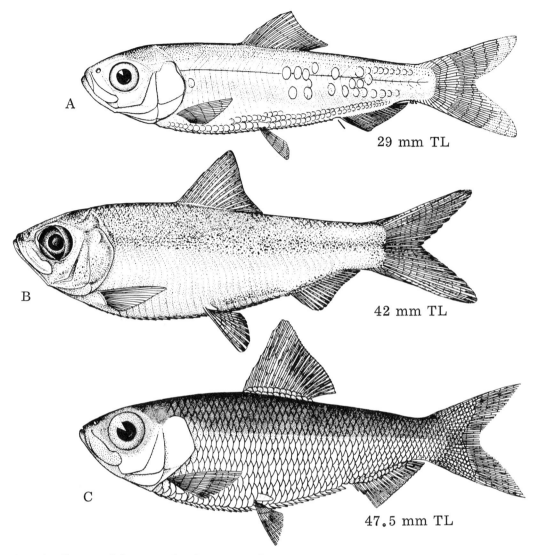

29 mm TL

42 mm TL

47.5 mm TL

Fig. 28. *Alosa pseudoharengus*, alewife. A. Juvenile, 29 mm TL, 22 mm SL. B. Juvenile, 42 mm TL, 34 mm SL. C. Juvenile, 47.5 mm TL. (A, C, *Hildebrand, 1963a: fig. 83*. B, *original drawing, A. J. Mansueti.*)

4 hours, 30 minutes—32-cell, 64-cell, and morula stages.

11 hours—gastrula; blastodermal tissue around 1/2 of yolk; yolk granulations less distinct.

12 to 15 hours—blastopore formed; yolk paler; less granular.

Ca. 24 hours—blastopore closed; embryo differentiated; yolk no longer granular.

65 hours—tail free; eyes, lenses, auditory vesicles, and 28 myomeres formed.

113 hours—heart, otoliths, pectoral buds, finfold, intestine, and vent formed; brown chromatophores over ventral 2/3 of yolk, sparsely scattered over eye, and in a line along ventral surface of gut; tail completely around yolk.

Incubation: 3–5 days at 20 C (AJM), 6 days at 15.6 C.[2]

YOLK-SAC LARVAE (Fig. 27 A-D)

Hatching length 3.5 mm (AJM) to 5.0 mm TL;[19] duration of stage 4–5 days (AJM).

Head flexed at hatching, straight or flexed at 1 day; mouth barely evident at hatching, non-functional at 1 day. Yolk initially hemispherical, pale amber; 1/2 absorbed by 1 day. Auditory vesicles triangular at hatching, much enlarged by 2nd day.

Pigmentation: Pigment pattern of yolk variable, typically with ca. 10 rows of melanophores across ventral half of yolk. A double row of ca. 20 melanophores along each side of ventral mid-line of tail. At 1 day, eye flecked with gold; few melanophores along dorsal and ventral surfaces of gut and in caudal region (AJM).

LARVAE (Fig. 27 E,F)

Size range described ca. 5.0 mm (AJM) to ca. 16.5 mm TL.[19]

Preanal myomeres 39 at 6.0 mm; vertebrae 38+42 at 8 days (ca. 7.0 mm).

Body long, narrow; head variable, rounded at ca. 6.0 mm, flattened by 8th day; lower jaw projected beyond upper at 8 days; mouth terminal at 6.0 mm (AJM); lower jaw with small teeth at 16.5 mm.[19] Gut straight at 6.0 mm (AJM), conspicuously convoluted posteriorly at 15 mm; gas bladder visible at 16.5 mm.[19] Caudal and pectorals with or without incipient rays up to 5.4 mm (AJM); preanal finfold retained to 16.5 mm.[19]

Pigmentation: At 6.0 mm, melanophores in a row on dorsal surface of anterior half of intestine and on dorsal and ventral midline of tail near developing caudal fin. At 8 days, ca. 12 melanophores along dorsal surface of anterior half of gut, 22–24 on ventral surface of posterior half of gut; scattered melanophores on lateral body wall and in area behind eye (AJM). At 15 mm, a few yellow spots apparent around pupil and an orange patch in region behind pectorals; at 16.5 mm, additional yellow spots on head, cheeks and throat.[19]

PREJUVENILES

Undescribed.

JUVENILES (Fig. 28 A-C)

Minimum size described 28 mm TL.[18]

Gill rakers 25–33 at 30–49 mm; 32–36 at 50–69 mm; 30–39 at 70–89 mm; 35–38 at 90–109 mm; 36–40 at 110–129 mm. Body depth 4 times in SL at 29 mm TL; depth adult-like at 100 mm.[2]

Scales first evident at 28 mm on side of tail along lateral line at about 43rd myomere.[18]

Pigmentation: At 35 mm, pigment forming two lunate patches at base of tail; minute black specks over entire dorsum, especially on head and tail; black specks also on premaxillaries, maxillaries, and mandible.[19]

Age and size at maturity: Freshwater populations mature earlier and at a smaller average size than saltwater populations; e.g., in Lake Ontario, males mature at minimum of ca. 1 year and ca. 95.5 mm SL, females at minimum of 2 years and ca. 110 mm SL. Atlantic males reach maturity at a minimum of 3 years (ca. 147.4 mm SL); females at minimum of 4 years (ca. 167.3 mm SL).[15]

LITERATURE CITED

1. Smith, H. M., 1907:123.
2. Hildebrand, S. F., 1963a:332–7, 340–1.
3. Greeley, J. R., 1935:89.
4. Ryder, J. A., 1887:505–6.
5. Bigelow, H. B., and W. W. Welsh, 1925:109.
6. Odell, T. T., 1934:118.
7. Hildebrand, S. F., and W. C. Schroeder, 1928:90, 93.
8. Bigelow, H. W., and W. C. Schroeder, 1953:103–4.
9. Massmann, W. H., 1958:4.
10. Fowler, H. W., 1906:97.
11. Nichols, J. T., and C. M. Breder, Jr., 1927:38.
12. Miller, R. R., 1957:99.
13. Rothschild, B. J., 1962:1, 35–6, 39.
14. Berry, F. H., 1964:726.
15. Graham, J. J., 1956:7, 8.
16. Mansueti, R. J., 1956:2, 3.
17. Edsall, T. A., 1964:226–7.
18. Huntsman, A. G., 1918:81.
19. Prince, E. E., 1907:106–7.
20. de Sylva, D. P., F. A. Kalber, Jr., and C. N. Shuster, Jr., 1962:18.

ADDITIONAL REFERENCES

Bean, T. H., 1902; Breder, C. M., Jr., and R. F. Nigrelli, 1936; Brice, J. J., 1898; Gross, R. W., 1959; Tracy, H. C., 1910; Wyman, J., 1856.

American shad

Alosa sapidissima (Wilson)

ADULT (Fig. 29 A)

D. 14–20; A. 18–25; P. 13–18;[17] V. 8–10.[2] Scale rows between gill opening and base of caudal 52–62; scale rows between base of pelvics and anterior dorsal rays 15–16;[4] vertebrae 51[2]–60;[17] gill rakers on lower limb of first arch 59[4]–76;[5] ventral scutes 34–40, 19–25 anterior to pelvics, 12–18 behind.[17]

Proportions as percent SL: Body depth 30.2–48; head length 23–28; eye diameter 3.8–5.7 (may include some juveniles).[4]

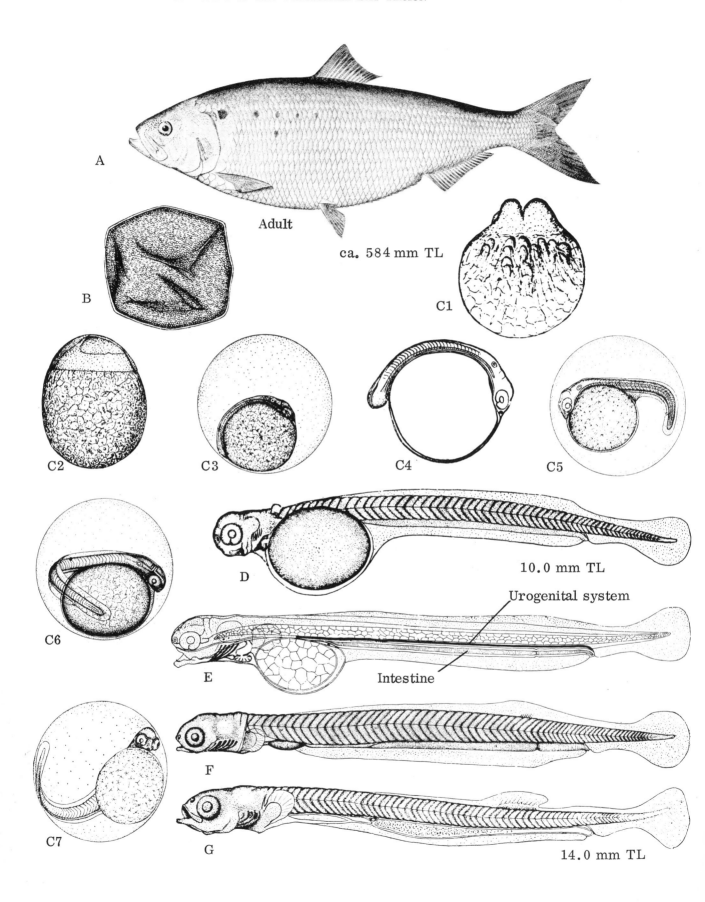

A

Adult

ca. 584 mm TL

B

C1

C2

C3

C4

C5

C6

D

10.0 mm TL

E

Urogenital system

Intestine

C7

F

G

14.0 mm TL

Dorsal profile of head nearly straight;[5] mouth oblique;[4] maxillary reaching slightly beyond posterior margin of eye;[5] upper outline of mandible only slightly concave and lacking sharp angle;[7] teeth absent.[4] Scales large,[7] moderately adherent.

Dorsal elevated anteriorly, margin slightly concave, origin an eye's diameter or less in front of ventrals; caudal rather deeply forked, lobes about equal and somewhat shorter than head; anal low; axillary scale equal to or little more than 1/2 length of ventrals.

Greenish or bluish above; bright silvery on sides; dark shoulder spot sometimes followed by one or more rows of smaller spots; fins pale to greenish, dorsal and caudal sometimes dusky; peritoneum pale to silvery.[4]

Maximum length ca. 760 mm.[6]

DISTRIBUTION AND ECOLOGY

Range: Newfoundland [29,31] to St. Johns River, Florida;[7] introduced on Pacific coast and now established from San Diego, California to Alaska;[18,27] also eastern shores of Kamchatka, U.S.S.R.[21]

Area distribution: "Virtually all streams tributary to Chesapeake Bay";[5] New Jersey, Delaware, and Virginia.[6]

Habitat and movements: Non-spawning adults—waters of continental shelf, appearing in schools near surface in spring, summer, and fall;[7] brackish estuaries;[4] rarely in freshwater outside the spawning season.[8] Maximum depth 50-68 fathoms. Maximum distance from coast 110 miles.[4]

Spawning adults—anadromous, ascending parental rivers to spawn,[10,11,19] with runs of 513 miles from sea reported.[33] Adults from rivers south of Chesapeake Bay die after spawning. Adults from Connecticut River to Chesapeake Bay migrate northward to Gulf of Maine, those from Canada move southward to same area with both populations remaining there throughout summer and fall. During winter this mixed population scatters throughout Middle Atlantic area. As spawning season approaches schools move shoreward and northward or southward to native streams.[19] Atypical "runs" may occur in November and December in Chesapeake Bay.[5]

Larvae—fresh to brackish water; maximum salinity ca. 7.0 o/oo;[2] movements generally downstream.[4]

Juveniles—usually in the sea after first fall, sometimes in estuarine waters;[4] near mouths of bays and rivers in northern parts of range during summer.[9] Move downstream when water temperature falls below ca. 16 C,[4] and to ocean,[6] although some remain in estuarine waters such as Chesapeake Bay for first winter,[4] and 1- and 2-year old shad are occasionally taken in brackish and fresh water in Potomac River.[11] Immature shad typically remain in ocean for 3 [1] to 6 [19] years; their whereabouts in southern parts of their range, during this time, are unknown, but in northern localities they tend to stay close inshore at least for first year.[4]

SPAWNING

Location: Mostly in tidal freshwater, less frequently in non-tidal water (WHM); possibly in brackish water in California.[2] Usually in river areas dominated by extensive flats;[13] also over sandy or pebbly shallows;[4,15] frequently near mouths of creeks.[1,5]

Season: First runs in St. Johns River, Florida in November and progressively later northward;[4] earliest individuals arrive in Maryland streams in February, but most abundant in April [1] with spawning activity apparently continuing for "several weeks".[6] Spawning may continue until May [23] or June in more northern localities of east coast [23,29,30] and in California.[24,25]

Time: Probably all hours of day and night with greatest activity apparently between noon and midnight [1,2,13] or from sunset to midnight.[26]

Temperature: Usually enter rivers when temperature exceeds 4 C;[14] spawning generally occurs at 12–20 C.[16]

Fecundity: 116,000 [12]–659,000.[16] Reports of lower fecundities (25,000–30,000) are apparently in error.[12,32]

Fig. 29. Alosa sapidissima, American shad. A. Adult female, ca. 584 mm TL. B. Egg, diameter ca. 1.8 mm. Ripe unfertilized, not water-hardened; small round vesicles under wrinkled egg capsule. C. Development of egg at 24 C. Diameter ca. 3.5 mm. C1. Two-cell stage, 1 1/3 hours; egg capsule removed. C2. Gastrula with embryonic shield; egg capsule removed. C3. Early embryo just after closure of blastopore. Egg capsule intact; 20 myomeres visible. C4. Tail-free embryo. Egg capsule removed; 32 myomeres visible; heart dark, thickened area posterior to eye. C5. Embryo, 44 hours. C6. Late embryo, ca. 48 hours. C7. Prehatching embryo, ca. 72 hours. Yolk covered with stellate chromatophores; mouth open; rudimentary gill arches and pectoral buds formed. D. yolk-sac larva, 10.0 mm TL, newly hatched. Preanal myomeres 43; pigmentation on yolk and along intestine not shown. E. Yolk-sac larva, 3 days. View of internal structures; urogenital system drawn as dark line over intestine. F. Larva, 5 days. Remnant of yolk remains; incipient rays present in dorsal and pectorals; eyes dark; pigmentation of ventral and dorsal surface of intestine not illustrated. G. Larva, 14.0 mm TL, 17 days. Nine incipient rays in dorsal; rudimentary gas bladder forming at 18th myomere. (A, *Goode, et al.* 1884: pl. 212. B-G, *Ryder, 1887: fig. 68, 78, 101, 102, 126, 127, 136, 141, 148–151*.)

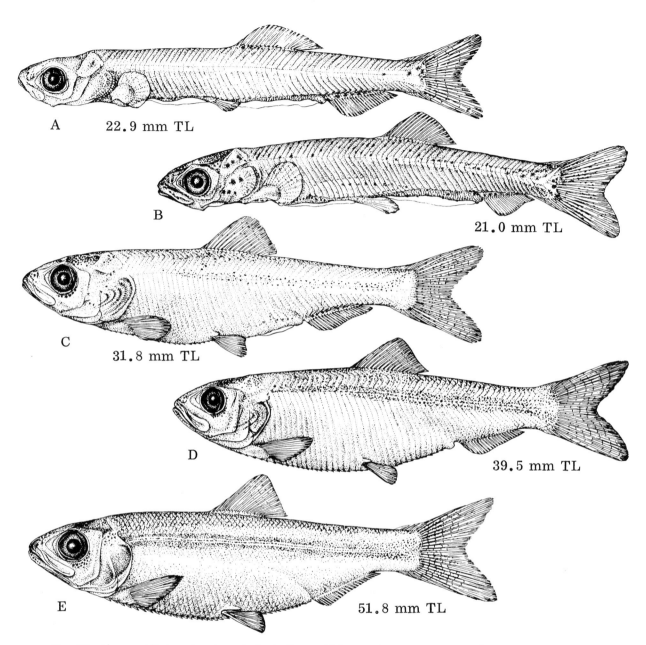

Fig. 30. *Alosa sapidissima*, American shad. A. Larva, 22.9 mm TL, 20.0 mm SL, 12 days. Hatchery reared; D. 17; A. 21; preanal myomeres 43; postanal myomeres 14; sparse pigmentation. B. Larva, 21.0 mm TL, 17.8 mm SL, 18 days. Hatchery reared; D. 16; A. 21; preanal myomeres 42; postanal myomeres 15; large gas bladder visible through body wall. C. Juvenile, 31.8 mm TL, 26.7 mm SL. D. 17; A. 21; preanal myomeres 38; postanal myomeres 15; remnant of preanal finfold remains; nictitating membrane and scutes developing; no scales. D. Juvenile, 39.5 mm TL, 33.5 mm SL; D. 17; A. 21; 33 scutes; preanal myomeres 38; postanal myomeres 16; scales forming above mid-lateral region; dark stripe along side. E. Juvenile, 51.8 mm TL, 41.5 mm SL; D. 17; A. 22; 37 scutes; almost fully scaled; lateral stripe still evident; pigmentation dense over back and head. (*Original drawings, A. J. Mansueti.*)

EGGS (Fig. 29 B-C)

Description: Demersal,[1,4] rolling about on bottom with current;[7] deposited at random, dropped "loosely and singly to the bottom."[4]

Unfertilized eggs—ca. 1.8 mm in diameter;[8] pale amber; with wrinkled egg capsule; micropyle single.[3]

Fertilized eggs—transparent, pale amber or pink,[1] nonadhesive,[4] spherical,[3] ca. 2.5[28]–3.5 mm in diameter.[2,4] Yolk distinctly granular; perivitelline space ca. 1/2 egg radius.

Development: At ca. 24 C.

Ca. 30 minutes—blastodisc formed.
Ca. 1 hour, 20 minutes—first cleavage furrow.
Ca. 2 hours—second cleavage.
Ca. 2 hours, 30 minutes—third cleavage.
4 to 5 hours—morula completed.
Beyond 5 hours—Blastula stage brief; blastocoel kidney-shaped when viewed from above, soon becoming crescent-shaped. Three or 4 somites evident at time of closure of blastopore; Kupffer's vesicle, optic and auditory vesicles, choroid fissure evident shortly thereafter; tail-bud stage with ca. 32 somites.
44 hours—yolk pigmented and finfold well formed.
Ca. 48 hours—tail recurved and incipient pectoral fins evident.

At 16–17 C:
6 hours—blastula.
20 hours, 30 minutes—late gastrula.
38 hours—early embryo.
42 hours—tailfree embryo.[15]

Incubation: Two days at ca. 27 C,[20] to 17 days at ca. 12 C.[3]

Optimum conditions for development: Temperature ca. 17 C, salinity ca. 7.5 o/oo, and darkness.[2]

YOLK-SAC LARVAE (Fig. 29 D,E)

Length at hatching ca. 7–10 mm TL; length at end of stage probably ca. 9–12 mm TL. Duration of stage 4–5 days at 17 C, ca. 7 days at 12 C.

Body slender, depth in advanced specimens 0.05 of TL.[4]

In newly hatched, yolk sub-spherical; head detached from yolk; mouth open but without free passage through esophagus;[3] eyes large, dark, protuberant.[4] By 3rd day, jaws, gill arches, and 2 pairs of recurved teeth in lower jaw forming; incipient rays of pectorals formed; notochord thick, distinctly granular; gut striated; renal apparatus conspicuous, extending from above yolk to anus.

Pigmentation: Body transparent.[4] Yolk sac covered with diffuse network of stellate chromatophores. Midventral line of pigment sometimes present on isthmus. A line of chromatophores along juncture of yolk sac and body and continuing along junction of intestine and body to anus. A closely approximated double line of pigment on ventral aspect of intestine from ca. 18th myomere to anus. A fine network of pigment usually present on lateral surface of intestine, most dense near anus. Stellate chromatophores on lateral surfaces of body, mostly between level of notochord and intestine, extending from yolk to beyond anus. Few spots above and below notochord in area of future caudal fin.[2]

LARVAE (Fig. 29 F,G; Fig. 30 A,B)

Size range 10.5[2] to ca. 27.0 mm TL (may include some prejuveniles). Duration of stage 21–28 days.[3]

At 21 to 22.9 mm, pectorals and ventrals still developing; P. 3–15; V. 5–7.[2] Total myomeres 55–57 at 21.0–22.9 mm (AJM); preanal myomeres 43–47 in specimens to 13 mm, 41–45 at 14–16 mm, 37–44 at 17–22 mm, 34–42 at 23–27 mm.[2]

Body long and slender, increasing in relative depth throughout stage. Auditory vesicles still evident at 21.0 mm. Gas bladder evident by 14 mm.

By 14 mm, finfold greatly reduced; anlage of dorsal fin developed; incipient caudal rays formed; urostyle directed slightly upward; rudimentary ventrals evident at 18 mm; preanal finfold retained throughout stage.

Pigmentation: Up to 13 mm, lines of pigment along venter and intestine broken into short dashes; pigment on isthmus decreased; a line of chromatophores dorsad from base of pectoral; 0–15 chromatophores ventrolaterally between head and caudal peduncle. At 14–16 mm, diverging lines of pigment along venter generally terminating at 14th or 15th myomere; chromatophores sometimes present along dorsal wall of intestine between dorsal fin and anus; few chromatophores on caudal fin. Larger specimens highly variable; additional pigment develops on snout, operculum, and dorsal surfaces of head and body. Specimens from fresh water apparently more heavily pigmented than those from brackish water.[2]

PREJUVENILES

Undescribed, although fin formation may be complete in specimens as small as ca. 20 mm.[15]

JUVENILES (Fig. 30 C-E)

Minimum size 25 to 28 mm TL.[2]

Total myomeres 54 at 32 mm (RJM); preanal myomeres

34–47 at 28–32 mm, 32–36 at 33–71 mm.[2] Gill rakers on lower limb of first arch 26–31 at 35–65 mm, 34–43 at 70–125 mm, 48–62 at 190–270 mm, and increasing with growth to ca. 300 mm.[4] Ventral scutes 33 at 39.5 mm, 37 at 51.8 mm. Greatest depth ca. 3.9 to 4.5 in SL at 26.7–51.8 mm (RJM); average depth 3.5 in SL at 35–100 mm.[5] Ratio between horizontal diameter of eye and distance from most anterior point of eye to tip of upper jaw in specimens 23–47 mm (thus possibly including some larvae and prejuveniles) 0.96–1.28.[2]

At 31.8 mm, nictitating membrane present; opercular apparatus not fully differentiated; remnant of preanal finfold present; axillary scales beginning to form. Scales first evident above mid-lateral region at 34.5 mm, nearly complete at 51.8 mm TL (RJM). Cheek more narrow and deep; angle of upper margin of mandible near middle and much lower and broader than in other young clupeids. Maxillary reaching middle of eye at 50 mm;[5] median notch on maxillary lacking below 150 mm;[4] teeth developed on anterior part of jaws, persisting to ca. 300 mm.[7] At 40–70 mm, tongue with 6–20 teeth; ca. 50 melanophores crowded in 2 or 3 rows on each half of tongue.[22]

Pigmentation: Dorsal and dorso-lateral aspects of body and head covered with dense pigment.[2] A 31.8 mm specimen has chromatophores over head, below eye, on opercle, along anal base, on caudal, in a district mid-lateral line, and along dorsum (AJM).

Age and size at maturity: 3–6 years, mostly at 4–5 years;[19] males ca. 305–447 mm FL, females 383–485 mm FL.[16]

LITERATURE CITED

1. Mansueti, R. J., 1955:1–2.
2. Leim, A. H., 1924:163–300.
3. Ryder, J. A., 1887:523–33.
4. Hildebrand, S. F., 1963a:293–308.
5. Hildebrand, S. F., and W. C. Schroeder, 1928:93–101.
6. Mansueti, R. J., and H. Kolb, 1953:3–20, 64–100.
7. Bigelow, H. B., and W. C. Schroeder, 1953:108–112.
8. Leach, G. C., 1925b:471.
9. Atkins, C. G., 1887:683–87.
10. Hollis, E. H., 1948:332.
11. Hammer, R. C., 1942:1–45.
12. Lehman, B. A., 1953:8.
13. Massmann, W. H., 1952:84, 90.
14. Massmann, W. H., and A. Pacheco, 1957:351–2.
15. Bigelow, H. B., and W. W. Welsh, 1925:118.
16. Walburg, C. H., 1960:498.
17. Hill, D. R., 1959:284–86.
18. Roedel, P. M., 1953:35.
19. Talbot, G. B., and J. E. Sykes, 1958:475.
20. Rice, H. J., 1878:106.
21. Svetovidov, A. N., 1963:354.
22. Dovel, W. L., A. J. Mansueti, and E. H. Oldmixon, 1965:4.
23. Leach, G. C., 1925a:408.
24. Ganssle, D., 1966:71.
25. Erkkila, L. F., J. W. Moffett, O. B. Cope, B. R. Smith, and R. S. Nielson, 1950:31.
26. Whitney, R. R., 1961:19.
27. McHugh, J. L., and J. E. Fitch, 1951:492.
28. Milner, J. W., 1874:428.
29. Hodder, V. M., 1966:228–9.
30. Foster, N. W., and C. G. Atkins, 1869:10–1.
31. Scott, W. B., and E. J. Crossman, 1964:17.
32. Davis, W. S., 1957:1.
33. Stevenson, C. H., 1899:110.

ADDITIONAL REFERENCES

Bean, T. H., 1892a, 1892b; Cable, L., 1948; Clark, F. N., 1885; Coleman, N., 1872; Collins, A. S., 1871; Ferguson, T. B., and P. W. Downes, 1876; Green, S., 1874; Hammer, R. C., 1943; Hartshorne, H., 1872; Lanman, C., 1874; Lennurt, J. T., 1883; McDonald, M., 1884; Meehan, O. L., 1907a, 1907b; Mihursky, J. A., 1962; Milner, J. W., 1877, 1878, 1880; Nichols, P. R., and R. V. Miller, 1966; Norris, T., 1868; Page, W. F., 1885; Rice, H. J., 1884; Ryder, J. A., 1882a, 1882b, 1884; Senior, H. D., 1909; Sykes, J. E., and B. A. Lehman, 1957; Tracy, H. C., 1910; Vladykov, V. D., 1950; Vladykov, V. D., and D. H. Wallace, 1937; Worth, S. G., 1893, 1898; Yarrow, H. C., 1874.

Atlantic menhaden

Brevoortia tyrannus (Latrobe)

ADULT (Fig. 31 A)

D. 18–24;[15] A. 18–24:[1] P. 13–19:[15] V. 7; scales in oblique series along middle of side 41–55;[1] modified scales anterior to dorsal fin 31–43;[2] ventral scutes 28–37;[15] vertebrae 45–50;[3] gill rakers on lower limb of first arch 150 to 160 in adults 330–360 mm long.

Proportions as percent of SL (based in part on juvenile specimens exceeding 55 mm SL): Body depth 30.0–40.0; head length 29.0–36.0; eye diameter ca. 5.0–8.0.

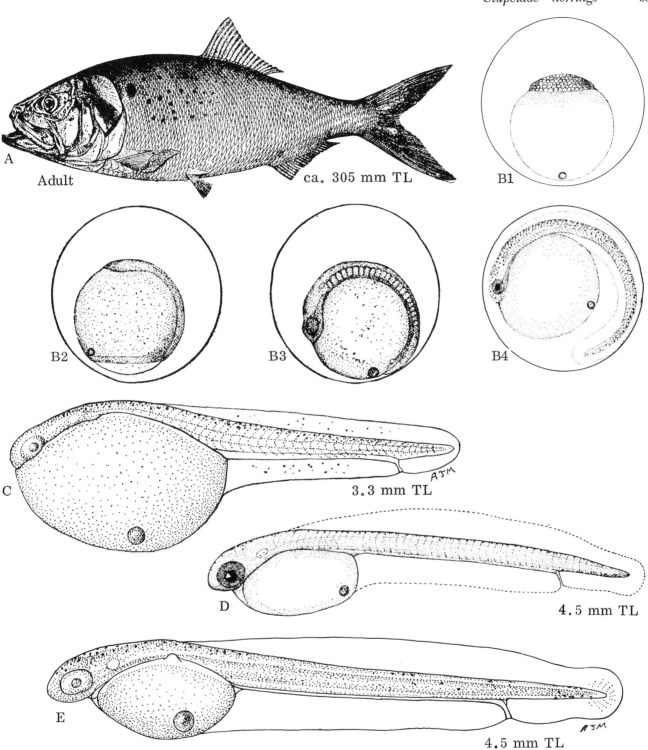

Fig. 31. Brevoortia tyrannus, Atlantic menhaden. A. Adult, ca. 305 mm TL. B. Development of egg. Diameter 1.04–1.95 mm. B1. Morula. B2. Early embryo before closure of blastopore. B3. Early embryo, 22–24 myomeres, blastopore closed. B4. Late embryo with scattered chromatophores over dorsal surface of body. C. Yolk-sac larva, 3.3 mm TL, 3.2 mm SL, just hatched. D. Yolk-sac larva 4.5 mm TL, recently hatched. E. Yolk-sac larva, 4.5 mm TL, 4.4 mm SL, recently hatched. (A, *Goode, et al., 1884: pl. 205.* B, D, *Kuntz and Radcliffe, 1917: fig. 76–81.* C, E, *original drawings, A. J. Mansueti.*)

Body elongate, compressed.[1] Maxillary scarcely reaching below posterior margin of eye; snout quite blunt with prominent median notch; cheek deeper than long; upper section of opercle with prominent radiating ridges. Scales adherent, exposed parts much deeper than long, posterior margins nearly vertical and strongly fimbriated; row of modified scales on each side of mid-line of back in front of dorsal fin; low sheath of scales at base of anal and dorsal. Margin of dorsal concave; origin of anal under or just behind tip of last dorsal ray; pectoral slightly falcate.[1]

Blue, green, blue-gray, or blue-brown above; sides, belly, and fins silvery with strong yellow or brassy lustre;[4] dark, round or vertically elongate shoulder spot usually followed by a number of smaller spots sometimes arranged in indefinite horizontal rows. Peritoneum black.

Maximum length reported at 500 mm,[1] but sizes above 470 mm are not authenticated.[23]

DISTRIBUTION AND ECOLOGY

Range: Nova Scotia[1] to St. Lucie River, Florida.[22]

Area distribution: "Nearly all sections" of Chesapeake Bay;[5] New Jersey, Delaware, and Virginia.[1,21]

Habitat and movements: Adults—near-surface waters overlying inner half of continental shelf during "warmer" months and in loose aggregations in deeper water during "colder" months;[17] also tributaries of Chesapeake Bay and middle Atlantic area during late winter and spring.[19] Undertake extensive migrations, moving northward along coast in spring. During summer, younger and smaller fish are found in southern parts of range and larger, older fish occur in more northerly latitudes. A southward withdrawal from summer grounds occurs in autumn.[17] Minimum salinity 20 o/oo.[20]

Larvae—pelagic, primarily downriver between fresh and brackish water in salinities of 2–3 o/oo; few individuals as much as 27 miles upstream from brackish water.[7] Move shoreward from spawning areas soon after hatching[6] and into estuarine nursery areas.[8,24]

Juveniles—generally pelagic, with smallest size groups furthest up river;[19] as much as 35 miles upstream from brackish water in Rappahannock River, Virginia;[9] also among rushes in intertidal zone of Delaware River estuary.[20] Emigrate to sea after first summer, generally in late August in northern estuaries and as late as January in southern waters.[19]

SPAWNING

Area: Chiefly at sea, closer to shore in northern parts of range,[1] as much as 40 miles offshore from mouth of Chesapeake Bay;[6] eggs have been taken ca. 25 miles south of Cape Lookout, N. C.,[18] lower Chesapeake Bay,[13] and in the Patuxent River north to Benedict. The latter suggests some spawning occurs within Chesapeake Bay (WLD).

Season: Almost every month in some part of range,[14,16] with fall and spring peaks apparently occurring in Chesapeake Bay region.[8]

Temperature: As low as 10 C to somewhat above 16 C.[12]

Fecundity: 38,000 to 631,000 eggs per season.[16]

EGGS (Fig. 31 B)

Description: Buoyant,[4] spherical, highly transparent;[10] diameter 1.3 (JWR)—1.95 mm, with summer eggs somewhat smaller than fall eggs[11] (a reported minimum diameter of 1.04 mm[12] is probably in error. JWR). Yolk ca. 0.9 mm; single, small oil globule, 0.12[10]–0.17 mm.[4] Egg capsule thin, horny; perivitelline space ca. 1/2 egg radius.

Development: Embryonic axis formed before closure of blastopore. At 22–24 somite stage, tail attached; Kupffer's vesicle conspicuous; blastopore closed; otoliths present; and eyes forming. Advanced embryo with elongate slender dorsolateral chromatophores from snout to tip of tail.[10] Just prior to hatching anus 9/10 distance from head to tip of tail (OES).

Incubation: Ca. 48 hours at 22 C.[10]

YOLK-SAC LARVAE (Fig. 31 C-E)

Hatching length 2.4[12]–ca. 4.5 mm.[10]

At 3.3 mm TL, ca. 35 preanal myomeres; head deflected over and attached to yolk; yolk mass large, ovoid; anus less than 1/8 TL from tip of tail; pectoral buds barely visible.

At 4.5 mm head less deflected; yolk mass ca. 1/2 absorbed; anus ca. 1/5 TL from tip to tail; additional pigment on ventral aspect of body posterior to yolk;[10] chromatophores lacking in finfold. Incipient rays in caudal (AJM).

Pigmentation: Eye unpigmented. Small, black chromatophores along entire dorsal surface and few scattered through dorsal and ventral finfolds (AJM).

LARVAE (Fig. 32 A-F)

Size range ca. 5.0–23.0 mm TL.

D. 16–18; A. 18–20 at 16.6–23.1 mm; C. 19; preanal myomeres 37–40; postanal myomeres 8–10 (AJM). Depth ca. 30 times in TL at 9.0 mm, 21 times in TL at 23 mm.[1]

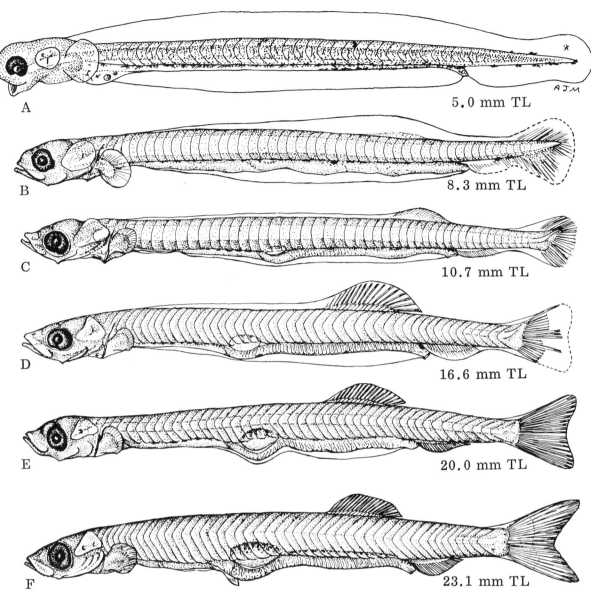

Fig. 32. Brevoortia tyrannus, Atlantic menhaden. A. Larva, 5.0 mm TL, 4.8 mm SL. B. Larva, 8.3 mm TL, 8.07 mm SL. Total myomeres 48; preanal myomeres 40. C. Larva, 10.7 mm TL, 10.4 mm SL. Total myomeres 47; preanal myomeres 37; gas bladder inflated, depressing intestine. D. Larva, 16.6 mm TL, 15.3 mm SL. Total myomeres 47; preanal myomeres 37. D.17; A.18. E. Larva, 20.0 TL, 17.9 mm SL. Total myomeres 46; preanal myomeres 38; D.16; A.18. F. Larva, 23.1 mm TL, 20.4 mm SL. Total myomeres 46; preanal myomeres 38; D.18; A.20; dark pigment over dorsal surface of gas bladder. (*Original drawings, A. J. Mansueti.*)

Head shape extremely variable. Choroid fissure retained to ca. 17 mm; auditory vesicle large and more or less triangular at 11.0 mm. Gas bladder first evident at ca. 11.0 mm, conspicuously bulged in some specimens (AJM). Gut initially straight, becoming convoluted with development; vent slightly behind a vertical from base of last dorsal ray at 25 mm.[1]

Finfold between dorsal and caudal lost between 8.3 and 10.7 mm; retained anterior to dorsal at least to ca. 17 mm,

and preanally to end of stage. Dorsal, anal, and caudal differentiating at 8.3 mm; caudal forked at 16.6 mm; ventrals forming towards end of stage. Notochord initially thick, occupying more than 1/2 thickness of body; urostyle directed upward at 10.7 mm (AJM).

Pigmentation: At 5.0 mm, pigmentation along entire dorsal surface of intestine and along posterior half of ventral surface; scattered chromatophores dorsally and in caudal region (AJM). At 5.7 mm, chromatophores no

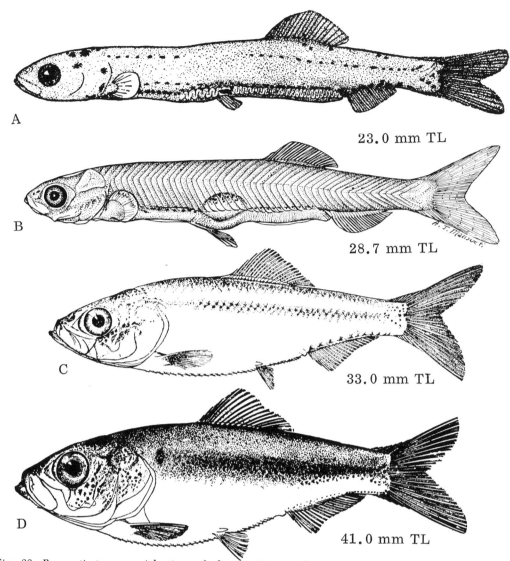

Fig. 33. Brevoortia tyrannus, Atlantic menhaden. A. Prejuvenile, 23.0 mm TL. B. Prejuvenile, 28.7 mm TL, 25.0 mm SL. Total myomeres 47; preanal myomeres 37; D. 19; A. 20. C. Juvenile, 33 mm TL. Scales and scutes present. D. Juvenile, 41 mm TL. (A, C, D, *Kuntz and Radcliffe, 1917: fig. 83–5.* B, *original drawing, A. J. Mansueti.*)

longer evident dorsally except near tip of tail; small group of ventral chromatophores in caudal region; and series along digestive tract from level of pectorals to vent. By end of stage, additional chromatophores over gas bladder, on nape and opercle; near caudal, anal, and dorsal bases; ventral to pectorals; and in series at dorsal level of notochord.

PREJUVENILES (Fig. 33 A,B)

Specimens described 23.0 mm TL to 35 mm TL.[10]

At 28.7 mm, preanal myomeres 37, postanal myomeres 9 (AJM).

Body elongate, somewhat deeper than in previous stage. Some specimens up to 35 mm with ventral aspect of chest and abdomen rounded and slightly flattened, with greatest depth contained 13 times in TL.[1]

Preanal finfold retained to 28.7 mm, but greatly reduced; pectorals rounded.

Pigmentation: At 28.7 mm, essentially as in previous stage (AJM). Specimens 35 mm long with a more or less definite lateral band of dark pigment spots.[1]

JUVENILES (Fig. 33 C,D)

Minimum size described ca. 30 mm TL. Gill rakers increasing with growth of fish; ca. 60 at 60 mm, ca. 100 at 100 mm,[1] 130 to 145 at 140–170 mm SL (FHB). Greatest depth ca. 6.7 times in SL at 30–35 mm, ca. 3.6–4.0 at 40–45 mm.

Cheek not deeper than long. Minute teeth on margin of maxillary below 60 mm;[1] tongue teeth 0–4.[25] Eye proportionately much larger at 41 mm than in adult.[4] Striations on upper plate of gill cover formed by 40–45 mm. Ventral scutes present in some 30-mm fish.[1] Scales present at 33 mm,[10] and scale edges irregular at 60 mm, with blunt serrae at 100 mm; scalation about complete at 40–45 mm, but modified predorsal scales not formed until ca. 125 mm TL; axillary scales of pectoral little developed at 50 mm, ca. 1/2 length of fin at 100 mm.[1]

Pigmentation: At 33 mm, back pigmented; distinct dark lateral stripe; melanophores on dorsal and caudal rays.[10] Silvery lateral band developed at 30–35 mm, blending with silvery abdomen at 40–45 mm.[1] At 41 mm, shoulder spot forming,[10] completed at 75 mm and followed by additional spots by 150 mm.[1]

Age at maturity: Few females at age 1, most at age 2 and all at age 3.[16]

LITERATURE CITED

1. Hildebrand, S. F., 1963a:346–62.
2. Hildebrand, S. F., 1948: Table 1.
3. Sutherland, D. F., 1963:3.
4. Bigelow, H. B., and W. C. Schroeder, 1953:113–8.
5. Hildebrand, S. F., and W. C. Schroeder, 1928:105.
6. Massmann, W. H., J. J. Norcross, and E. B. Joseph, 1962:43–4.
7. Massmann, W. H., C. L. Ladd, and H. N. McCutcheon, 1954:20–2.
8. McHugh, J. L., R. T. Oglesby, and A. L. Pacheco, 1959:160–1.
9. Massmann, W. H., 1954: 78.
10. Kuntz, A., and L. Radcliffe, 1917:119–23.
11. Richards, S. W., 1959:106–7.
12. Wheatland, S. B., 1956:249–50.
13. Pearson, J. C., 1941:83.
14. Nichols, J. T., and C. M. Breder, Jr., 1927:41–2.
15. June, F. C., 1958:30–3.
16. Higham, J. R., and W. R. Nicholson, 1964:263, 267.
17. June, F. C., 1961:1–13.
18. Reintjes, J. W., 1961:2.
19. June, F. C., and L. Chamberlin, 1959:42.
20. de Sylva, D. P., F. A. Kalber, Jr., and C. N. Shuster, Jr., 1962:19.
21. Goode, G. B., 1879:41.
22. Reintjes, J. W., 1964:111.
23. Cooper, R. A., 1965:412.
24. Lewis, R. M., 1965:409.
25. Dovel, W. L., A. J. Mansueti, and E. H. Oldmixon, 1965:3.

ADDITIONAL REFERENCES

Ellison, W. A., Jr., 1951; Goode, G. B., 1884; Gunter, G., and J. Y. Christmas, 1960; Marak, R. R., and J. B. Colton, Jr., 1961; Marak, R. R., J. B. Colton, Jr., and D. B. Foster, 1962; Marak, R. R., J. B. Colton, Jr., D. B. Foster, and D. Miller, 1962; McCutcheon, H. N., 1953; Pacheco, A., and G. C. Grant, 1965; Pearson, J. C., 1941; Perlmutter, A., 1939; Westman, J. R., and R. F. Nigrelli, 1955.

Atlantic herring

Clupea harengus Linnaeus

ADULT (Fig. 34 A)

D. 16 [1]–21; [21] A. 14 [59]–20; [21] C. 17–20; [59] P. 14–20; [57] V. 6–10; [59] scales between gill openings and caudal base ca. 56–62; ventral scutes weakly developed, ca. 39–46; [1] vertebrae 49 [60,61]–60; [21] gill rakers on lower limb of first arch 37–52.

Proportions as percent of SL (may include some juveniles): Body depth 20.0–25.8; head length 22.6–26.4; eye diameter 5.3–7.7.

Body compressed. Maxillary rounded posteriorly, not quite reaching middle of eye, its margin with minute serrae; teeth on lower jaw, tongue,[1] and in oval patch on vomer.[7] Dorsal origin about midway along trunk, usually closer to caudal base than tip of snout.

Body iridescent, bluish above, silvery on sides and belly.[6]

Maximum length ca. 450 mm.[1]

DISTRIBUTION AND ECOLOGY

Range: North to edge of polar ice, rarely beyond; [53] in the western Atlantic, Greenland,[21] and Labrador [10] to Cape Hatteras, North Carolina; in the eastern Atlantic, Iceland, Spitsbergen, Novaya Zamlya, White and Baltic Seas, and Gulf of Finland,[21] south along coast of Europe to Straits of Gibraltar.[1]

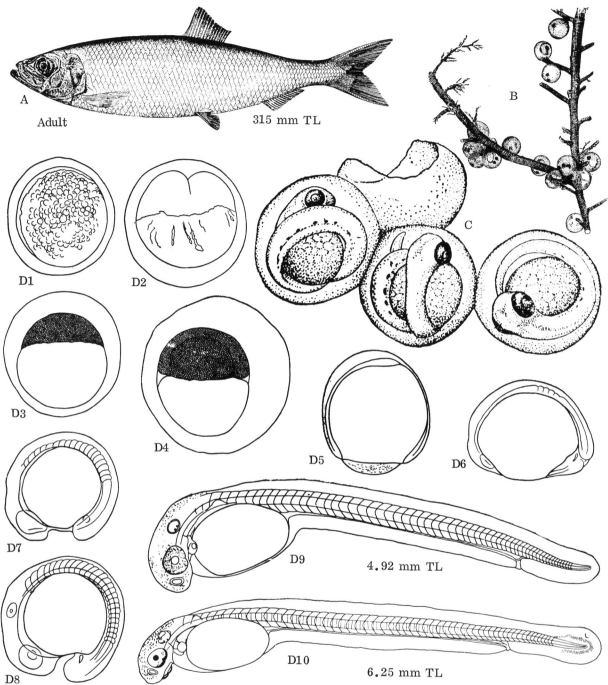

Fig. 34. *Clupea harengus*, Atlantic herring. A. Adult, 315 mm TL. B. Egg clusters attached to seaweed. C. Cluster of eggs containing advanced embryos. D. Development of egg. Yolk granular throughout incubation although not illustrated; D5-D10 with capsule removed. D1. Early blastodisc, 34 minutes, 17 C. Egg diameter 1.12 mm; yolk diameter 0.95 mm. D2. Two-cell stage, 2 hours, 17 C. Egg diameter 1.2 mm; yolk diameter 1 mm; depth of blastomeres 0.55 mm and 0.45 mm. D3. Morula, 8 hours, 11 C. Egg diameter 1.15 mm; yolk diameter 0.9 mm; depth of blastoderm 0.3 mm. D4. Blastula, 12 1/2 hours, 23 C. Egg diameter 1.2 mm; yolk diameter 0.75 mm. D5. Embryo, 26 hours, 15 C. Embryonic axis visible. D6. Embryo, 25 1/2 hours. Three myomeres, and optic vesicles visible. D7. Embryo, 33 hours. Eighteen myomeres, and Kupffer's vesicle visible. D8. Embryo, tail bud stage, 38 hours. Twenty-seven myomeres, auditory vesicles visible. D9. Embryo, 4.92 mm TL, 5 1/2 days, 14.8 C. Melanophores scattered over head. D10. Embryo, 6.25 mm TL, 6 1/2 days, 15.8 C. Just before hatching; lower jaw formed; eye pigmented. (A, *Hildebrand, 1963a: fig. 66.* B, *Bigelow and Schroeder, 1953: fig. 42 (after Ehrenbaum 1909).* C, *Berg, et al. 1949: 121.* D1-D10, *Krevanovski, 1956: fig. 21, 23, 26.*)

Area distribution: Chesapeake Bay to vicinity of Solomons Island, Maryland[15] and in Patuxent River to Lower Marlboro (WLD); also off New Jersey,[1] Delaware,[10] and Maryland.[14,16]

Habitat and movements: Adult—a pelagic, schooling species found mainly offshore in deeper water[1] but with some populations moving shoreward during spawning season;[1,33] undertake vertical migrations, rising at night and sinking by day.[3,42,43,44] Movements typically local and probably of short range,[1] although specimens of unknown age are known to make long oceanic excursions; e.g., from east coast of Iceland to southern Norway.[5] Maximum depth ca. 273 fathoms, but typically no deeper than 30 or 60 fathoms (HCB). Salinity typically ca. 35 o/oo,[33] ranging from 0.0 o/oo in European lakes[21] to 45 o/oo under experimental conditions[33] but not below 2.8 o/oo along American coast.[1]

Larvae—initially in vicinity of spawning beds at bottom,[12] making short upward movements and sinking back to bottom;[31,58] may make horizontal movements within 2 hours of hatching[30] and form discrete swarms within 6 hours.[29,30] Vertical movements upward at night with their magnitude increasing directly with size of larvae.[8] Ultimately dispersed by current at lengths of 18[55]–25 mm,[40] e.g., from Georges Bank toward Nova Scotia and New Jersey.[17] Recorded at depths of 7–700 meters.[21] Experimental optimum salinity 10–15 o/oo,[39] but able to withstand 1.4–60.1 o/oo for at least 24 hours.[31,32]

Juveniles—drifting with current,[1] sometimes as far as 800 miles;[21] initially at surface;[45] inshore after metamorphosis,[31] often in estuaries;[50,62] also in open sea.[21,72] Specimens 90 mm long and longer have been experimentally maintained at a salinity of 45 o/oo.[33]

SPAWNING

Location: Vicinity of fjords, bays, straits, and estuaries; also oceanic banks;[1,13,21] greatest concentration of spawning activity off eastern United States at Georges Bank ca. 100 miles off Cape Cod;[10] sometimes on slopes of banks situated near underwater "valleys" along which fish approach shore.[53] Usually over rocky, pebbly, or gravel bottoms; sometimes over clay; probably never over soft mud;[7] in areas with or without vegetation.[9,12] Depth 1 foot[11] to 240 meters,[43] but usually at 40–80 meters;[53] rarely in intertidal water in Newfoundland.[11]

Season: Variable, depending on locality;[1,10,69] year round in coastal Gulf of Maine, but with peak activity in September and October; on Georges Bank, late August to March (HCB); outer coast of Nova Scotia with two peaks, a major one in May or early June, a minor one in September; New Jersey and Maryland populations probably autumn spawners.[10]

Salinity: 4.0–35.9 o/oo[21] with some populations spawning in water that is "nearly fresh".[7] Salinities of 1.7 o/oo have been recorded in European spawning grounds,[38] and eggs have been successfully fertilized, developed, and hatched at 52.5 o/oo.[32] In American waters, not below 31.9 o/oo or above 33.0 o/oo.[1]

Temperatures: 0.0[31]–15.0 C.[10]

Fecundity: 3,000[53,67]–107,000,[68] with summer-autumn spawners in some areas having significantly higher production than spring spawners.[53]

EGGS (Fig. 34 B-D; Fig. 36 A)

Description: Demersal, adhesive.[1] In Western Atlantic sometimes deposited on algae, anchor ropes,[7] and even on free living animals such as Toad crabs, genus *Hyas*;[42] but most often in large "sheets"[9] directly on stones, gravel,[20] and shells[13] in beds which may cover 375,200 square meters.[12] Egg sheets may be 4–8 layers[20] or as much as 35.5 mm thick at center.[9] In English Channel attached to large rocks in long, narrow beds which are oriented with their greatest length lying in the direction of tidal movements;[47] sometimes close inshore[37] and occasionally washed up on beaches.[13]

Ripe ovarian eggs—0.92[59]–1.7 mm[7] in diameter; transparent;[50] almost globular;[29] egg capsule thick, somewhat bossed;[54] yolk transparent; micropyle single.[29]

Unfertilized eggs—0.86–1.01 mm, yellow.[55]

Fertilized eggs—diameter, typically 1.0–1.4 mm in American waters but varying from 0.36 mm in vicinity of Ireland to 3.0 mm in Keil Canal.[21] Size influenced by size of female,[30] time of spawning,[53] and salinity of environment.[32] Mean yolk diameter 0.81–0.92 mm with yolk decreasing 4.4–7.9% of original size during first three hours of development. Perivitelline space ca. 23.2–29.6% of egg diameter.[30] Transparent bluish-grey when first deposited, becoming whitish during hatching.[66] Parthenogenesis occurs.[28]

Development: At 17–24 C.

1 hour, 45 minutes—1-cell stage.
2 hours, 5 minutes—2-cell stage.
8 hours, 20 minutes—morula.
14 hours, 45 minutes—early gastrula.
24 hours—closure of blastopore.
25 hours, 30 minutes—eyes forming; 3 somites present.
29 hours—Kupffer's vesicle evident.
31 hours—9 somites.
36 hours—24 somites; auditory vesicles forming.
38 hours—27 somites.

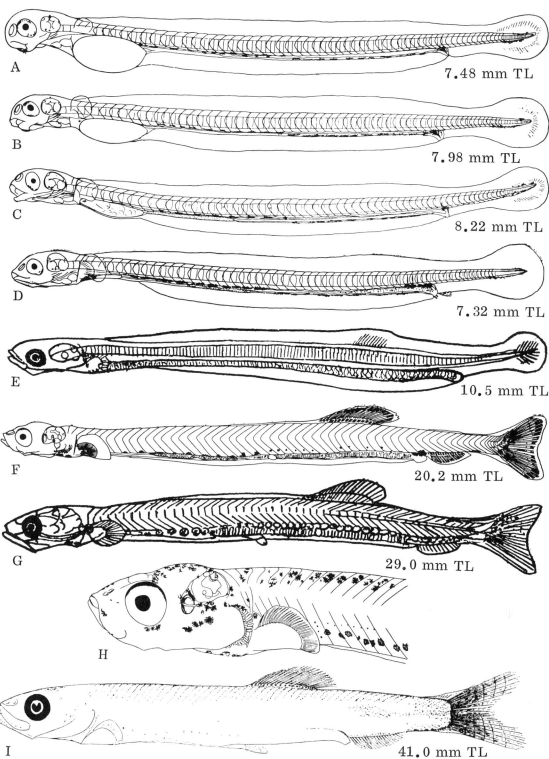

Fig. 35. *Clupea harengus,* Atlantic herring. A. Yolk-sac larva, 7.48 mm TL, 13.2 C. Just hatched, 8 days after fertilization. B. Yolk-sac larva, 7.98 mm TL, 14.8 C. Nine days after fertilization. C. Yolk-sac larva, 8.22 mm TL, 15.8 C. Ten days after fertilization. D. Larva, 7.32 mm TL, 19.7 C. Eleven days after fertilization, E. Larva, 10.5 mm TL. F. Larva, 20.2 mm TL. Preanal finfold retained. G. Larva, 29.0 mm TL. H. Head of larva of 29.0 mm TL. I. Prejuvenile, 41.0 mm TL. (A-D, F, H, *Krevanovski, 1956: fig. 27, 28, 30, 31.* E, G, *Ehrenbaum, 1909: fig. 139.* I, *Fage, 1920: fig. 42.*)

51 hours—45 somites; tail free.

109 hours—59 somites.

120 hours—Kupffer's vesicle no longer evident; incipient pectoral buds visible; pigmentation in eye begun.

174 hours—head not sharply deflected over yolk; pigment developed along lower edge of intestine and above and below body in caudal region.[23] At time of tail-free stage, yolk assumes a somewhat elongate shape, but becomes round when embryo surrounds entire yolk.

Incubation: Ca. 4.3[30] to 56 days,[54] depending primarily on temperature, but with period also lengthened by siltation[30] and decreased salinity.[32]

    0.1 C–47–50 days.[4,21]
    5.0 C–24 days.[24]
    8.0 C–15 days.[71]
    12.0 C–10 days.
    14.0 C–7.5 days.[24]

Probable time in Gulf of Maine, 10–15 days.[2] Optimum developmental salinity 20–35 o/oo.[32]

YOLK-SAC LARVAE (Fig. 35 A-C)

Hatching length 4.0[18]–10.0 mm TL,[40] with larvae hatched at low temperatures tending to be longer and having less yolk. Hatching length also influenced by salinity, with largest larvae produced at 15 o/oo.[35] Length at end of stage 6.5[70]–12.0 mm.[37]

Duration of stage varies with temperature and locality; 2½ days at 14.5 C;[25] 4½ to 14 days at 8 C;[24] 50% yolk absorption in 36 days at mean temperature of 5.1 C.[27]

Total myomeres 56[37,49]–67, increasing during stage.[64] Preanal myomeres 47,[37,49] fixed throughout stage.[64] Four gill arches developed, the fifth forming at hatching.[29]

Depth contained 24 times in TL; vent less than 1/5 TL from tip of tail.

Body very slender;[1] head rounded at ca. 7.5 mm.[23] Yolk mass oval at salinities of 5.9–22.7 o/oo, spherical at 33.6–45.0 o/oo.[32] Mouth open,[29] non-functional at hatching;[31] sometimes functional prior to yolk absorption.[22,37] Eye protuberant; choroid fissure evident. At hatching, gut straight,[31] sometimes with opening from mouth; 2 primitive excretory ducts present; gas bladder not evident.[29] At ca. 6.0 mm, heart a straight tube constricted at middle.[40] Anus fixed in position throughout stage.[64]

Pectoral fin distinctly rounded at ca. 7.5 mm. Origin of dorsal finfold initially above pectoral origin; preanal finfold long and wide; by 8.22 mm, finfold reduced in region of future caudal peduncle.[23]

Pigmentation: Body transparent;[1] eye uniformly black[29] or silvery with black pupil.[54] A line of chromatophores between body and intestine on anterior half of body, ventrally along intestine on posterior half; a concentration of pigment in vent region.[23] Few chromatophores on tail; "a little red pigment" located between yolk sac and anus.[45]

LARVAE (Fig. 35 D-H; Fig. 36 B-C)

Size range described 6.5[70]–34.0 mm TL.[3]

Preanal myomeres 46–47 at 10–20 mm, 41–46 in specimens longer than 20 mm;[37] "vertebral myomeres" 53–60,

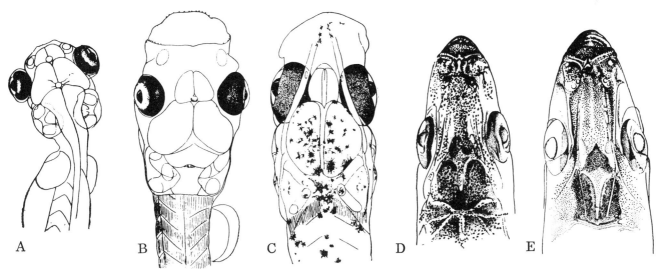

Fig. 36. Clupea harengus, Atlantic herring. Dorsal views of head at various stages. A. Embryo, 7.0 mm TL. B. Larva, 18.0 mm TL. C. Larva, 19.0 mm TL. D. Prejuvenile, 50.0 mm TL. E. Juvenile, 150.0 mm TL. (*Krevanovski, 1956; fig. 34, 35.*)

not countable until after formation of urostyle.[52] Tail less than 1/6 TL in specimens 20 mm long and longer.[37,49]

Head becoming elongate at ca. 7.8 mm, but nearly as broad as long at 10.5 mm. At beginning of stage, anterior margins of upper and lower lips equal and level.[27] Jaw with toothlike serrations and branchial arches evident at 14.5 mm. Opercle forming at 20 mm. Finfold no longer continuous at 20.0 mm, but remnant retained anterior to dorsal fin to end of stage.[23]

Incipient dorsal rays first evident in some specimens at 10.5 mm;[3,22] dorsal fin complete by 15[7]–29 mm.[36] Anal fin first evident at 16[26]–29 mm;[1] incipient rays at 17.0[3]–20.2 mm; stainable rays at 17.5–20.0 mm;[26] anal fin complete at least by 30 mm.[37] Ventrals first evident at 20.2[23]–29.9 mm,[26] usually appearing near 24th myomere[37] and usually in front of 1st dorsal ray.[48]

Vertebral centra stainable at mid-body at ca. 20 mm; entire column developed at 24–25 mm.[26,35] Urostyle first directed upward at ca. 16[52]–17 mm, completely oblique at 21 mm or more.[37]

Pigmentation: Body transparent. Pigment increased in density at 7.32 mm, especially in region of anus and below pectoral fins. At 20.2 mm, a series of chromatophores ventrally on body; heavy concentration of pigment above anus; few chromatophores at caudal base.[23] At ca. 25 mm, a longitudinal row of black dots on wall of abdominal cavity; fine black spots on dorsal surface, especially on roof of brain.[40] At 29 mm, additional pigment on head and in dorso-lateral region of body.[23]

PREJUVENILES (Fig. 35 I; Fig. 36 D)

Size range described 30[35,48]–50 mm TL.

Vent ca. 1/3 TL from tip of tail. Premaxilla and posterior supramaxilla developed at 34 mm.[34] Pyloric caecae developing at 33 mm;[37] gas bladder evident at 30–35 mm.[22,65] Scales first evident at 24[50]–48 mm;[37] urostyle still evident at 41 mm.[3] Anal and ventrals forward of earlier relative position.[1]

Pigmentation: At 41 mm, pigment over back, along lateral surface on posterior part of body, over gut, along posterior half of venter, and on dorsal and caudal fins;[3] at 50 mm, pigment over most of head;[23] at sizes larger than 35 mm operculum silvery.[40]

JUVENILES (Fig. 36 E)

Minimum size ca. 30[35]–60 mm TL.[37]

Gill rakers on lower limb of first arch 25–36 in specimens 36–70 mm long.

Depth 5.2–9.5 times in SL in specimens 40–70 mm SL.

Gill rakers at angle of arch not as long as eye in "young."[1] Teeth developed "late in life"; a minute row on maxilla and 3–4 on premaxilla.[34] Pyloric caecae fully developed at 70 mm.[56]

Pigmentation: "Adult pigmentation" at least by 45 mm in some populations.[50]

Age and size at maturity: 2[21]–7 or possibly 9 years.[53] Possibly 100 mm[59] in European populations, but ca. 181–185 mm SL in American populations.[19]

LITERATURE CITED

1. Hildebrand, S. F., 1963a:275–83, 290.
2. Bigelow, H. B., and W. W. Welsh, 1925:93–4.
3. Ehrenbaum, E., 1909:365.
4. Norman, J. R., 1949:330.
5. Fridriksson, A., and O. Aasen, 1950:27.
6. Hildebrand, S. F., and W. C. Schroeder, 1928:81.
7. Bigelow, H. B., and W. C. Schroeder, 1953:81, 88, 91.
8. Colton, J. B., Jr., K. A. Honey, and R. F. Temple, 1961:187.
9. McKenzie, R. A., 1964:203–4.
10. Scattergood, L. W., C. J. Sindermann, and B. F. Skud, 1959:166–7.
11. Tibbo, S. N., 1956:460.
12. Tibbo, S. N., D. J. Scarratt, and P. W. G. McMullan, 1963:1073–4, 1077.
13. Moore, H. F., 1898:408, 411.
14. Schwartz, F. J., 1961:391.
15. Mansueti, R. J., 1962a: 2.
16. Schwartz, F. J., 1964a: 179.
17. Tibbo, S. N., J. E. H. Legare, L. W. Scattergood, and R. F. Temple, 1958: 1467.
18. Jean, Y., 1956:35.
19. Scattergood, L. W., 1952:6.
20. Parrish, B. B., A. Saville, R. E., Craig, I. G. Baxter, and R. Priestley, 1959:447.
21. Svetovidov, A. N., 1963:122, 128–9, 136–43, 154–6, 162–3, 173–4.
22. Marshall, S. M., A. G. Nicholls, and A. P. Orr, 1937: 245, 248, 252.
23. Krevanovski, S. G., 1956a: figs. 21–26.
24. Blaxter, J. H. S., and G. Hempel, 1963:215–6, 221.
25. Rannak, L. A., 1959:15.
26. Blaxter, J. H. S., 1962: 13.
27. Blaxter, J. H. S., 1956:10, 15.
28. Volodin, V. M., 1956:6–7.
29. Brook, G., 1885:32–4, 47–8.
30. Toom, M. M., 1962, 10–12.
31. Blaxter, J. H. S., and F. G. T. Holliday, 1963:274, 283, 289, 294.

32. Holliday, F. G. T., and J. H. S. Blaxter, 1960:594–5, 602.
33. Holliday, F. G. T., and J. H. S. Blaxter, 1961:37–8.
34. Bamford, T. W., 1941:427–8, 436.
35. Blaxter, J. H. S., and G. Hempel, 1961:282.
36. Wells, F. R., 1923:1213–1228.
37. Lebour, M. V., 1921:448–9, 451, 455.
38. Buckmann, A., W. Harder, and G. Hempel, 1953: 22–42.
39. Bishai, H. M., 1961:177.
40. John, C. C., 1932:113–7.
41. Galkov, A. A., 1958:9.
42. Runnström, S., 1941:23.
43. Solovyev, B. S., and A. A. Degtyarev, 1957:81–4.
44. Ryzhenko, M., 1961:29–30.
45. Balls, R., 1951:298.
46. Brawn, V. M., 1960a:699.
47. Bolster, G. C., and J. P. Bridger, 1957:638.
48. Ford, E., 1930:746.
49. Saville, A., 1964:3.
50. Parrish, B. B., and A. Saville, 1965:323–73.
51. Ewart, J. C., 1884a:68.
52. Hempel, G., and J. H. S. Blaxter, 1961:343.
53. Marty, Y. Y., 1959:10, 53, 61.
54. Williamson, H. C., 1910a:120, 122.
55. Liamin, K. A., 1959:199.
56. Nikolsky, G. V., A. V. Chepurnov, and M. I. Shatunovsky, 1963:41.
57. Saville, A., G. McPherson, and B. B. Parrish, 1965: 178–9.
58. Ewart, J. C., 1886:46.
59. Matthews, J. D., 1886:91–2, 95–6.
60. Leim, A. H., 1957a:10.
61. Leim, A. H., 1957b:27.
62. Wood, H., 1960:23.
63. Bowers, A. B., and F. G. T. Holliday, 1961:11.
64. Blaxter, J. H. S., 1957:5, 7.
65. Bhattacharyya, R. N., 1957:4–5.
66. Fridriksson, A., and G. Timmermann, 1951:261.
67. Bezrukova, E. A., 1938:17.
68. Brook, G., 1886a:253.
69. Williamson, H. C., 1910b:65.
70. Hardy, A. C., 1924:4.
71. Huxley, [T. H.], 1881:610.
72. McKenzie, R. A., and B. E. Skud, 1958:1343.

ADDITIONAL REFERENCES

Anokhina, L. E., 1959; Baxter, I. G., 1959; Blaxter, J. H. S., and G. Hempel, 1966; Bowers, A. B., and D. I. Williamson, 1951; Boyar, H. C., 1965; Brawn, V. M., 1960b, 1960c; Bridger, J. P., 1961; Brook, G., 1886b, 1886c; Bückman, A., 1950; Colton, J. B., and R. F. Temple, 1961; Couch, J., 1869; Cunningham, J. T., 1888, 1889; Das, N., and S. N. Tibbo, 1962; Day, L., 1957a, 1957b, 1957c; Duge, F., 1903; Dunn, H. D., 1897; Ehrenbaum, E., 1904; Ewart, J. C., 1883, 1884b, 1884c, 1888; Farran, G. P., 1938; Farrin, A. E., L. W. Scattergood, and C. J. Sinderman, 1957; Fish, C. J., and M. W. Johnson, 1937; Ford, E., 1929; Gilpin, J. B., 1963, Graham, J. J., and H. C. Boyar, 1966; Graham, M., 1936; Graham, T., 1962; Harder, W., 1952, 1953, 1954, 1960; Heincke, F., 1898, 1899; Hela, I., and T. Laerastu, 1962; Hempel, G., 1953; Hentschel, E., 1950; Hickling, C. F., 1940; Hinkelmann, A., 1902, 1908; Hjort, J., 1908; Hoek, P. P. C., 1903; Holliday, F. G. T., 1958; Holliday, F. G. T., J. H. S. Blaxter, and R. Lasker, 1964; Holstvoogd, C., 1957; Holt, E. W. L., 1889; Huntsman, A. G., 1919; Johansen, A. C., 1924; 1925; Jones, F. R. H., 1962; Kändler, R., and S. Dutt, 1958; Knox, R., 1834; Kotthaus, A., 1939; Krebs, W., 1911; Krevanovski, S. G., 1956b; Kupffer, C., 1878; Maier, H. N., and L. Scheuring, 1923; Marak, R. R., and J. B. Colton, Jr., 1961; Marak, R. R., J. B. Colton, Jr., D. B. Foster, and D. Miller, 1962; Masterman, A. T., 1896; Merriman, D., and R. U. Sclar, 1952; Meyer, H. A., 1878a, 1878b, 1878c, 1879, 1880; Mielck, W., 1925; Mitchell, J. M., 1861, 1863a, 1863b, 1864; Nature, 1876; Nikitinskaya, I. V., 1958; Nilsson, S., 1860; Naumor, V. M., 1959; Okonski, S., and H. Konkol, 1957; Petersen, C. G. J., 1901; Prince, E. E., 1907; Ramanujam, S. G. M., 1929; Rogalla, E. H., and D. Sahrhage, 1960; Sanders, H. L., 1952; Scattergood, L. W., 1957; Schach, H., 1939; Schnakenbeck, W., 1929; Silliman, R. P., 1950; Simroth, H. R., 1910; Skud, B. E., and H. C. Boyar, 1958; Soleim, P. A., 1942; Steele, J. H., 1961; Tibbo, S. N., 1957a, 1957b; Tibbo, S. N., and J. E. H. Legare, 1960; Valenciennes, A., 1847; Warren, R., 1906; Watson, J. E., 1963, 1964; Williamson, H. C., 1911a, 1911b.

Gizzard shad

Dorosoma cepedianum (LeSueur)

ADULT (Fig. 37 A)

D. 10–13; A. 25–36; C. 19; P. 14–17; V. 7–8; scales in lateral series 52–70; scales around body 36–45; scale rows between dorsal and anal fins 19–24. Ventral scutes 27–32; prepelvic scutes 17–20; postpelvic scutes 10–14. Vertebrae 48–51; gill rakers 412 in a specimen 157 mm long.

Proportions as times in SL (based in part on juvenile specimens): Head length 3.0–3.9; body depth 2.3–3.1;

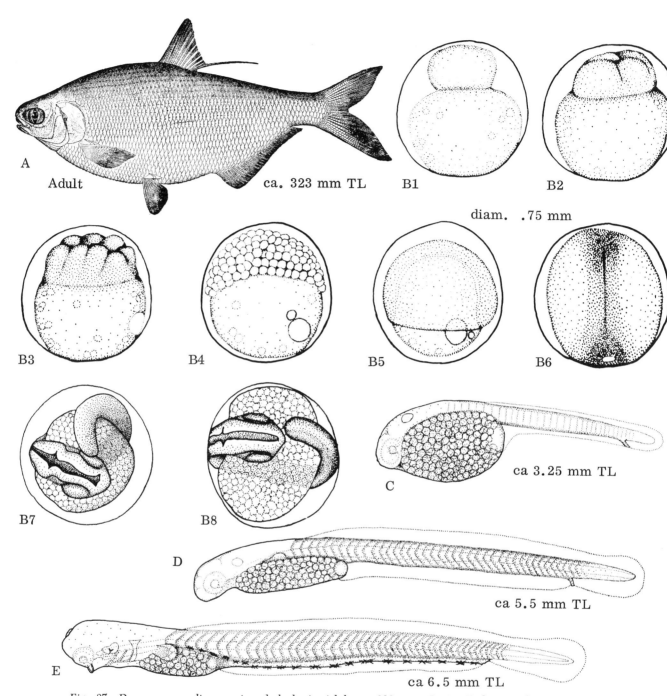

Fig. 37. *Dorosoma cepedianum*, gizzard shad. A. Adult, ca. 323 mm TL. B. Embryonic development. All except B1 raised at 16.6 C. Egg diameter 0.75 mm. B1. Blastodisc, 15–20 min., 26.6 C. B2. Four-cell stage, 3 hours. B3. Eight-cell stage. Larger oil globules visible. B4. Morula, 5 1/2 hours. B5. Late gastrula, 15 1/2 hours. B6. Embryonic axis, 25 1/2 hours; blastopore closing. B7. Tail-free embryo, 60 hours. B8. Late embryo, 70 hours. C. Yolk-sac larva, ca. 3.25 mm TL. Just hatched; 32 myomeres. D. Yolk-sac larva, ca. 5.5 mm TL, 3 days old. E. Yolk-sac larva, ca. 6.5 mm TL; 3 days old. (A, *Goode, et al., 1884: pl. 217A.* B1-D, *Warner, 1940: pl. 1, 2.* E, *Miller, 1960: fig. 3.*)

predorsal length 1.85–2.05; prepelvic length 2.0–2.35; anal origin to caudal base 2.4–2.8; anal base 3.2–3.9; dorsal filament 3.1–6.5.

Scales comparatively small, cycloid, thin. Teeth absent. Maxillary with 2 supramaxillary bones. Ridge on back before dorsal fin naked.

Silvery-blue above, milky-white below, often with brassy or golden reflections; ca. 6–8 horizontal dark stripes along upper sides above middle of shoulder spot; dorsal almost uniform, dusky; caudal dusky, darkest on outer third; anal dusky, lighter basally; top of head, snout, upper jaw and upper part of opercle pigmented; remainder of head silvery.

Maximum length ca. 520 mm [7] (average ca. 254–356 mm).[1,20]

DISTRIBUTION AND ECOLOGY

Range: North Dakota,[13] central Minnesota, and the Great Lakes drainage, south through the Mississippi River system; southern New York south along the Atlantic slope to the Gulf coast of the United States and to the basin of the Rio Panuco in eastern Mexico.[1]

Area distribution: Chesapeake Bay,[11] Virginia,[8] and New Jersey.[12]

Habitat and movements: Adults—open quiet surface waters which may be clear to very silty; abundant in rivers of Chesapeake Bay region throughout year; and in Bay itself in fall.[1] Maximum salinity 33.7 o/oo.[2] Maximum depth 108 feet.[9]

A fall "run" in Chesapeake Bay in September and October,[11] spring "runs" in North Carolina [15] and up Mississippi River.[4]

Juveniles—in greatest abundance well upstream from brackish water [8] with very young individuals apparently never entering brackish water.[11] Reported from beds of spatterdock; close inshore, usually in shallow water; [1] primarily over mud bottom.[16]

SPAWNING

Location: Fresh water [19] near surface in sloughs, ponds, lakes, and large rivers; [1] sometimes at depth of 6–12 inches along shoreline.[3]

Season: Mid-March to late August, but principally during April, May and June in temperate waters of the United States; [1] early summer in area of Chesapeake Bay.[11]

Time: Mid-day.

Temperature: 10–23 C, usually on rising temperature, and most active above ca. 18 C.[1,21]

Fecundity: Range 22,405–543,912; average 59,480 at age group I to 378,990 at age group II; declining with age to 215,330 at age group VI.[5]

EGGS (Fig. 37 B)

Description: Dermersal; adhesive, attaching to contacted objects. Irregular shaped and wrinkled when first extruded, becoming spherical in water.

Fertilized eggs—creamy-yellow; nearly transparent; 0.75 mm diameter.[1] Egg capsule smooth, tough; [14] micropyle single.[1] Yolk finely granular with single large oil globule and 1–5 smaller ones.

Development: At ca. 27 C.

15–20 minutes—blastodisc formed.
ca. 1 hour—first cleavage.

At ca. 17 C.

3 hours—4-cell stage.
5 hours, 30 minutes—morula.
25 hours, 30 minutes—closure of blastopore.
33 hours, 30 minutes—2 somites; embryo around 7/8 of yolk; neural keel deep in yolk; optic vesicles and neural cord evident.
43 hours, 30 minutes—9 somites.
52 hours, 30 minutes—17 somites; optic cup formed; caudal region barely delineated from underlying yolk; embryo encircling entire yolk.
60 hours—tail free and overlapping head slightly; three primary lobes of brain distinguishable.[14]

Incubation: Ca. 36 hours to 1 week depending on temperature; [5] 95 hours at ca. 17 C, 36 hours at ca. 27 C.[1]

YOLK-SAC LARVAE (Fig. 37 C-E)

Average hatching length 3.25 mm TL. Maximum size described 6.5 mm.

Total myomeres ca. 32 at hatching, 40 at 5.5 mm. Four gill arches but no filaments at 6.5 mm. Body elongate at hatching; depth, including finfold, 0.2 mm; head flexed downward 90° over yolk. Head straight at 5.5 mm. Yolk mass initially oval and 0.8 mm in length, cylindrical by 2nd day, greatly reduced by 3rd (6.5 mm). Oral plate perforated at 1 day, but pharynx not open into mouth; cartilage of lower jaw forming at 6.5 mm; choroid fissure wide, closed in 1 day.

Gut nearly straight at hatching; anus at margin of finfold at hatching, close to body in notch in finfold at 6.5 mm. Anlagen of pectorals present at 5.5 mm, small and paddle-like at 6.5 mm; finfold slightly constricted in caudal region at hatching.

Pigmentation: Pigment lacking at birth and at 1 day; at

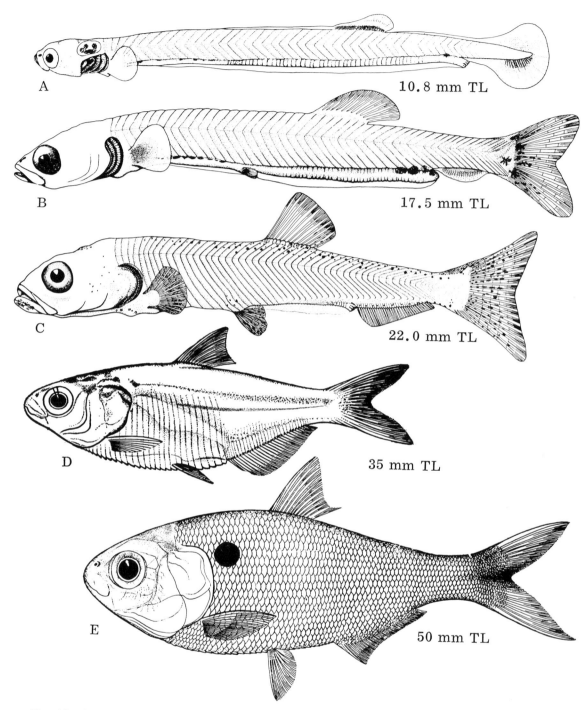

Fig. 38. Dorosoma cepedianum, gizzard shad. A. Larva, 10.8 mm TL. Total myomeres 48; preanal myomeres 44. B. Larva, 17.5 mm TL. D. 12; A. with 22 incipient rays; total myomeres 49; preanal myomeres 39. C. Prejuvenile, 22.0 mm TL. D. 13; A. 34; total myomeres 54; preanal myomeres 39. D. Juvenile, 35 mm TL. E. Juvenile, 50 mm TL. Last ray of dorsal fin starting to elongate. (A-C, *Warner, 1940: pl. 3, 4.* D, *Fowler, 1935: fig. 2.* E, *Fowler, 1945: fig. 7.*)

3 days (6.5 mm), a line of chromatophores on each side of body starting dorsad to yolk and extending to preanal finfold.[1]

LARVAE (Fig. 38 A,B)

Specimens described 10.8 to 17.5 mm TL.

A. 22 at 17.5 mm. At 10.8 mm, total myomeres 48, preanal myomeres 44; at 17.5 mm, total myomeres 49, preanal myomeres 39.

Body long and slender. Incipient gill filaments present at 10.8 mm; posterior development of opercle rapid during stage; nostril dividing at 17.5 mm. Internal folds of intestine developing at 10.8 mm; gut 1.5 to 2.0 times TL.[1]

Finfold reduced dorsally at 10.8 mm; only preanal present at 17.5 mm. Anal with incipient rays at 17.5 mm; caudal rounded and with 14 incipient rays at 10.8 mm, bifurcate at 17.5 mm; pectoral "paddle-like", more ventral by 10.8 mm, with primitive rays by 17.5 mm. Order of fin development; dorsal, caudal, pectoral, ventral and anal. Urostyle directed upward at 17.5 mm.

Pigmentation: Additional chromatophores anterior to vent and along each side of dorsal wall of anterior third of gut; scattered over caudal fin and base, and along each side of anal.[14]

PREJUVENILES (Fig. 38 C)

Minimum size described ca. 20 mm.

Gill rakers as low as 90 at ca. 20 mm. At 22 mm, body minnow-like, cylindrical. Few minute teeth on lower edge of maxillary. Gut with 4 flexures, but lacking pyloric caeca.[1]

Pigmentation: An irregular triangle of chromatophores on crown; ca. 20 chromatophores in 2 irregular rows on lower jaw plus few on lower lip and chin; scattered chromatophores on preopercle and throat; 3 rows on dorso-lateral surface; a short fourth row along base of caudal; a row along anal base; and many on caudal fin.[14]

JUVENILES (Fig. 38 D,E)

Minimum size described 26 mm TL.

Gill rakers greater than 300 at 65 mm SL, ca. 350 at 95 mm. Upper jaw lacking median notch and with row of fine teeth in young.[10] Dorsal filament becoming elongate at ca. 50 mm.[18] Scales apparently not formed, but ventral scutes present at 35 mm;[17] scalation complete at ca. 50 mm.[18] Caecae arise from duodenum by 27.5 mm; liver, intestine, and gizzard well developed by 26 mm.

Pigmentation: Young-of-the-year (up to 114 mm) with dorsal and caudal fins uniformly sprinkled with chromatophores; pectorals and ventrals almost unpigmented.[1]

Age and size at maturity: Usually 2nd or 3rd year; some females apparently at 1 year.[5] Typically 178–279 mm,[10] possibly 151 mm.[6]

LITERATURE CITED

1. Miller, R. R., 1960:371–88.
2. Gunter, G., 1945:31.
3. Langlois, T. H., 1954:224.
4. Gowanloch, J. N., 1933:215.
5. Bodola, A., 1955:1–130.
6. Vladykov, V. D., 1945:35, 37.
7. Trautman, M. B., 1957:182.
8. Massmann, W. H., 1953:441.
9. Cady, E. R., 1945:114.
10. Miller, R. R., 1963:444–6.
11. Hildebrand, S. F., and W. C. Schroeder, 1928:106–8.
12. Abbott, C. C., 1861:365.
13. Carufel, L. H., and A. Witt, 1963:178.
14. Warner, E. N., 1940:7, 9, 17–8.
15. Smith, H. M., 1907:119.
16. Nash, C. B., 1950:562.
17. Fowler, H. W., 1935: Fig. 2.
18. Fowler, H. W., 1945: Fig. 7.
19. Gunter, G., 1938a:71.
20. Miller, R. R., 1950:392–4.
21. Bodola, A., 1966:392, 417.

Round herring

Etrumeus teres (DeKay)

ADULT (Fig. 39 A)

D. 16–22; A. 10–12; V. 8; P. 14–17; scale rows between upper angle of gill opening and base of caudal ca. 48–55; branchiostegal rays 14–15; gill rakers on lower limb of first arch 27–38; vertebrae 48–56.[1,6]

Proportions as percent of SL: Body depth 16.0–18.5; depth of caudal peduncle 6.7–8.2; head length 24.0–29.0;

base of anal fin 5.6–6.9; length of pectoral 14.0–17.0; length of ventral 8.9–11.5.

Body nearly round, its greatest thickness 80% of depth. Caudal peduncle compressed. Scales deciduous with even edges; scutes lacking. Head low, moderately long. Eye with much adipose tissue. Maxillary obliquely rounded posteriorly, reaching about under anterior margin of eye. Gill rakers slender, close set. Single series

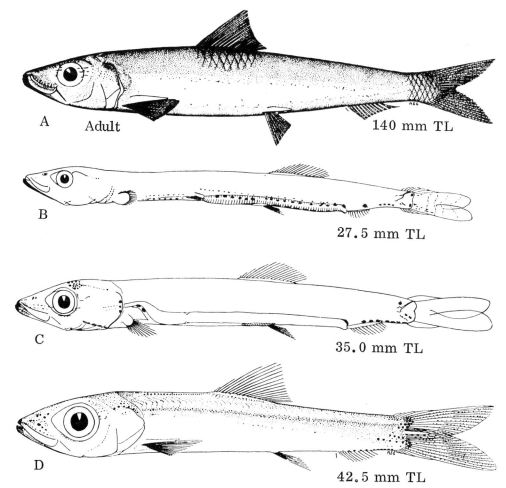

Fig. 39. *Etrumeus teres*, round herring. A. Adult female, 140 mm TL. B. Larva, 27.5 mm TL. C. Pre-juvenile, 35.0 mm TL. D. Juvenile, 42.5 mm TL. (*Hildebrand, 1963a: fig. 62–3*).

of teeth on mandible; row on margin of maxillaries; few on pre-maxillaries; and very small granular teeth on vomer, palatines, pterygoids, and tongue. Ventrals inserted somewhat posterior to a vertical from base of last dorsal ray; pectorals reaching less than halfway to ventrals.

Olive-green above, silvery below.[1]

Maximum length ca. 380 mm.[4]

DISTRIBUTION AND ECOLOGY

Range: Bay of Fundy to Cape Kennedy, Florida and Gulf of Mexico; [1] also the American Pacific Coast, eastern coast of South Africa, southern coast of Australia, Japan, Galapagos Islands, eastern Mediterranean, and the Red Sea.[6]

Area distribution: One specimen 6 miles southwest of Cape Charles, Virginia; [2] large schools off New Jersey in some years; [5] possibly off Ocean City, Maryland (taken from stomach of white marlin).[3]

Habitat and movements: Adult—a pelagic, schooling species whose pattern of movement is unknown; primarily an inhabitant of offshore waters although occasionally entering bays and rivers.[1,7]

SPAWNING

Location: Larvae recorded off northern Florida and from the Gulf of Mexico ca. 17 miles off the Mississippi Delta.

Season: Probably winter.[1]

EGGS

Undescribed.

LARVAE (Fig. 39 B)

Size range described 25–28 mm TL.

Body depth contained 16 to 24 times in SL; snout 1.5 to 2.0 times length of eye.

Jaws weakly developed; teeth absent. At 27.5 mm,

opercle developing; caudal fin deeply bifurcate; pectorals and ventrals incompletely developed; urostyle directed obliquely upward; gut striated.

Pigmentation: Single, slightly broken line of chromatophores on chest; two diverging lines on abdomen; dark spots along each side of anal base; single, dark median lines behind anal fin; several dark spots on base of caudal.[1]

PREJUVENILES (Fig. 39 C)

Specimens described 33.0–35.0 mm TL.

Body proportionately much deeper than in previous stage; nostril divided; gut still visible.

Pigmentation: Virtually same as in larvae, but with chromatophores on top of head and opercle, and abdominal pigment reduced.[1]

JUVENILES (Fig. 39 D)

Single specimen described 42.5 mm TL.

Axillary process of pectoral present, that of ventral lacking; urostyle and gut no longer visible.

Pigmentation: Rows of small chromatophores on dorsum and along upper sides; scattered chromatophores on snout, posterio-dorsal region of head, caudal peduncle, caudal fin, and ventrally between anal and caudal. General pigmentation scarcely complete at 55 mm TL.[1]

Age and size at maturity: Unknown.

LITERATURE CITED

1. Hildebrand, S. F., 1963a:263–6.
2. Massmann, W. H., 1960:70.
3. de Sylva, D. P., and W. P. Davis, 1963:94.
4. Breder, C. M., Jr., 1948:63.
5. Perlmutter, A., 1961:287.
6. Whitehead, P. J. P., 1963:321–8.
7. Bigelow, H. B., and W. C. Schroeder, 1953:88.

Atlantic thread herring   *Opisthonema oglinum* (LeSueur)

ADULT (Fig. 40)

D. 17–22; A. 21–25; P. 15–19; V. 8–9; scale rows between gill opening and base of caudal 42–50; vertebrae 45–49. Total ventral scutes 32–36; prepelvic scutes 17–19; post pelvic scutes 13–17.[1,7] Total gill rakers ca. 125–158; epibranchial 50–61; ceratobranchial 29–46; hypobranchial 42–62; lower limb 80–100 (FHB).

Proportions as percent SL: Body depth 30.0–40.0; caudal peduncle depth 8.5–11.0; head length 19.0–28.0; eye

diameter 6.0–8.5; maxillary length 8.8–12.0; anal fin base 16.7–21.5; ventral fin length 8.5–11.5; pectoral fin length 17.0–21.0; length of anterior lobe of dorsal fin 15.1–20.8; length of last dorsal ray 33.3–40.3.

Body elongate, rather strongly compressed; ventral outline convex; dorsal outline only gently convex. Head small; snout lacking definite median notch; maxillary broadly rounded, reaching anterior margin of pupil; mandible slightly projecting, its upper margin forming

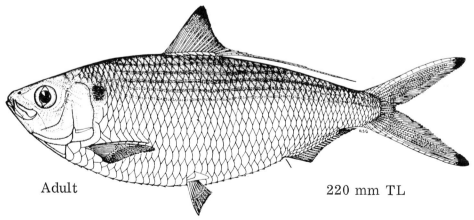

Adult   220 mm TL

Fig. 40. Opisthonema oglinum, Atlantic thread herring. Adult, 220 mm TL, 167 mm SL. (Hildebrand, 1963b: fig. 94.)

obtuse angle; jaws toothless; longest gill rakers ca. 1/3 eye diameter. Scales thin, deeper than long, with somewhat irregular membranous edges; predorsal median line scaled to nape; anal and dorsal bases with low sheath of scales.

Bluish-green above, silvery on sides and below; usually with dark shoulder spot; dorsal scale rows with more or less definite dark lines; fins translucent, dorsal and caudal usually with dark tips.

Maximum length ca. 300 mm.[1,7]

DISTRIBUTION AND ECOLOGY

Range: Gulf of Maine[8] to Santa Catarina, Brazil;[7] also Bermuda[5] and West Indies.[1]

Area Distribution: Chesapeake Bay,[2] to Annapolis;[3] Ocean City, Maryland;[6] New Jersey.[9]

Habitat and movements: Adults—a surface schooling species found chiefly in tropical and subtropical waters.
    Juveniles—Three- to 4-inch specimens abundant in Beaufort harbor, North Carolina in August and September;[4] sometimes in great abundance in Chesapeake Bay during summer months.[3] Minimum salinity probably 10–15 o/oo.[10]

SPAWNING

Location: Apparently at sea.

Season: Probably May and June at Beaufort, North Carolina.[1]

EGGS

Undescribed.

YOLK-SAC LARVAE

Undescribed.

LARVAE

Undescribed, although fish 22–25 mm long have been tentatively identified as this species.[1]

JUVENILES

Minimum size described 30 mm TL.

Body generally more slender than in adults in specimens up to 75 mm long. Number of gill rakers increasing with size; 40–50 on lower limb of first arch at 40–60 mm TL; at 40–50 mm SL, ca. 24–35 epibranchial, 22–27 ceratobranchial, and 23–31 hypobranchial. Ventral scutes developed at 30 mm or less;[1] caudal elements fully formed at 75 mm;[5] last ray of dorsal prolonged in some 30 mm specimens.

Pigmentation: Variable; a silvery band, occasionally with small, dark spots, generally merges with silvery color of sides at 35–40 mm, but can remain distinct up to ca. 50 mm. Shoulder spot present in some specimens at 35 mm. Peritoneum black, often visible through body wall.

Size at maturity: 150 mm.[1]

LITERATURE CITED

1. Hildebrand, S. F., 1963a:381–84.
2. Hildebrand, S. F., and W. C. Schroeder, 1928:102.
3. Schwartz, F. J., 1960a:210–11.
4. Smith, H. M., 1907:130.
5. Hollister, G., 1936a:284–86.
6. Fowler, H. W., 1914:3.
7. Berry, F. H., and I. Barrett, 1963:126, 150.
8. MacCoy, C. V., 1931:21.
9. Fowler, H. W., 1906:103.
10. Beaven, G. F., 1960:9–10.

Anchoa hepsetus

Anchoa mitchilli

Anchoviella eurystole

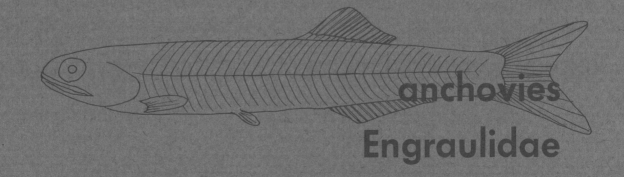

anchovies

Engraulidae

ADULT (Fig. 41 A)

D. 13–16; A. 18–23; P. 13–15; scales from upper angle of gill opening to base of caudal ca. 37–43; vertebrae 40–44; gill rakers 15–20+18–24.

Proportions as percent SL: Body depth 18.5–22.0; head length 25.0–30.0; diameter of eye 7.2–8.7.

Body slender, moderately compressed; cheek little longer than eye, its posterior angle ca. 45°. Maxillary quite pointed, reaching nearly to margin of opercle. Origin of dorsal about equidistant between base of caudal and middle of eye; ventrals inserted about equidistant between anal origin and pectoral base.[2] Pale gray and irridescent; upper surface of head with some green and yellow; back with dusky spots;[4] a prominent, silver, lateral band, its width highly variable;[2] dorsal and caudal sometimes more or less dusky.[4]

Maximum length 153 mm.[2]

DISTRIBUTION AND ECOLOGY

Range: Nova Scotia to Montevideo, Uruguay.[2]

Area distribution: Delaware,[10] Maryland, New Jersey, and Virginia.[3]

Habitat and movements: Adults—Usually in large schools near shore; frequently in shallow, grassy areas in North Carolina.[1] Salinity range 2.5[7] to 75–80 o/oo.[8] Greatest recorded depth 30–40 fathoms.[2] Oceanic movements largely unknown; apparently withdraws from Chesapeake Bay during winter.[5]

Larvae—salt and brackish water; hatched at surface, but majority apparently descend to bottom at an early stage.[1] Recorded along edge of Continental Shelf off Delaware and Virginia (OES).

SPAWNING

Location: Along outer banks at Beaufort, North Carolina; also in harbor and nearby sounds and estuaries;[1] not more than 10 miles offshore and in water no deeper than 12 fathoms (OES).

Season: Ripe individuals in March to early May in Tampa Bay, Florida;[6] mid-April through July with peak activity in May in North Carolina.

Time: Early evening.[1]

Minimum temperature: 16 C (OES).

EGGS (Fig. 41 B)

Description: Ripe ovarian eggs—ca. 1.2 mm in diameter, white, oval.[11]

Fertilized eggs—buoyant, transparent,[1] elliptical.[2] Major axis 1.2[9]–1.66 (OES), minor axis 0.7[2]–0.94 mm (OES). Yolk segmented into large cell-like masses,[2] stated to lack oil globules,[2,9] but illustrations indicate a single globule.

Development: Eggs collected before any cleavage occurred, developed at ca. 19–21 C.

> Within 1 hour—8-cell stage; early cleavage furrows deep.
> 12 hours—Embryonic axis.
> Just before hatching—Heart action and embryonic movement apparent.

Incubation: 48 hours at ca. 18.9–21.1 C.[1]

YOLK-SAC LARVAE (Fig. 41 C)

Hatching length ca. 3.6–4.0 mm TL. Maximum size described 4.5 mm TL. Duration of stage ca. 24 hours.[2]

Body long, slender,[1] thread-like;[2] head somewhat decurved;[1] dorsal outline slightly concave.[2] Yolk mass elongate, tapering to a point posteriorly. Anus slightly behind beginning of posterior 1/4 of body at hatching. Fins lacking; finfold continuous from first somite to vent and forward over posterior 1/3 of yolk.

Pigmentation: Body highly transparent; slight, greenish shade on head, but no definite chromatophores.[1]

LARVAE (Fig. 41 D,E)

Specimens described 5.0–13.0 mm TL.

Body very slender at 5.0 mm, slightly deeper at 10.0 mm. Mouth oblique; gape extending to eye at 5.0 mm, beyond anterior margin of eye at 10.0 mm. Myomeres visible only in posterior region at 10.0 mm. Gut almost straight, but with striated appearance at 5.0 mm; not invaginated at 10.0 mm.

Dorsal, anal, caudal, and pectoral fins evident, but lacking rays, at 5.0–6.0 mm. Incipient ventrals at ca. 13 mm; caudal definitely forked at 10.0 mm. Finfold constricted in region of future caudal peduncle and deeply scalloped behind future dorsal at 5.6 mm. Notochord somewhat oblique posteriorly at 5.0, strongly oblique at 10.0 mm.

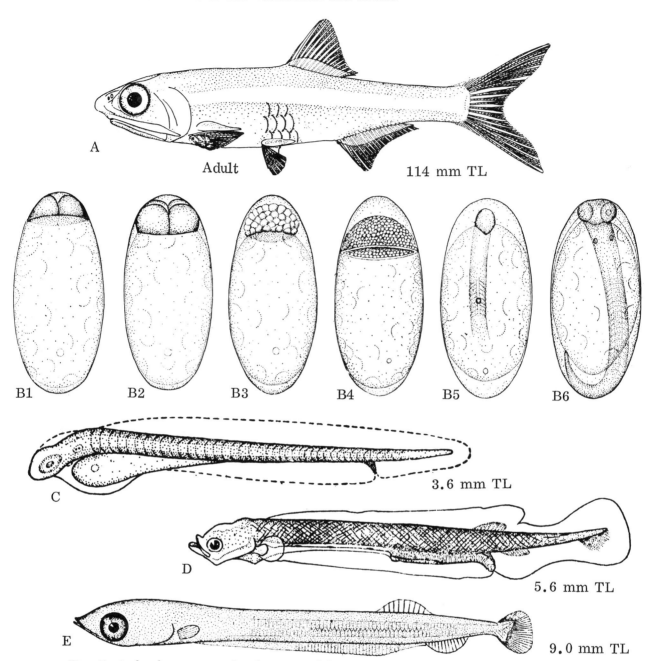

Fig. 41. *Anchoa hepsetus*, striped anchovy. A. Adult, 114 mm TL. B. Development of egg. Major axis ca. 1.5 mm; minor axis ca. 0.8 mm. B1. Two-cell stage. B2. Four-cell stage. B3. Early morula. B4. Late morula. B5. Early embryo. Eight somites visible; Kupffer's vesicle present. B6. Embryo just before hatching. C. Yolk-sac larva, 3.6 mm TL, newly hatched. D. Larva, 5.6 mm TL; few chromatophores along anterior dorsal half of intestine not illustrated. E. Larva, 9.0 mm TL. (A, *Hildebrand, 1963b: fig 40.* B-E, *Hildebrand and Cable, 1930: fig. 3–11*).

Pigmentation: At 5.0 mm, ca. 5 very small, elongate chromatophores near ventral outline posterior to head. At 10.0 mm, few chromatophores on midline of chest and along venter from anal base to caudal.[1]

PREJUVENILES (Fig. 42 A,B)

Specimens described 15.0–25.0 mm TL.

Depth ca. 8 times in SL at 25 mm TL. Mouth terminal; jaws somewhat curved; gape extended beyond posterior margin of eye at 15 mm. At 25 mm, mouth slightly inferior; jaws bent upward anteriorly. Gut fully enclosed in body wall at 25 mm. Caudal fin definitely homocercal; notochord no longer visible at 15 mm.

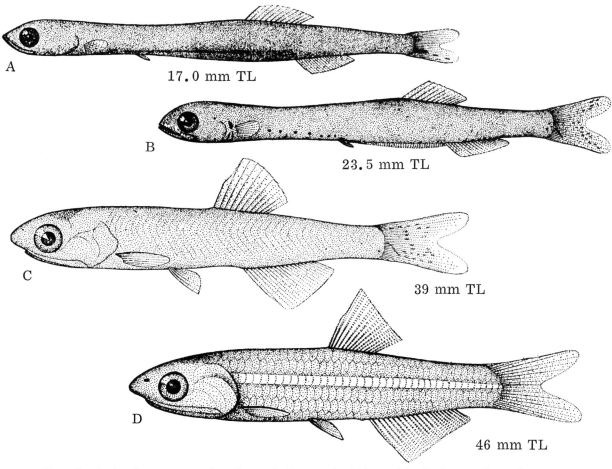

Fig. 42. Anchoa hepsetus, striped anchovy. A. Prejuvenile, 17.0 mm TL. B. Prejuvenile, 23.5 mm TL. C. Juvenile, 39 mm TL. D. Juvenile, 46 mm TL. Silvery band distinct. *(Hildebrand and Cable, 1930: fig. 12–15.)*

Pigmentation: At 15 mm, additional pigment at upper margin of eye. At 25 mm, a continuous dark line mid-ventrally from gill covers to opposite pectoral bases; 2 or 3 elongate spots behind opercle; a ventro-lateral series of chromatophores between pectorals and ventrals; scattered chromatophores on caudal base and fin.[1]

JUVENILES (Fig. 42 C,D)

Minimum size described 35 mm TL.

Depth ca. 6 times in SL at 35 mm TL; body very nearly as deep as in adult at 45 mm. At 35 mm, head conical, snout fully developed. Scales evident at 45 mm. Origin of anal under posterior 1/2–1/4 of dorsal base; vent definitely posterior to vertical from origin of dorsal.

Pigmentation: At 35 mm, pigment developed on dorsum,

a conspicuous brownish area on top of head; silvery, lateral band present but narrow and indistinct.

Age and size at maturity: Ca. 1 year; minimum ca. 75 mm.[1]

LITERATURE CITED

1. Hildebrand, S. F., and L. E. Cable, 1930:388–94.
2. Hildebrand, S. F., 1963b:194–8.
3. Hildebrand, S. F., 1943a:58.
4. Bigelow, H. B., and W. C. Schroeder, 1953:119.
5. Hildebrand, S. F., and W. C. Schroeder, 1928:111.
6. Springer, V. G., and K. D. Woodburn, 1960:20.
7. Gunter, G., 1945:33.
8. Simmons, E. G., 1957:182.
9. Kuntz, A., and L. Radcliffe, 1917:90.
10. de Sylva, D. P., F. A. Kalber, Jr., and C. N. Shuster, Jr., 1962:20.
11. Stevenson, R. A., Jr., 1958:30.

ADULT (Fig. 43 A)

D. 14–16;[3] A. 23[4]–30; P. 11–12; scales from upper angle of gill opening to base of caudal ca. 38–44; vertebrae 38–44; gill rakers 15–19+20–26.

Proportions as percent SL: Body depth 16.0–27.0; head length 22.0–26.5; diameter of eye 5.8–8.2.

Body rather slender, moderately compressed; cheek short, broad, about as long as eye, its posterior angle ca. 60°; maxillary pointed, extending nearly to margin of opercle.

Anal origin under or slightly posterior to dorsal origin. Ventrals small, not quite reaching halfway to anal origin, and inserted nearer anal origin than pectoral base.

Greenish above with bluish reflections, silvery below; an ill-defined, silvery, lateral band from gill opening to caudal fin; many dark dots on body and fins and two more or less definite rows of dusky punctations on back posterior to dorsal fin.[3,5]

Maximum length 102 mm TL.[4]

DISTRIBUTION AND ECOLOGY

Range: Gulf of Maine to Yucatan, Mexico.

Area distribution: Chesapeake Bay,[3] New Jersey, Delaware, Maryland, and Virginia.[4]

Habitat and movements: Adults—euryhaline, 40 miles above brackish water in Virginia rivers.[7] Primarily estuarine and coastal waters; in bayous;[9] off sandy beaches;[10,11] in open bays and muddy coves;[8] grassy areas along beaches;[3] around mouths of rivers;[5] and in both shallow and deeper offshore waters.[3] Maximum salinity 80 o/oo.[12] Maximum recorded depth 15–20 fathoms.[3] Present in Chesapeake Bay throughout the year, concentrating in deeper water during colder months;[8] oceanic movements unknown, apparently restricted to localized inshore-offshore migrations.[3]

Larvae—apparently hatched mainly near surface but majority descend to bottom before reaching 12 mm; recorded from both salt and brackish waters.[1].

Juveniles—euryhaline, ascending rivers in Virginia 40 miles above brackish water;[7] also shallow grassy areas and deeper water.[1]

SPAWNING

Location: Typically in water less than 20 meters deep,[6] although possibly to edge of continental shelf on basis of putative eggs (OES). In the harbor, estuaries, sounds, and along outer banks near Beaufort, North Carolina.

Season: Late April to early September in North Carolina,[1] with peak activity in July;[2] May through August in Chesapeake Bay;[8] early June to September in Long Island Sound.[6]

Time: Typically early evening, 6:00 to 9:00 p.m.[1]

EGGS (Fig. 43 B)

Description: Buoyant when newly spawned, but apparently becoming demersal with advancing development.

Fertilized eggs—slightly elongate,[2] rarely spherical;[3] major axis 0.65[2]–1.24 mm (WLD), minor axis 0.64[2]–1.12 mm (WLD); eggs apparently smaller as season progresses.[6,15] Yolk segmented into large cell-like masses;[2] oil globules absent;[16] perivitelline space very narrow.

Development: At unspecified temperature.

5 hours—cleavage regular and rapid; late morula.
10 hours—blastopore closed and embryo slightly longer than 1/2 greater circumference of egg.
Soon after closure of blastopore, Kupffer's vesicle formed; 18–20 somites present; optic and otic buds visible.

Incubation: Ca. 24 hours at average temperature of ca. 27.2–27.8 C.[2]

YOLK-SAC LARVAE (Fig. 43 C; Fig. 44 A,B)

Hatching length 1.8–2.7 mm.[2] Maximum size described 3.75 mm (WLD). Duration of stage 15–18 hours.[12]

Snout to anus 2.02 mm at 2.75 mm TL, 2.51 mm at 3.70 mm TL (WLD).

Body elongate, flattened, rather slender; head deflected downward over yolk at hatching, straight at 2.6–2.8 mm. Yolk pear-shaped, tapering to a point posteriorly, and more than 1/2 absorbed in 12 hours.[2] Incipient rays in caudal at 3.7 mm (WLD). Notocord thick, granular. Gut apparently a straight tube.

Pigmentation: Pigment initially lacking;[2] at 3.7 mm, a few chromatophores ventrally between anus and caudal fin (WLD).

LARVAE (Fig. 44 C-G; Fig. 45 A-D)

Specimens described 2.7–15.0 mm TL.[2]

At 12.0 mm, D. 15–16; A. 23–31 (NSS).

Body long and slender. Mouth terminal, apparently functional at 2.7 mm. Finfold somewhat constricted in caudal region at 2.9 mm; relative depths of finfolds decreased

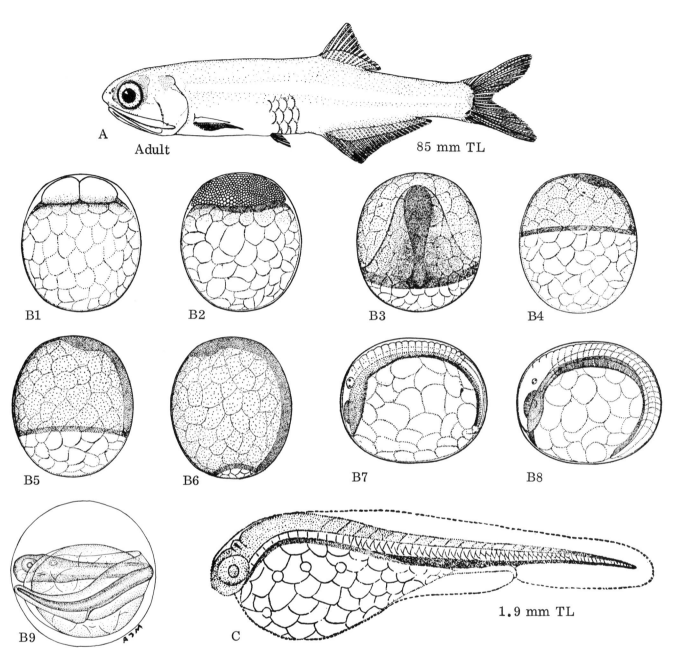

Fig. 43. *Anchoa mitchilli,* bay anchovy. A. Adult, 85 mm TL. B. Egg diameters (except B9), major axis 0.64 to 1.05 mm, minor axis 0.64 to 0.92 mm. B1. Two-cell stage. B2. Morula, ca. 5 hrs. B3. Gastrula. Egg at angle to show formation of embryonic shield. B4. Lateral view of same stage. Blastoderm almost 1/2 around yolk; germ ring distinct. B5. Late gastrula. Blastoderm 2/3 around yolk. B6. Early embryo just before closure of blastopore at ca. 10 hours. B7. Embryo with 18–20 somites and Kupffer's vesicle. B8. Later embryo, 29 somites. B9. Pre-hatching embryo, egg diameters-major axis 1.06 mm, minor axis 1.01 mm. C. Yolk-sac larva, 1.9 mm TL, recently hatched. (A, *Hildebrand, 1963b: fig. 31.* B1-B8, C, *Kuntz, 1914: fig. 25, 28, 31–37.* B9, *original drawing, A. J. Mansueti.*)

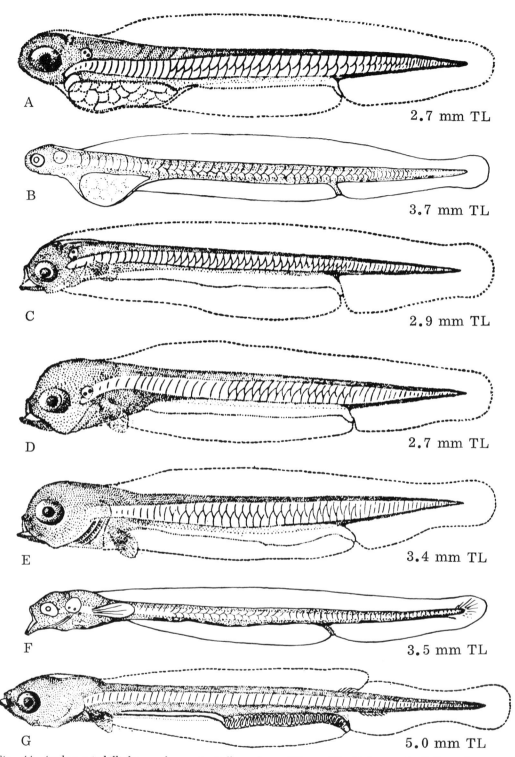

2.7 mm TL

3.7 mm TL

2.9 mm TL

2.7 mm TL

3.4 mm TL

3.5 mm TL

5.0 mm TL

Fig. 44. Anchoa mitchilli, bay anchovy. A. Yolk-sac larva, 2.7 mm TL; 12 hours. B. Yolk-sac larva, 3.7 mm TL. Snout to anus length 2.5 mm; few chromatophores in caudal region. C. Larva, 2.9 mm TL, 36 hours. D. Larva, 2.7 mm TL, 3 days old. E. Larva, 3.4 mm TL. F. Larva, 3.5 mm TL. Ventral row of chromatophores and incipient rays in caudal area. G. Larva, 5.0 mm TL. Fin ray bases of dorsal and anal formed; posterior half of intestine convoluted. (A, C-E, G, *Kuntz, 1914: fig. 38–42.* B, F, *original drawings, A. J. Mansueti.*)

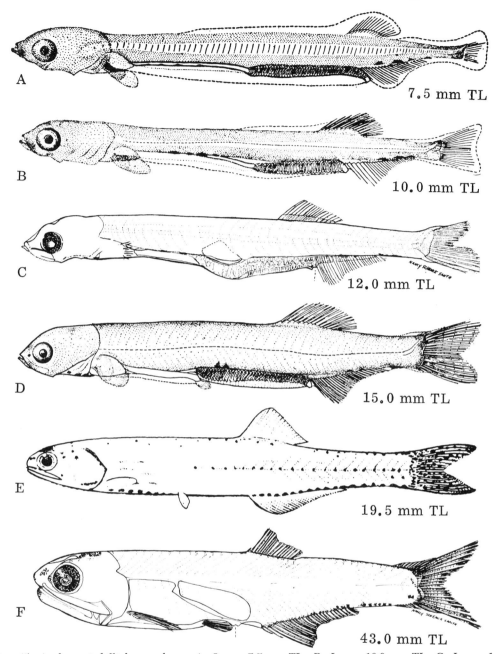

Fig. 45. *Anchoa mitchilli,* bay anchovy. A. Larva, 7.5 mm TL. B. Larva, 10.0 mm TL. C. Larva, 12.0 mm TL, 11.3 mm FL. Intestine bulged below expanded gas bladder. D. Larva, 15.0 mm TL. Ventral buds formed. E. Juvenile, 19.5 mm TL. F. Juvenile, 43.0 mm TL, 39.5 mm FL. Gas bladder visible. (A, B, D, *Kuntz, 1914: fig. 43–45.* C, F, *original drawings, N. S. Smith.* E, *Fowler, 1945: fig. 34.*)

by 3.0–4.0 mm. Posterior region of gut convoluted at 5.0 mm. Anlage of pectoral present at 2.7 mm; incipient dorsal and anal at 5.0 mm; some specimens with full anal count by 7.0–8.0 mm; caudal slightly forked at 10.0 mm; pelvics forming at 15 mm, but apparently without rays. Urostyle oblique at 7.5 mm.

Pigmentation: Highly transparent, becoming less so with growth. At 3.5 mm, double row of chromatophores along venter (WLD). At 7.0–8.0 mm, few chromatophores on ventral aspect of thoracic region and at base of caudal.[2]

PREJUVENILES AND JUVENILES (Fig. 45 E,F)

Limits of stages unknown.

Depth 12 times in body length at 16 mm, 9 times at 20 mm, 5.5 times at 25 mm.[8]

Projecting snout developed at ca. 20–25 mm.[3] Posterior convolutions of gut no longer visible externally at 20 mm.[2] Anal origin slightly behind dorsal origin; vent under or slightly anterior to dorsal origin.[1]

Pigmentation: Individuals may remain quite transparent until mature;[3] at 19.5 mm, a series of chromatophores ventrally between operculum and ventral fins; a similar series from origin of anal to caudal base; mid-lateral row of chromatophores on posterior 2/3 of body; scattered chromatophores on dorso-lateral surface; a dark blotch between eyes on top of head; caudal fin heavily pigmented.[13] At 43 mm, a row of chromatophores along anal base and continuing to caudal fin; few chromatophores on head (NSS).

Age and size at maturity: Minimums ca. 2 1/2 months (based on putative identification), between 35 and 40 mm.[14]

Silver anchovy

ADULT

D. 13–16; A. 15–19; P. 15–16; scales between upper angle of gill opening and caudal base 40–45; vertebrae 43–45; gill rakers 24–28+27–33.

Proportions as percent of SL: Body depth 15.4–19.0; head length 25.0–28.5; snout length 3.85–5.0; eye diameter 5.7–7.0; postorbital distance 13.8–15:5; maxillary length 15.8–17.8; mandibular length 15.0–18.5; anal fin base 12.5– 16.0; pectoral fin length 12.5–13.7.

Body slender, not strongly compressed. Snout projecting half its length beyond mandible. Maxillary rather narrow, rounded distally and not reaching joint of mandible. Dorsal low anteriorly, longest ray failing to reach tip of last ray if deflected. Origin of dorsal usually somewhat nearer tip of snout than base of caudal. Anal origin wholly behind dorsal base. Ventrals inserted nearly an eye's diameter in advance of dorsal.

Preserved specimens pale or bluish above; sides of head and lower sides sometimes silvery; a silvery lateral band about as broad as eye in small specimens, becoming obscure along ventral margin in large specimens.

Maximum length 155 mm TL.[2]

DISTRIBUTION AND ECOLOGY

Range: Lynn Harbor, Massachusetts[3] to Beaufort, North Carolina.[6]

LITERATURE CITED

1. Hildebrand, S. F., and L. E. Cable, 1930:388–89, 393–95.
2. Kuntz, A., 1914:13–19.
3. Hildebrand, S. F., 1963b:176–79.
4. Hildebrand, S. F., 1943a:90, 92.
5. Bigelow, H. B., and W. C. Schroeder, 1953:118–19.
6. Richards, S. W., 1959:107, 109.
7. Massmann, W. H., 1954:76.
8. Hildebrand, S. F., and W. C. Schroeder, 1928:109–10.
9. Springer, V. G., and K. D. Woodburn, 1960:21.
10. Reid, G. K., Jr., 1954:18.
11. Kilby, J. D., 1955:193.
12. Simmons, E. G., 1957:182.
13. Fowler, H. W., 1945; Fig. 34.
14. Stevenson, R. A., Jr., 1958:1, 30, 34–5.
15. Wheatland, S. B., 1956:249.
16. Herman, S. S., 1958:23.

Anchoviella eurystole (Swain and Meek)

Area distribution: Unknown from Chesapeake Bay, rarely taken in coastal waters of New Jersey.[2]

Habitat and movements: Adults—coastal waters; primarily pelagic, although recorded inshore at Mullet Pond on Shakleford Banks, North Carolina [4] and in Brigantine Bay, New Jersey; possibly seaward to within Gulf Stream.[2,5]

Larvae—putative stages from edge of continental shelf off Montauk and New York (OES).

SPAWNING

Area: Probably offshore waters.[1] Presence of putative larvae suggest spawning as far south as off the Chesapeake Capes (OES).

Season: July [2] to early August;[1] possibly early spring based on putative larvae taken near edge of continental shelf in April (OES).

Time: Probably during evening.[1]

EGGS (Fig. 46 B)

Description: Buoyant,[2] highly transparent, oblong;[1] major axis 1.02 (OES)–1.25 mm,[1] minor axis 0.50 (OES)– 0.80 mm. Yolk coarsely granular.

Development: Unspecified rearing temperature. Embryonic axis evident when blastoderm covers less than 1/4 of

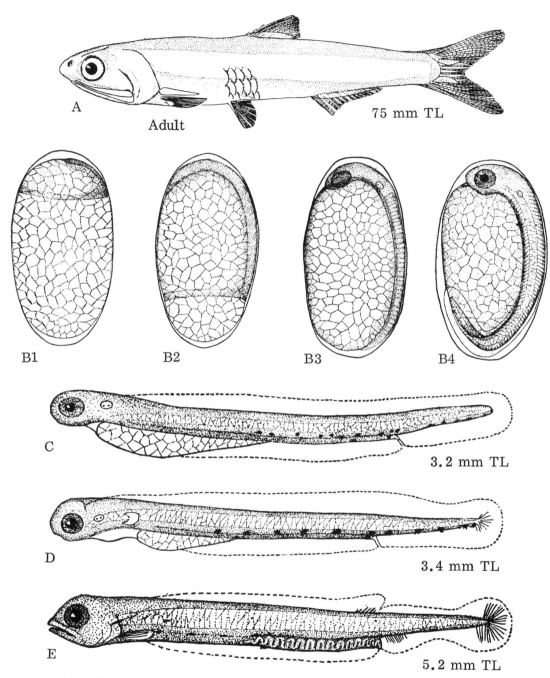

Fig. 46. Anchoviella eurystole, silver anchovy. A. Adult, 75 mm TL. B. Development of egg. Major axis 1.15–1.25 mm. B1. Formation of embryonic axis. B2. Early embryo before closure of blastopore. B3. Embryo shortly after closure of blastopore. B4. Late embryo. C. Yolk-sac larva, 3.2 mm TL, 8 hours. D. Yolk-sac larva, 3.4 mm TL, 1 day. E. Larva, 5.2 mm TL. (A, *Hildebrand, 1963c: fig. 44.* B-E, *Kuntz and Radcliffe, 1917: fig. 69–75.*)

yolk. Shortly after closure of blastopore, somites, auditory vesicles, Kupffer's vesicle and anlagen of eyes differentiated. When fully differentiated, embryo lies parallel to major egg axis with head deflected sharply over yolk. Advanced embryo, apparently without pigment, extends ca. 2/3 around yolk; notochord thick and vesicular.[1]

YOLK-SAC LARVAE (Fig. 46 C,D)

Length at hatching ca. 3.0 mm TL; at 1 day, ca. 3.4 mm.

Body elongate. Head not deflected over yolk at 8 hours after hatching. Yolk mass elongate, tapering to point posteriorly; more than 1/2 absorbed by first day. Gut apparently a straight tube at hatching; anus about 1/4 length of body from posterior end.

Dorsal finfold originates just behind auditory vesicles. Finfold straight-edged in newly hatched larvae; scalloped above region of future caudal peduncle in 1 day old fish. Preanal finfold extends forward about halfway across yolk. Incipient rays forming in caudal and anlagen of pectorals present in 1 day old specimen. Notochord reticulate.

Pigmentation: At hatching, or within first 8 hours, melanophores in series along intestine posterior to yolk and at base of ventral finfold posterior to vent; melanophores considerably larger at 1 day.[1]

LARVAE (Fig. 46 E)

One specimen described 5.2 mm TL.[1]

Body deeper anteriorly. Mouth large, oblique, terminal;[2] gape reaching middle of eye. Opercle well differentiated. Incipient rays forming in dorsal, anal, caudal, and pectoral. Pectoral fin rounded, ventrals lacking.

Dorsal finfold reduced in front of and strongly notched at posterior region of developing dorsal fin; preanal finfold extending slightly forward of distal end of pectoral fin and about to below anterior end of dorsal finfold. Notochord conspicuously thickened, reticulate. Intestine convoluted posteriorly.

Pigmentation: Body almost colorless; melanophores of earlier stages less conspicuous.[1]

JUVENILES

Undescribed.

LITERATURE CITED

1. Kuntz, A., and L. Radcliffe, 1917:90, 116–19.
2. Hildebrand, S. F., 1963b:208–10.
3. Hubbs, C. L., 1953:194.
4. Hildebrand, S. F., 1941:224.
5. Nichols, J. F., and C. M. Breder, Jr., 1927:44.
6. Radcliffe, L., 1914:414.

Umbra pygmaea

mudminnows
Umbridae

Eastern mudminnow

Umbra pygmaea (DeKay)

ADULT (Fig. 47 A)

D. 2–3 unbranched, 12–14 branched; A. 4 unbranched, 5–8 branched; [6] V. 6; P. 12 [10]–16; [4] scales in mid-lateral series 28–35, transversely between dorsal and ventral origins 12–15. [6] Body depth 4.5 times in TL; [8] eye 3.4–5.0 times in HL. [6] Head short and broad. [8] Premaxillaries not protractile; [10] gill rakers short and numerous. Scales cycloid. Lateral line lacking.

Yellowish-green with 10–12 narrow, lateral, dark stripes; dark stripe through eye; a black basicaudal bar; [8] lower jaw pale; [13] fins plain. [8] During spawning season ground color black or grey. [14]

Maximum length ca. 152 mm or larger. [6]

DISTRIBUTION AND ECOLOGY

Range: Southeastern New York (ECR) to northeastern Florida [11] (records from New England [2] are doubtful); introduced and established in Belgium [4] and France. [12]

Area distribution: Tidal tributaries of Chesapeake Bay in Virginia; [19] coastal streams and ponds in Maryland (JDH) and New Jersey. [20]

Habitat: Adults—lowland streams, ponds, pools, [16] and swamps; [17] in heavy vegetation over soft, silty bottoms in sluggish streams. [3] Maximum natural salinity 4 o/oo; [9] experimentally survive at 10 o/oo, but not at 15 o/oo. [3]
   Larvae—remain in algal nest for ca. 6 days. [18]
   Juveniles—among aquatic vegetation along edges of shallow barrier beach ponds adjacent to Chesapeake Bay (JDH); specimens 15–22 mm TL tend to travel in schools of 10–12 individuals. [7]

SPAWNING

Location: In hollows formed in masses of algae. [17,18]

Season: March and April in aquaria; [4,14] early spring (to at least April) under natural conditions. [5,18]

Temperature: 14–15 C.

Fecundity: 300–400. [4,14]

EGGS (Fig. 47 B)

Description: Placed in special algal nest [18] and guarded by parents.
   Fertilized eggs—diameter 1.6 mm. Slightly viscous; [14]

perivitelline space ca. 1/9 yolk radius; yolk with numerous oil globules of various sizes. [1]

Incubation: 6 [18] to 14 days. [14,16]

YOLK-SAC LARVAE (Fig. 47 C,D)

Specimens described 5.4 and 6.0 mm TL.

Head deflected downward at hatching, but apparently not attached to yolk; yolk mass somewhat flattened at hatching, more than half absorbed by 6.0 mm. Mouth open at 6.0 mm.

Anlagen of pectorals formed at hatching. Finfold apparently continuous around and beyond yolk at hatching; constricted at mid-body and in area of vent and bluntly pointed at posterior end at 6.0 mm. Incipient rays in caudal at 6.0 mm.

Pigmentation: Chromatophores on dorsal surface of head and eye, and above and below body in basicaudal region at hatching. At 6.0 mm, chromatophores along dorsal surface of body, in a line between body and yolk, in a heavy blotch ventrally in region of future anal fin, throughout eye, and on top and sides of head and snout. [1]

LARVAE (Fig. 47 E,F)

Specimens described 6.5–10.0 mm TL.

Urostyle turning upward at 6.5 mm. Incipient rays in dorsal at 8.5 mm. Finfold constricted near caudal region and with distinct postdorsal notch at 8.5 mm. [1]

JUVENILES (Fig. 47 G,H)

Minimum size described 14.3 mm TL (JDH).

Body shape similar to adult at 15 mm. [1] Nostril an elongate slit at 22.2 mm. Scales forming at 14.7 mm.

Preanal finfold 2/3 distance to opercle at 14.3 mm, to base of ventrals at 21.1 mm; lacking at 16.0 mm. Dorsal finfold forward to a point above pectoral tips at 14.3 mm; reduced to a small remnant at 16.0 mm (JDH). Urostyle external and projecting above dorsal margin of caudal fin at 15.0 mm, gradually absorbed into caudal fin thereafter. [1]

Pigmentation: At 14.3 mm, uniformly and heavily pigmented except in thoracic region, with most dense pigment on head and in region of developing caudal stripe. Rays of fins with numerous large chromatophores. Internal chromatophores visible from eye to opercular

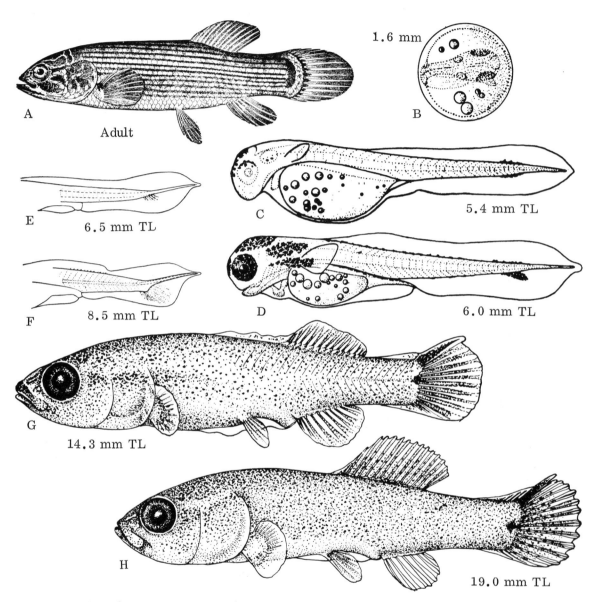

Fig. 47. *Umbra pygmaea,* Eastern mudminnow. A. Adult. B. Egg, diameter 1.6 mm; embryo just before hatching. C. Yolk-sac larva, 5.4 mm TL. Newly hatched. D. Yolk-sac larva, 6.0 mm TL, 3 days. E. Tail of larva 6.5 mm TL. Urostyle turning upward. F. Tail of larva 8.5 mm TL. Prolonged urostyle established. G. Juvenile, 14.3 mm TL, 12.5 mm SL. Pigment spot at base of caudal and along urostyle. H. Juvenile, 19.0 mm TL, 16.5 mm SL. (A, *Jordan, 1905: fig. 152.* B-F, *Breder, 1933: fig. 1, 2.* G, H. *Original drawings, A. J. Mansueti.*)

region and over gas bladder (JDH). At 15–22 mm, projecting urostyle nearly black.[7]

Age and size at maturity: Unknown.

LITERATURE CITED

1. Breder, C. M., Jr., 1933b: Figs. 1 and 2.
2. Sterba, G., 1962:80.
3. Hoese, H. D., 1963:165.
4. Poll, M., 1949:8–10.
5. Raney, E. C., 1950:172.
6. Fowler, H. W., 1917a:95–6..
7. Gordon, M. S., 1948:224.
8. Smith, H. M., 1907:141–42.
9. Schwartz, F. J., 1964b:13–15.
10. Jordan, D. S., and B. W. Evermann, 1896:623–24.
11. Briggs, J. C., 1958:257.
12. Spillmann, J., 1959:401–02.
13. Schultz, L. P., 1929:73–82.
14. Carbonnier, M. P., 1874:665–71.
15. Brimley, C. S., 1896:944.
16. Gill, T., 1906:818–19.
17. Gray, W. B., 1923:67.
18. Aquatic Life, 1918:12–13.
19. Massmann, W. H., 1958:4.
20. Fowler, H. W., 1906:182–83.

Esox americanus americanus

Esox niger

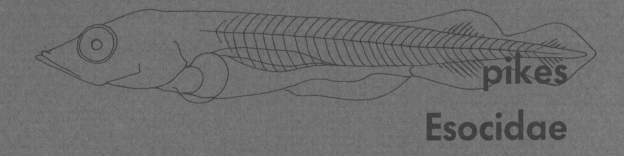

pikes
Esocidae

Esocidae—pikes

ADULT (Fig. 48 A)

D. 17–19; A. 14–17;[15] P. 13–17; V. 8–10;[4,9,10] scales along lateral line 94–117;[15] vertebrae 44[3]–51;[10] branchiostegals 11–16;[3] submandibular pores 7–9.[13]

Proportions as times in SL: Greatest depth 5.2–6.1;[2] snout length 7.9–9.5.[10]

Body robust; cross-section circular with flattened somewhat concave dorsal surface. Snout short, broad, spatulate;[3] mouth horizontal; lower jaw extended slightly beyond upper;[2] teeth moderately large, those in front of upper jaw and several along each side of ramus a little enlarged;[6] cheek and opercle fully scaled.[14]

Olivaceous to black above; belly white, sometimes mottled with dark; 12–16 irregular light bands on sides running upward and back; suborbital bar black, curved back ventrally; fins bright carmine; pupil green; iris gold.[3]

Maximum length ca. 356 mm. Larger specimens (up to ca. 483 mm) may be hybrids (EJC).[7]

DISTRIBUTION AND ECOLOGY

Range: South shore of St. Lawrence River, Quebec; through the Champlain Valley in southern New Hampshire and New York, south along eastern seaboard to Lake Okeechobee, Florida;[3,8] introduced in mountainous regions of Maryland.[12]

Area distribution: Tidal tributaries in Chesapeake and Delaware Bay region.[1,5]

Habitat and movements: Adults—in sluggish streams, sloughs, drainage ditches, ponds, lakes and swamps; usually associated with heavy emergent vegetation and often in tea-colored water of pH 4.2–4.9.[2,3] Maximum salinity 8.7 o/oo.[1]

   Larvae—sometimes in very shallow water in roadside ditches (JDH).

   Juveniles—Young-of-the-year in flood pools and rivulets among exposed roots, twigs, leaves, and grass in 3–4 inches of water.[3]

SPAWNING

Location: Flood plains, grassy banks, and overflow ponds in areas of heavy vegetation, sometimes in water less than 1 foot deep.

Season: February and March in North Carolina with spawning possibly lasting 1 month.

Temperature: Ca. 10 C.

Fecundity: In fish 3–4 years old, 186–542 ripe eggs (average 269.4).[3]

EGGS

Description: Scattered in small numbers among aquatic vegetation,[3] not in long strings as has been reported.[16]
   Ripe ovarian eggs: 1.6–2.3 mm in diameter.[3,11] Golden yellow or amber, clear.

Incubation: Probably 12–14 days in North Carolina.[3]

LARVAE (Fig. 48 B,C)

Specimens described 11.6–17.8 mm TL.

At 11.6 mm, preanal myomeres ca. 31; postanal myomeres 15+; myomeres no longer distinct at 17.8 mm. Snout elongates with growth, still quite blunt at 11.6 mm, more elongate at 17.8 mm. Cleithrum and outline of auditory vesicles visible; gill rakers formed and visible through opercle at 11.6 mm; choroid fissure still evident at 17.8 mm.

Dorsal finfold extended forward beyond level of ventrals at 11.6 mm, wholly behind ventrals at 17.8 mm. Ventral buds formed at 11.6 mm; incipient rays in caudal and anal at 11.6 mm, in dorsal by 17.8 mm. Urostyle oblique; caudal finfold bilobed, adjacent to, but not continuous with dorsal and ventral finfold at 17.8 mm.

Pigmentation: At 11.6 mm, conspicuously darker below than above; lower fourth of abdomen clear except for heavy, mid-ventral, dark stripe. Dorsolateral regions with large brown stellate chromatophores; a mid-dorsal light stripe lacking chromatophores; sides of tail posterior to anus with light and dark chromatophores; a dark stripe along snout and continuous behind eye to pectorals. At 17.8 mm, abdomen conspicuously lighter; mid-ventral line reduced; number of dorsal chromatophores increased and concentrated over brain and in dark band between pectoral fins (JDH).

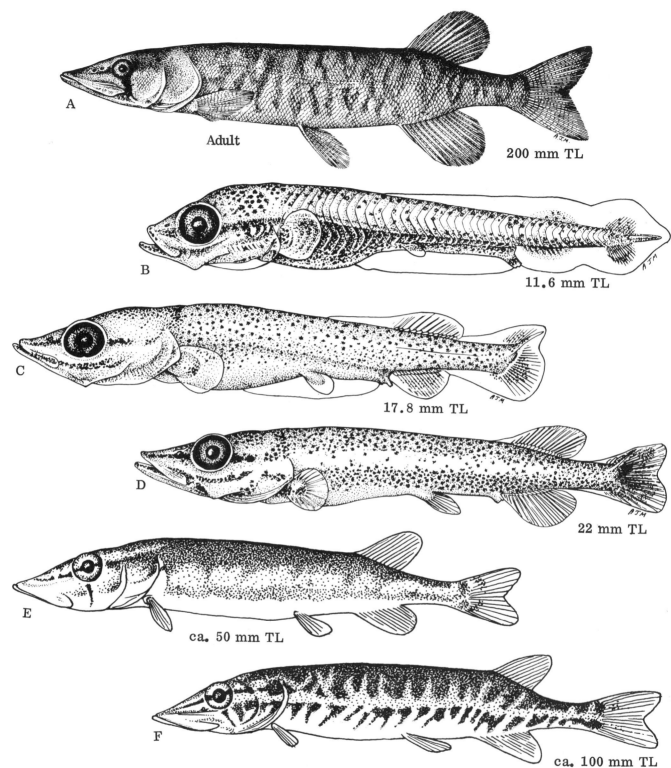

Fig. 48. *Esox a. americanus*, redfin pickerel. A. Adult, 200 mm TL, 172 mm SL. B. Larva, 11.6 mm TL, 11.4 mm SL. Preanal myomeres 31; postanal myomeres 15 +. C. Larva, 17.8 mm TL, 16.9 mm SL. D. Prejuvenile, 22 mm TL, 20 mm SL. E. Juvenile, ca. 50 mm TL. Unpigmented lateral band, straight to moderately wavy. F. Juvenile, ca. 100 mm TL. Lateral band changing to adult pattern with vertical bars prominent. (A-D, *original drawings, A. J. Mansueti.* E, F, *Redrawn from Crossman, 1962b: fig. 2.*)

PREJUVENILE (Fig. 48 D)

Specimens described 20 [3]–22 mm TL.

Eye proportionately larger than in adult; urostyle still evident; caudal fin lobed; finfold absent at 22 mm TL.

Pigmentation: Sides with scattered stellate chromatophores, denser below than above and enclosing an unpigmented, poorly defined, mid-lateral band which extends from operculum to region above posterior margin of anal fin. Dense stripe on snout and behind eye; vertical band below eye not yet developed. Mid-ventral row of chromatophores still evident; clear area on abdomen much reduced. A conspicuous, bright red blotch at base of caudal fin (JDH).

JUVENILES (Fig. 48 E,F)

Specimens described ca. 50–100 mm TL.

Snout length 8.7 or more times in TL (7.5 times in SL) at sizes less than 150 mm. Scales first evident at ca. 50 mm behind head and in lateral band behind ventrals; at 65 mm, scales complete except on venter. Vertebral column completely segmented by 65 mm.

Pigmentation: Under 60 mm, a straight to moderately wavy, unpigmented, lateral band from snout to caudal peduncle, which separates an upper band of olive or black and a lower band of grey. "Young" with red color-

ing limited to fin bases, and with a lustrous, silver-green, mid-dorsal band from tip of snout to caudal base. At 60–100 mm, mid-dorsal and lateral bands inconspicuous; vertical bars forming on sides. Adult pattern developed in excess of 150 mm.

Age and size at maturity (minimums): Possibly 1 year (EJC), definitely 2 years.[16] Males 128 mm FL, females 132 mm FL [3] (also reported as ca. 99 mm TL).[14]

LITERATURE CITED

1. Schwartz, F. J., 1964b:14.
2. Dick, M. M., 1964:558–9.
3. Crossman, E. J., 1962a:114–23.
4. Hildebrand, S. F., and W. C. Schroeder, 1928:132.
5. Massmann, W. H., 1958:4.
6. Fowler, H. W., 1906:175.
7. Westman, J. R., 1950:52.
8. Carr, A., and C. J. Goin, 1955:47.
9. Raney, E. C., 1955:11–12.
10. Crossman, E. J., and K. Buss, 1965:1270, 1275.
11. Sturtdevant, E. L., 1877:494.
12. Schwartz, F. J., 1960b:26.
13. Crossman, E. J., 1962b:7.
14. Karvelis, E. G., 1964:10–11.
15. Crossman, E. J., 1966:4–5, 8, 16.
16. North Carolina Wildlife Resources Commission, 1962:13.

Chain pickerel

Esox niger LeSueur

ADULT (Fig. 49 A)

D. 17 [19]–21,[32] including rudiments; A. 15 [19]–19,[32] including rudiments; P. 25–30 (both fins); V. 18–21 [19] (both fins); scales in lateral line, 112–135; [29] branchiostegals 14–17; [16,23] submandibular pores 9–11; [15] vertebrae 49–54.[32] Body depth 5.3–6.6 times in SL; [2] snout 2.2–2.4 times in HL,[20] 6.13–6.83 in SL.[32]

Body rather slender, somewhat compressed, deepest near middle. Head large, depressed above, profile slightly concave over snout; snout long, broad; mouth large, nearly horizontal; lower jaw projecting; maxillary to, or slightly beyond, anterior margin of pupil; teeth present on jaws, vomer, palatines, and tongue; lateral teeth on lower jaw and vomer enlarged; [2] cheek and opercle fully scaled.[20]

Greenish above, sometimes very dark; [29] venter pale; scales above with golden lustre; [2] laterally with light areas enclosed by dark chain-like markings; dark upper side interrupted by light vertical bars; suborbital bar

almost vertical or with slight posterior slant; rays of dorsal, anal, pectorals, and ventrals with light interradial membranes.[19]

Maximum length ca. 838 mm or large.[31]

DISTRIBUTION AND ECOLOGY

Range: Southern tributaries of St. Lawrence and Lake Ontario drainages south (EJC), east of mountains, to Florida; in Mississippi valley to Texas, southern Missouri and Alabama; introduced outside original range as far west as State of Washington,[21] and in Appalachian mountains.[35]

Area distribution: Throughout area, tidal tributaries of Chesapeake Bay [2,11] and Delaware River.[4]

Habitat and movements: Adults—prefer shallow, warm water over mud bottoms with abundant vegetation [17] in lakes, ponds, and sluggish streams; [28,31] less frequently in deep, cold water with little or no vegetation.[17] Migrate

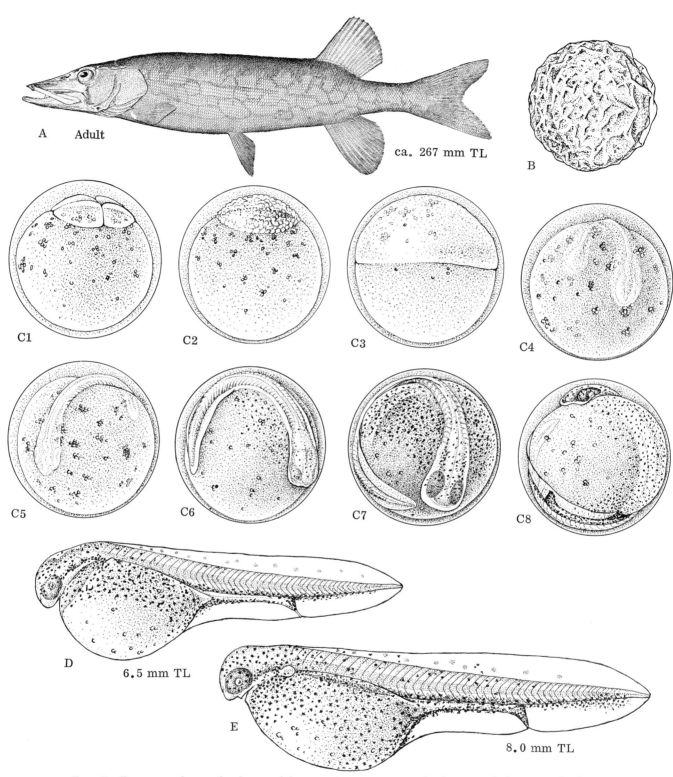

A   Adult
ca. 267 mm TL

B

C1   C2   C3   C4

C5   C6   C7   C8

D   6.5 mm TL

E   8.0 mm TL

Fig. 49. Esox niger, chain pickerel. A. Adult, ca. 267 mm TL. B. Unfertilized egg, before water hardening. Diameter 2.0 mm. C. Development of egg at ca. 12–16 C. Diameter ca. 2.5 mm. C1. Four-cell stage, 6 1/2 hours. Small oil globules dispersed through yolk. C2. Morula, 12 hours. C3. Gastrula, 1 day. Oil globules more concentrated under blastoderm in early cleavage, more diffuse in later stages. C4. Early embryo, 2 days, notochord formed. C5. Early embryo, 3 days, myomeres forming. C6. Tail-free embryo, 4 days, ca. 41 myomeres. C7. Embryo, 5 days, just before hatching; head view, brown pigmentation intense, embryo with chartreuse coloration. C8. Embryo, 5 days, just before hatching, lateral view. D. Yolk-sac larva, 6.5 mm TL, just hatched. Chartreuse pigment spots along dorsal finfold. E. Yolk-sac larva, 8.0 mm TL, two days, preanal myomeres 31. (A, *Goode, et al., 1884: pl. 183.* B-E, *original drawings, A. J. Mansueti.*)

to deeper water during winter,[3,4,25] undertaking shoreward spawning migrations soon after spring ice disappears. Maximum depth 15 or 20 feet.[24] Maximum salinity 22 o/oo.[31]

Yolk-sac larvae—able to swim when hatched but generally attached to submerged debris or aquatic vegetation and lying on sides on bottom.[24]

Larvae—hide among vegetation.[10] "Fry" sometimes landlocked by receding water and killed.[24]

Prejuveniles and juveniles—at ca. 25 mm, tend to lie motionless near shore or bury themselves in mud beneath debris.[22] At 28–101 mm SL, near edges of ponds seldom in water more than 2 feet deep. Larger juveniles present at all depths to 11 feet, especially during night hours.[12]

SPAWNING

Location: Usually in water a few inches to 10 feet deep in coves, mouths of inlets, approaches to outlets, swampy streams, ditches, and flooded lowlands; often among terrestrial vegetation,[24] or cattail marshes.[3,7,10,24,28]

Season: Migrations begin at ca. 4.0 C.[24] February to June in New York;[7] early March[23] to mid-April in Maryland;[11] possibly during late fall in some areas.[18]

Temperature: 5.8 C[23]–18.3 C, usually between 10 and 15.5 C.[24]

Fecundity: 6,000[8]–30,000.[17,30]

EGGS (Fig. 49 B,C)

Description: Demersal when first deposited,[11] but apparently becoming semibuoyant to buoyant at eyed stage;[3,22] temporarily adhesive, but lose this characteristic after water-hardening;[11,24] not deposited in long strings as frequently reported,[3,7,25,27,31] but distributed over comparatively large area by vigorous spawning activity.[6]

Ovarian eggs—2.0 mm in diameter; yellowish or amber.[22]

Unhardened eggs—bright amber; capsule clear, rugose.

Water-hardened, unfertilized eggs—diameter 2.35–2.70 mm, mean ca. 2.5 mm; many small, diffuse, oil globules.

Fertilized eggs—diameter 2.25–2.95 mm, mean ca. 2.5 mm; yolk diameter 1.5–2.3 mm. Usually spherical, sometimes ovoid (AJM); amber-colored, translucent; egg capsule tough, finely granulated.[11]

Development: At 12.2–16.6 C.

1 hour, 30 minutes—diameter of blastodisc 1.2 mm; oil globules concentrated in area of blastoderm.

6 hours—2-cell stage.

6 hours, 30 minutes—4-cell stage.

8 hours—8-cell stage.

10 hours—16-cell stage.

12 hours—early morula.

13 hours, 30 minutes—late morula.

ca. 48 hours—early embryo formed; oil globules more evenly distributed; scattered dark brown chromatophores in yolk.

ca. 72 hours—eyes with lens; somites faintly visible.

ca. 96 hours—embryo thicker, extended 2/3 around yolk; tail free and with finfold; 41 somites; brown chromatophores over head, body and yolk adjacent to embryo.

ca. 120 hours (just before hatching)—anus visible; eyes pigmented; heavy concentration of brown and chartreuse chromatophores over embryo and yolk adjacent to embryo.

Incubation: 5 (AJM) to 12[24] days depending on temperature; 5–6 days at 12.2–16.6 C (AJM); 11 days at 10 C;[18] hatching over period of 2–3 days at ca. 17.2 C.[24]

YOLK-SAC LARVAE (Fig. 49 D,E; Fig. 50 A,B)

Size at hatchings 5.0–7.9 mm TL, mean 7.2 mm (AJM); mean size at end of stage 10.2 mm;[10] duration of stage 6–8 days.[8,10]

Preanal myomeres 30–34 by 3rd day. Head slightly deflected over yolk at hatching, straightened by 5th day at ca. 10 mm. Yolk more or less oval at hatching, 1/2 absorbed by 3rd day (AJM), or by 8.5 mm.[24] Mouth open by ca. 8.0 mm (AJM). Gas bladder visible on 5th day at ca. 10 mm. Incipient rays in caudal by 9.0[9]–10.0 mm. Pectoral buds present at hatching, flattened by 2nd day or ca. 8.0 mm, fan-shaped and with incipient rays by 3rd day or 9.1 mm (AJM). Notocord granular at 9.0 mm.[9]

Pigmentation: Newly hatched live specimens with dorsal finfold and body chartreuse; dark brown chromatophores scattered over head, dorsolateral yolk, along gut, and beneath tail. Pigment increased on yolk and head by 2nd day; extended to ventral yolk and increased caudally by 3rd day; eye black at ca. 10 mm (AJM).

LARVAE (Fig. 50 C,D)

Size range ca. 9.8[24]–14.0 mm TL.

Total myomeres ca. 53–54; snout becoming elongate at beginning of stage; lower jaw definitely longer than upper; eye extended into dorsal profile by 7th day or at ca. 10–11 mm (AJM); choroid fissure visible and auditory vesicles elongate at 11.5 mm.[9]

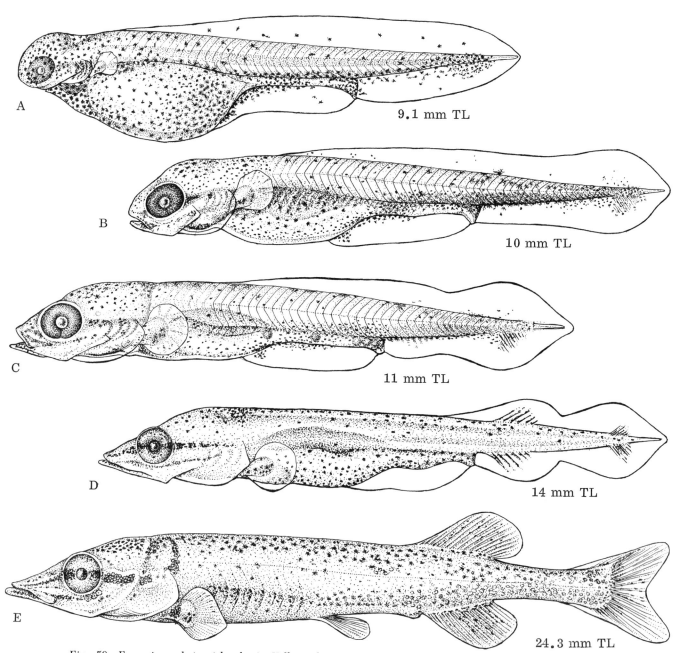

Fig. 50. Esox niger, chain pickerel. A. Yolk-sac larva, 9.1 mm TL, 3 days. B. Yolk-sac larva, 10 mm TL, 5 days. Large gas bladder visible. C. Larva, 11 mm TL, 9 days. Total myomeres 53 +. D. Larva, 14 mm TL. Pigmented streak through eye. E. Prejuvenile, 24.3 mm TL. Scales in caudal aréa. (*Original drawings, A. J. Mansueti.*)

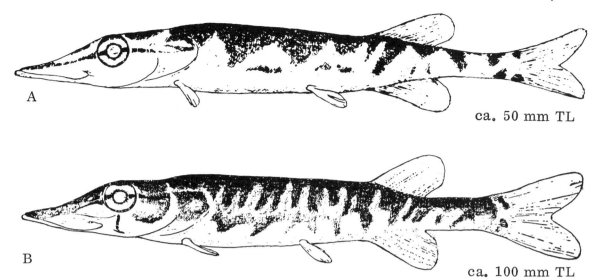

ca. 50 mm TL

ca. 100 mm TL

Fig. 51. Esox niger, chain pickerel. A. Juvenile, ca. 50 mm TL. Distinctive dorso-lateral pigmentation developing. B. Juvenile, ca. 100 mm TL. Lateral, barred pattern established. (*Reprinted from* THE GRASS PICKEREL, *Esox americanus vermiculatus* LeSueur in Canada *by E. J. Crossman, fig. 2.* Copyright © 1962 by Royal Ontario Museum. Used by permission of the author and publisher.)

Anlage of dorsal visible at ca. 14 mm and that of anal at ca. 10–11.8 mm (AJM); pectoral with incipient rays at 11.5 mm; [9] urostyle straight to at least ca. 14 mm.

Pigmentation: A conspicuous band of pigment through eye at ca. 14 mm (AJM).

PREJUVENILES (Fig. 50 E)

Specimen described 24.3 mm TL.

Myomeres still visible in thoracic region; scales visible in caudal area.

Pigmentation: Dark streak through eye; body chartreuse (AJM).

JUVENILES (Fig. 51 A-C)

Minimum size unknown.

Ratio of TL/snout length 7.0 or less; [13] HL/snout length 2.2–2.5. [14]

Pigmentation: At ca. 25–50 mm, greenish or yellowish throughout with suggestions of dusky punctations; black stripe from tip of snout through eye to margin of opercle; subocular bar downward and obliquely forward from eye. [19,22] With increased size, narrow, pale, verticle bars appear on upper sides; [2] adult pattern appears at lengths in excess of 200 mm. [13,21] Bean [26] notes that in "young" a pale stripe extends along mid-line of posterior half of body.

Age and size at maturity: 1 [10,28]–3 years; [24] minimum length ca. 185 mm. [10,24]

LITERATURE CITED

1. Hubbs, C. L., and K. F. Lagler, 1947:76.
2. Hildebrand, S. F., and W. C. Schroeder, 1928:132–34.
3. Kendall, W. C., 1919:28.
4. de Sylva, D. P., F. A. Kalber, Jr., and C. N. Shuster, Jr., 1962:20.
5. Adams, C. C., and T. L. Hankinson, 1928:389–90.
6. Embody, G. C., 1918:253.
7. North Carolina Wildlife Resources Commission, 1962:13.
8. Schwartz, F. J., 1960b:25.
9. Ryder, J. A., 1887: Fig. 28–9.
10. Underhill, A. H., 1949:378–80, 386, 391.
11. Mansueti, A. J., and R. J. Mansueti, 1955:2.
12. Raney, E. C., 1942a:58–60.
13. Crossman, E. J., 1962a:116.
14. Bailey, R. M., 1938:182.
15. Crossman, E. J., 1962b:7.
16. Crossman, E. J., 1960:365.
17. Karvelis, E. G., 1964:7.
18. Miller, J. G., 1962:323.
19. Raney, E. C., 1955:5, 11–12.
20. Moore, G. A., 1957:72–3.
21. Trautman, M. B., 1957:210–11.
22. DeJeane, J. A., 1951:10, 17, 21.
23. Sanderson, A. E., Jr., 1950:36.
24. Underhill, A. H., 1948:27–117.
25. Kendall, W. C., 1918:581.

26. Bean, T. H., 1892a:90–1.
27. Meehan, W. E., 1907:54.
28. Migdalski, E. C., 1962:255.
29. Slastenenko, E. P., 1958:145.
30. Needham, J. G., 1920:165.
31. Shoemaker, M. E., 1945:163–64.
32. Crossman, E. J., and K. Buss, 1965:1268, 1273, 1284.

33. McCabe, B. C., 1958:22.
34. Schwartz, F. J., 1964b:14.
35. Elser, H. J., and R. J. Mansueti, 1961:5.

ADDITIONAL REFERENCES

Raney, E. C., and D. A. Webster, 1952; Wich, K., 1958.

Synodus foetens

Trachinocephalus myops

lizardfishes
Synodontidae

ORDER MYCTOPHIFORMES
Synodontidae—lizardfishes

Inshore lizardfish   *Synodus foetens* (Linnaeus)

ADULT (Fig. 52 A)

D. 9 [13]–13; A. 10–14; P. 12–15; [14] V. 8; [24] lateral line scales 56–65; predorsal scales 20–30; scales between dorsal base and lateral line 4–6; [14] total vertebrae 58; trunk vertebrae 38. [15]

Proportions as percent of SL: Depth at base of ventrals 9.8–14.4; HL 20.6–26.3; eye diameter 3.4–6.2; anal fin bases 9.0–13.9.

Body slender, cylindrical; scales small; lateral line well-marked. [14] Head depressed, broader than deep, [1] slightly rugose above; snout triangular and moderately sharp, typically longer than diameter of eye in specimens larger than 200 mm SL; [14] depressible teeth present on upper jaw, [1] tongue, and lower pharyngeals; [7] gill rakers rudimentary. [12]

Color variable with both locality [14] and immediate background; [16] dorsum brownish or olivaceous [1] and with overall greenish cast, [14] sometimes with distinct blotches; [9] head brownish with light vermiculations on top and sides, pale yellow below; sides with ca. 8 obscure blotches in some specimens; belly white, [17] silvery-white, [1] or yellowish, sometimes with brownish punctations; [14] pectorals dusky, [17] yellowish, or light green; adipose with dark spot posteriorly. [1]

Maximum size confirmed at 405 mm SL, [14] but reported to reach ca. 610 mm. [17]

DISTRIBUTION AND ECOLOGY

Range: Cape Cod, Massachusetts south to Santa Catarina, Brazil; also Bermuda and the West Indies. [14]

Area distribution: Chesapeake Bay north to vicinity of Annapolis; also tidal portions of Patuxent, Choptank, [10] and Potomac Rivers; Maryland seaside [21,22,24] and Indian River Bay, Delaware. [25]

Habitat and movements: Adults—a bottom species [1] found on both shallow and deep sand flats among grass; [3,4,7] inshore in salt-water creeks, rivers, bays, sounds, [14] and deep channels within lagoons; [7] possibly more common over mud than shell or calcareous bottom; [26] also found in open ocean over continental shelf. Migrating northward seasonally, not found north of North Carolina from January through May. [14] In southern waters, as in South Carolina, found in deeper coastal waters throughout the year, in shallow water from June to October. [18] Salinity range 13.7 [6]–60.0 o/oo. [5] Maximum depth 100 fathoms. [14]

Larvae—recorded from offshore waters of Virginia in May (WHM).

Prejuveniles—apparently pelagic until ready to metamorphose; [9] readily collected from open ocean, usually near land in vicinity of or in shallow water; found at surface at night; collections recorded for February, May to August, November, and December. [11] Transformation to juvenile form probably completed in less than one week, and accompanied by assumption of benthic existence and burial in substrate. [8] Specimens less than ca. 50 mm dredged at 9 fathoms off Beaufort, North Carolina; [17] "young" taken at 75 fathoms; [20] other small specimens (exact stage unknown) from deep, sandy flats. [4,7]

Juveniles—47.1–87.2 mm specimens from bayous in vicinity of Tampa Bay, Florida. [3]

SPAWNING

Location: Unknown.

Season: Probably concentrated in spring, [3,6] although prejuveniles have been taken in all seasons. [11]

Temperature: Unspecified, but said to spawn on a rising or high temperature. [6]

Fecundity: Unknown.

EGGS

Undescribed.

LARVAE (Fig. 52 B)

Specimen described 10 mm TL.

Preanal myomeres 42, postanal myomeres 17. Auditory vesicle large, triangular, about equal to eye.

Incipient dorsal, anal, and pectoral rays present; pectoral with fleshy base; caudal somewhat bifurcate and apparently with definite rays; origin of dorsal finfold in

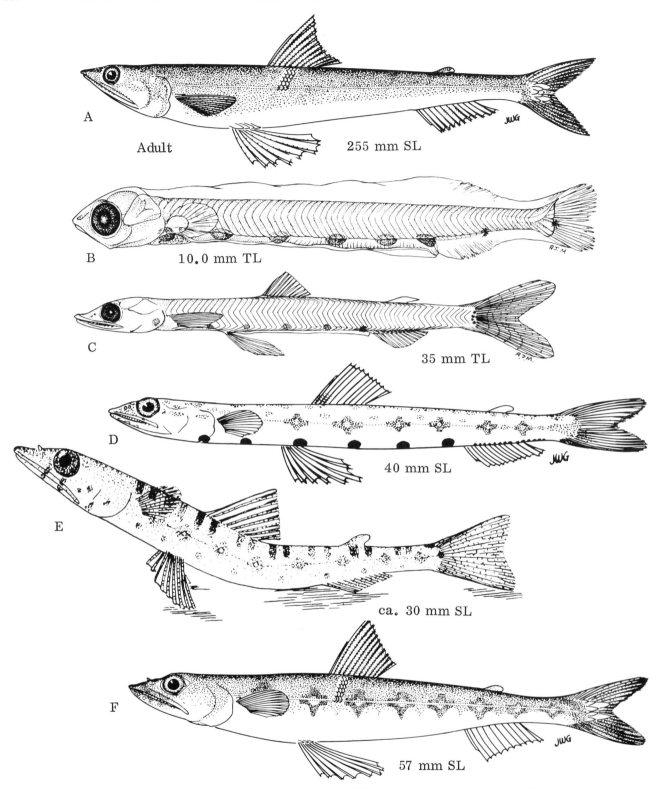

Fig. 52. *Synodus foetens,* inshore lizardfish. A. Adult, 255 mm SL. B. Larva, 10.0 mm TL, 9.2 mm SL. Dorsal finfold ballooned in this specimen. C. Prejuvenile, 35 mm TL, 30 mm SL. Total myomeres 58; preanal myomeres 39; postanal myomeres 19. D. Prejuvenile, 40 mm SL. Lateral pigmentation in crosses. E. Juvenile, ca. 30 mm SL. Fish in natural pose resting on bottom ready to strike at food. F. Juvenile, 57 mm SL. Lateral crosses still visible. (A, D, F, *Anderson, Gehringer, and Berry, 1966: fig. 9, 24, 25. B, C, original drawings, A. J. Mansueti. E. Breder, 1944: text-fig. 1.*)

occipital region; preanal finfold small, short; urostyle oblique.

Pigmentation: Six prominent ventro-lateral peritoneal spots; a small spot at caudal base and another at anal insertion (AJM).

PREJUVENILES (Fig. 52 C,D)

Size range described 15.8[11]–42 mm TL.[12]

Body transparent, sub-leptocephalic.[9] At 40 mm SL, depth 11.5 times in SL;[23] teeth conspicuous;[14] anus nearer caudal than ventrals.[23] Urostyle oblique at 28 mm.[15]

Pigmentation: A row of six conspicuous ventro-lateral spots of about equal size and equally spaced,[14] with each spot much smaller than the interspace,[11] extending from edge of gill cover[23] to point just in front of anal origin. Snout, lower jaw, and back lightly pigmented. A series of cross blotches developing along lateral line. Pigment along anterior base of dorsal.[14] A dark, chevron-like, basicaudal mark with short, narrow line extending forward from its apex.[11] Just prior to transformation, a pale dorsal pattern develops.[9]

JUVENILES (Fig. 52 E,F)

Minimum size described 30 mm SL.[9]

Snout slightly shorter or equal to diameter of eye in specimens under 200 mm SL;[14] eye diameter 5 times in HL in "young".[12] At 57 mm SL, a flap of tissue on edge of anterior nasal opening.[14]

Pigmentation: In recently transformed, body opaque; internal pigment patches retained but overlaid by dermal pigmentation.[9] At 57 mm SL, ventro-lateral spots missing; belly immaculate; ca. 8 very distinct blotches along lateral line arranged as crosses with light centers. Caudal and dorsal pigmented throughout; pigment developing at base of adipose.[14] Color of "half-grown" specimens variable with surroundings; typically creamy white to pale yellow; dorsal surface crossed by eleven brownish bands or blotches equally spaced, the first between the eyes, all double except the last which lies at caudal base. Ten diamond-shaped spots along lateral line and a second series of spots of lighter shade below and alternating with them. Dorsal, caudal, and proximal half of pectoral same color as body; other fins transparent.[7]

Age and size at maturity: Unknown.

LITERATURE CITED

1. Hildebrand, S. F., and W. C. Schroeder, 1928:130–1.
2. Briggs, J. C., 1958:257.
3. Springer, V. G., and K. D. Woodburn, 1960:21–2.
4. Reid, G. K., Jr., 1954:19.
5. Simmons, E. G., 1957:182.
6. Gunter, G., 1945:41, 175.
7. Longley, W. H., and S. F. Hildebrand, 1941:22.
8. Breder, C. M., Jr., 1962:565.
9. Breder, C. M., Jr., 1944a:14–5.
10. Schwartz, F. J., 1960a:211.
11. Gibbs, R. H., Jr., 1959:232–36.
12. Norman, J. R., 1935:102, 119.
13. Jordan, D. S., and B. W. Evermann, 1896:538.
14. Anderson, W. A., J. W. Gehringer, and F. H. Berry, 1966:68–73.
15. Hollister, G., 1937:391, 395.
16. Mast, S. O., 1916:181.
17. Smith, H. M., 1907:139.
18. Holbrook, J. E., 1860:189.
19. Hildebrand, H. H., 1954:290.
20. Evermann, B. W., and M. C. Marsh, 1902:93.
21. Uhler, P. R., and O. Lugger, 1876:130.
22. Uhler, P. R., and O. Lugger, 1877:86.
23. Nichols, J. T., 1911:278.
24. Truitt, R. V., B. A. Bean, and H. W. Fowler, 1929:53.
25. de Sylva, D. P., F. A. Kalber, and C. N. Shuster, 1962:21.
26. Hildebrand, H. H., 1955:201.

ADULT (Fig. 53 A)

D. 11–14; A. 14–18; P. 11–13; V. 8;[5] lateral line scales 51[18]–61;[19] scales between dorsal base and lateral line 3;[5] vertebrae 55[8]–58[5] (46 trunk).[8]

Proportions as percent of SL: Depth at ventral base 15.5–21.5; HL 25.2–28.6; eye 3.2–6.3; anal fin base more than 23.0.

Body slender, slightly compressed; scales moderate; lateral line poorly marked. Head compressed, upper surface strongly rugose; snout blunt and shorter than eye diameter; lower jaw projecting; large, compressed teeth in narrow band on upper and lower jaw with inner ones larger and depressible; teeth also present on tongue, hyoid bone and palate. Origin of anal fin about midway between base of caudal and insertion of pectorals.[5]

Golden-brown above, yellowish below;[16] back with ca. 5 indistinct saddles; sides with ca. 4 faint yellow longitudinal stripes, indistinct in larger specimens; opercle with black spot at upper angle; pectoral, ventral, and anal fins pale yellowish; dorsal and caudal dusky.[5]

Maximum recorded length 375 mm.[9]

DISTRIBUTION AND ECOLOGY

Range: Warm waters of all oceans but not reported from the eastern Pacific off the American continents;[1,5] in the western Atlantic from Cape Cod south to Brazil.[5]

Area distribution: Off New Jersey at 40° 04′N, 70° 33′W.[4]

Habitat: Adults—reported from inshore habitats[1,2] but apparently more common in offshore waters; over sand, shell, rock and mud bottoms; sometimes burrowed in substrate with only eyes exposed. Depth usually 20–50 fathoms.[5]

Prejuveniles and juveniles—in or near Gulf Stream over more than 1,000 fathoms of water;[4] also in coastal waters;[7] sometimes washed ashore during rough weather.[5,10] Maximum depth 212 fathoms.[5]

SPAWNING

Location: Ripe or nearly ripe individuals recorded near both islands and major land masses, such as St. Helena,[11] the Grenadines, B.W.I.,[12] and off the West African coast.[17]

Season: Probably prolonged; a fully ripe female has been recorded in July,[12] a nearly ripe male in late February or March,[11] and prejuveniles in July, August, October, and November.[4]

EGGS

Undescribed.

LARVAE

Undescribed.

PREJUVENILES (Fig. 53 B)

Size range described 27[7]–48 mm TL[13] or larger.[6]

Branchiostegals 13–14 at 35–42 mm. At 35–42 mm, body depth 10.33–11.50, and HL 5.25–5.75 times in TL; body width 1.25–1.33 times in depth; eye 3.50–3.75 times in HL.[10]

Body slender, considerably less deep than in adult,[4] elongate, slightly compressed, and of almost equal depth throughout; abdomen with narrow, smooth band, separating terminations of muscle rings and deeply grooved along each side. Head small with short, rounded snout; interorbital region narrow, concave;[10] mouth nearly straight; lower jaw included; gape extending to just beyond posterior margin of eye; a single row of palatine teeth on each side;[4] pseudobranchiae present; gill rakers minute, tubercular.[10] Lateral line developed at 28[4]–42 mm;[10] at 48 mm, scales of lateral line developed but not imbricated, scales developing on caudal peduncle and posteriorly on body but only indicated by pits on anterior half of body.[13] Urostyle oblique at 29–39 mm.[8] At 27–35 mm, dorsal above myomeres 16–23; anal below myomeres 37–45.[7] Third and 4th dorsal rays, 4th anal ray, and 6th ventral ray the longest. Adipose fin inserted above 3rd quarter of anal.

Pigmentation: Six pairs of large, preanal, ventro-lateral blotches, with the anterior-most partially on opercle, the posterior 4 sometimes confluent below forming a bluish band.[10] At 27–35 mm, body transparent; a semi-circle of chromatophores in occipital region, its curve directed posteriorly; a prominent spot at base of adipose fin; scattered chromatophores over head, dorsally between dorsal and adipose fins. At 27 mm TL to 43.0 mm SL, a mid-lateral row of chromatophores, the anterior-most conspicuously stellate. At 28–43.0 mm, a dark blotch at caudal base; small chromatophores beneath eye, on cheek, and in series on each side of posterior half of anal.[4,5,7,10,14,15]

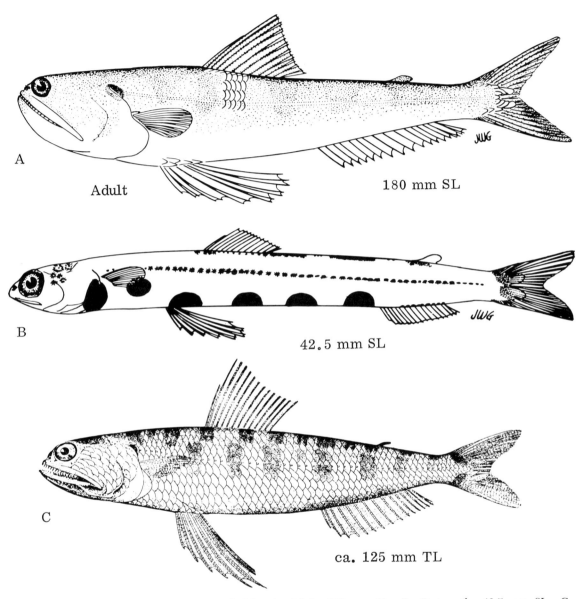

A Adult   180 mm SL

B   42.5 mm SL

C   ca. 125 mm TL

Fig. 53. *Trachinocephalus myops,* snakefish. A. Adult, 180 mm SL. B. Prejuvenile, 42.5 mm SL. C. Juvenile, ca. 125 mm TL. (A, B, *Anderson, Gehringer, and Berry, 1966: fig. 8, 14.* C, *Jordan and Evermann, 1900: pl. 88, fig. 235.*)

JUVENILES (Fig. 53 C)

Minimum size unknown.

Eye 4.5 times in HL in "young."[6] At ca. 125 mm TL, eye larger than in adult; mouth less oblique; blotches developed dorsally and laterally.[3]

Size at maturity: A female 168 mm long was fully ripe.[12]

LITERATURE CITED

1. Briggs, J. C., 1960:172.
2. Briggs, J. C., 1958:257.
3. Jordan, D. S., and B. W. Evermann, 1896:533.
4. Gibbs, R. H., Jr., 1959:234–36.
5. Anderson, W. W., J. W. Gehringer, and F. H. Berry, 1966:44, 47–48.
6. Norman, J. R., 1935:122.
7. Gopinath, K., 1946:11–12.
8. Hollister, G., 1937:387–88, 390.
9. Fowler, H. W., 1956:91.
10. Ogilby, J. D., 1898:249–95.
11. Cunningham, J. T., 1910:95.
12. Beebe, W., and G. Hollister, 1935:211–12.
13. Waite, E. R., 1904:233.
14. Fowler, H. W., 1959:83.
15. Weber, M., and L. F. deBeaufort, 1913:145–49.
16. Marshall, T. C., 1965:71.
17. Poll, M., 1953:75–6.

Carassius auratus

Cyprinus carpio

Hybognathus nuchalis

Notemigonus crysoleucas

Notropis amoenus

Notropis analostanus

Notropis bifrenatus

Notropis chalybaeus

Notropis hudsonius

Semotilus corporalis

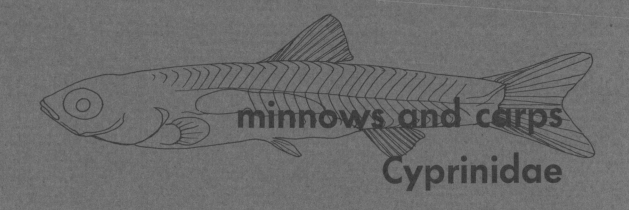

minnows and carps
Cyprinidae

ORDER CYPRINIFORMES
Cyprinidae—minnows and carps

Goldfish

Carassius auratus (Linnaeus)

ADULT (Fig. 54 A)

D. III [7]–V,[27] 14–19; A. II–III, 5 [7]–7; C. 19–20; P. 13 [26]–16; V. I, 8; [6] lateral line scales 25 [11,30]–34; vertebrae 28–32; [51,7,30] gill rakers on first arch 37[11]–50; [7] pharyngeal teeth 4–4.[30] Body depth 2.0 or less to 2.9 times in SL.[7]

Body stout, rather high, compressed.[6] Head scaleless,[26] somewhat depressed; interorbital space broad; snout longer than eye diameter; maxillary reaching posterior nostril or not quite to eye; [6] barbels lacking on upper jaw.[9] Last unbranched ray of dorsal and anal spinous with posterior edge serrated.[6]

Natural color slaty- or brownish-olive above with bronzy sheen; sides lighter; yellowish-white or white below. Color varieties include scarlet, red, pink, silver, brown, white, black and combinations of these colors.[9]

Maximum length ca. 457 mm.[5]

DISTRIBUTION AND ECOLOGY

Range: Native to eastern Asia and Europe,[8] but widely introduced throughout world; [12] in the United States most concentrated in vicinity of Lake Erie, absent from southern Florida.[9]

Area distribution: Fresh and brackish waters of Chesapeake Bay tributaries in Maryland [17] (RJM).

Habitat: Adults—usually a bottom species, but sometimes in schools at surface; [6] shallow water with dense vegetation in warm lakes, reservoirs, rivers, and quiet streams [7,11,12,30] (RJM). Maximum recorded salinity 17 o/oo,[10] but apparently unable to withstand prolonged exposures above 15 o/o.[11,14]

Larvae—cling to plants [13] or remain quietly on bottom when first hatched; [21] free-swimming after 1–2 days; [28] near surface after yolk absorption.[2]

SPAWNING

Location: Shallow water among weeds,[1,6] often where willow roots grow exposed in water.[20]

Season: Intermittently from late March [21] to about middle of August with first spawn of season the largest; [1] peak activity in April and May; individual fish spawn 3–10 lots of eggs at intervals of 8–10 days.[21]

Time: Recorded from just before dawn [3] to mid-afternoon.[4]

Temperature: Ca. 16.4 C [25,29] to 23 C.[13]

Fecundity: 2,000 [21]–400,000.[30]

EGGS (Fig. 54 B; Fig. 55 A-D)

Description: Attached singly, rarely in twos and threes, at intervals of ca. 12–25 mm on aquatic plants [1,28] and other fixed objects.[16]

Unfertilized eggs—diameter ca. 1.6 mm; [29] outer covering slightly wrinkled, loose; [21] micropyle apparently single.[18]

Fertilized eggs—spherical; [1,21] diameter 1.0–1.7 mm,[6] with smaller fish apparently developing smaller eggs.[29] Eggs just after fertilization slightly oblong; verticle axis 1.05 mm, horizontal axis 1.14 mm.[24] Variously described as transparent,[21,29] semi-transparent,[24] pale yellow,[21] cream colored,[1] and grayish-green.[7] Entire surface adhesive until water-hardened and attached.[1] Egg capsule smooth,[21] described as both "thin" [3] and "heavy"; perivitelline space narrow, 0.1 mm; yolk coarsely granular; oil globules 0.01–0.05 mm, sparsely scattered, and tending to disappear during later stages of development.

Development: At 24–28 C (constant temperature of 25 C following late cleavage stages).

30 minutes—first cleavage.

45 minutes—2nd cleavage [1] (at which time rhythmic contractions of the egg have been observed).[24]

2 hours—morula.

7 hours—blastoderm extended to equator of egg.

9 hours—blastopore formed.

11–12 hours—axis of embryo nearly encircling yolk, and head region visible as a somewhat oval expansion.

12 hours—3–4 somites, notochord differentiated.

15 hours—oval optic evaginations, 8–10 somites.

17 hours—auditory vesicles, olfactory pits, and 18 somites formed.

24–27 hours—tail and head free from yolk; narrow finfold around tail extending anteriorly on dorsal surface to mid-point of body; 25 somites, optic cup, and lens formed; pigment absent.

45–50 hours—embryo longer than yolk circumference; yolk sac divided into anterior spherical or oval

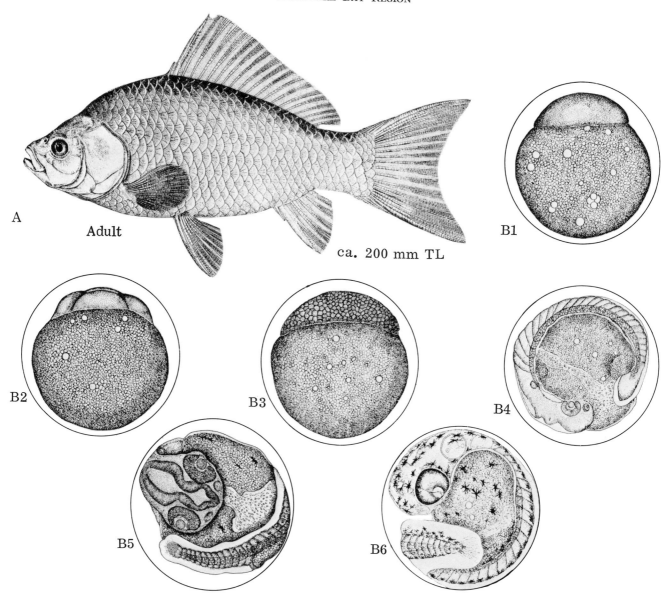

Fig. 54. *Carassius auratus*, goldfish. A. Adult, ca. 200 mm TL. B. Development of egg at 24–28 C (constant temperature of 25 C maintained following late cleavage stages). B1. Blastodisc. B2. Four-cell stage, 45 minutes. B3. Morula, 2 hours. B4. Embryo, 24–27 hours. Finfold on tail and to mid-point on dorsum; 25 somites formed. B5. Embryo, 45 hours. Eyes starting to pigment; 32 somites; pectoral buds visible, and circulation over yolk established. B6. Late embryo, 4.4 mm TL, 65 hours, just prior to hatching. Melanophore pattern distinct over head, yolk sac, and body; eye pigmented. (A, *Goode, et al., 1884: pl. 231.* B, *Battle, 1940: fig. 1, 3, 4, 13, 14, 16.*)

division and posterior cylindrical parts; 20–22 + 10–12 myomeres; pectoral buds formed; stellate chromatophores over head, yolk sac and along dorsum and primitive intestine.

60–65 hours—otoliths and rudimentary semi-circular canals formed; dorsal finfold to first myomere; pectorals free from yolk surface; 21–22 + 11–12 myomeres; heavy, stellate melanophores over head, yolk sac, along dorso-lateral and ventral musculature, and ventrally over region of intestine; eye densely pigmented.[1]

Incubation: 46 hours [3] to 14 days [4] depending on temperature; 8–10 days at 15 C, 5 days at 20 C,[6] 46–54 hours at 29 C.[3]

YOLK-SAC LARVAE (Fig. 56 A-C)

Hatching length 3.0 [22]–5.0,[6] possibly to 8.0 mm TL; [23] minimum size at end of stage 6.5 mm TL.[6]

Myomeres 21–22 + 11–12. Yolk initially with anterior oval and posterior cylindrical sections; almost tubular and much reduced at 5.8 mm; represented by few abdominal granules at 6.8 mm. Head not deflected over yolk, mouth open at 5.8 mm. Mouth much enlarged with lower jaw movable at 6.8 mm. Opercular membrane growing posteriorly over gills at 5.8 mm and well developed at 6.8 mm; [1] gills visible at edge of operculum by 3rd day. Gas bladder apparent within 20 hours of hatching,[3] partially inflated at 5.8 mm. Gut a straight tube, somewhat dilated behind gas bladder at 5.8 mm, enlarged anteriorly at 6.8 mm. Liver a reddish-yellow, ventral, triangular mass posterior to heart at 6.8 mm.[1]

Dorsal first indicated at 5.5–6.8 mm, with incipient rays at 6.2 mm; anal anlage visible at 7.0 mm. Caudal anlage with incipient rays in ventral lobe at 4.5–6.8 mm; caudal more or less truncate at 6.2–6.8 mm, somewhat forked at 7.0 mm. Pectoral buds small at hatching, with incipient rays at 6.2 mm.[1,27] Urostyle oblique at 6.0[27]–6.8 mm.[1]

Pigmentation: Variable at hatching; melanophores on jaws, dorsal surface of head and back, on sides at level of lateral line, and concentrated on anterior aspects of yolk; heavy sub-surface melanophores above gill arches; double or triple series on dorsal surface of intestine,[1] extending beyond vent to tip of notochord. Some specimens light-green with guanophores scattered among melanophores,[6] others uniformly covered with black pigment [21] or silvery-grey.[25] At 5.8 mm, density of pigment increased, especially in eye; xanthophores developed along dorsal musculature and on head. At 6.8 mm, dense yellow pigment on entire body; melanophores developed on ventral margin of operculum and dorsal surface of gas bladder.[1] At 5 days, round pigment cells along dorsal and ventral edge of notochord.[3]

LARVAE (Fig. 56 D-F)

Specimens described 6.5 [6]–11.6 mm TL.[1]

D. 9 at 9.4 mm; myomeres 22 + 12. At 7.9 mm, otoliths about equal to size of lens; gills completely covered by operculum; lips with minute, partly pigmented elevations; gas bladder partially divided into 2 chambers.

Finfold lobed in region of future dorsal and anal at

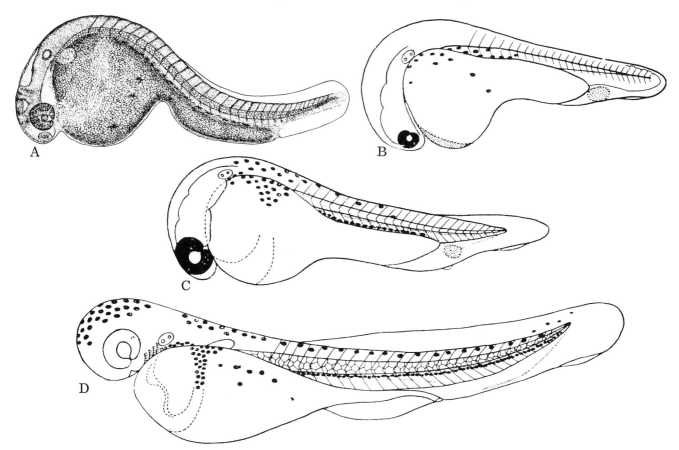

Fig. 55. Carassius auratus, goldfish. Embryos removed from eggs (A developed at 25 C, B-D developed at ca. 21 C). A. Embryo, 45 hours. B. Embryo, 50 hours. First appearance of melanophores. C. Embryo, 60 hours. Heart pulsating; circulation evident. D. Hatching embryo, 100 hours. (A, *Battle, 1940:* fig. 15. B-D, *Kajishima, 1960:* fig. 22, 23, 25.)

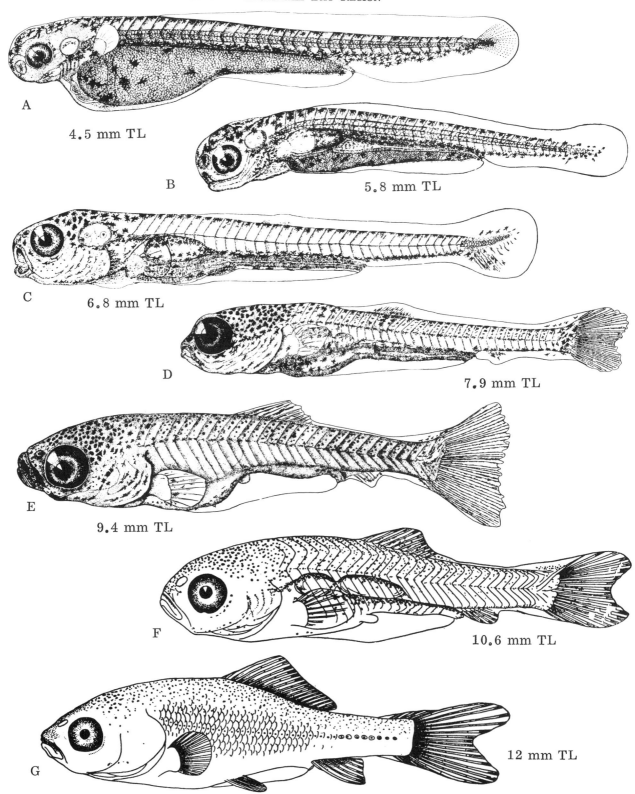

4.5 mm TL

5.8 mm TL

6.8 mm TL

7.9 mm TL

9.4 mm TL

10.6 mm TL

12 mm TL

Fig. 56. Carassius auratus, goldfish. A. Yolk-sac larva, 4.5 mm TL, 4.3 mm SL, newly hatched. B. Yolk-sac larva, 5.8 mm TL, 5.2 mm SL, ca. 2 days. C. Yolk-sac larva, 6.8 mm TL, 6.1 mm SL, 7–8 days. Yolk vestigial; gas bladder one-chambered. D. Larva, 7.9 mm TL, 7.0 mm SL, 15–18 days. Gas bladder constricting. E. Larva, 9.4 mm TL, 8.3 mm SL. Dorsal with 9 rays; ventral buds formed. F. Larva, 10.6 mm TL. Gas bladder 2-chambered. G. Prejuvenile, 12 mm TL. (A–E *Battle, 1940: fig. 17–21.* F, G, *Dmitrieva, 1957: fig. 6.*)

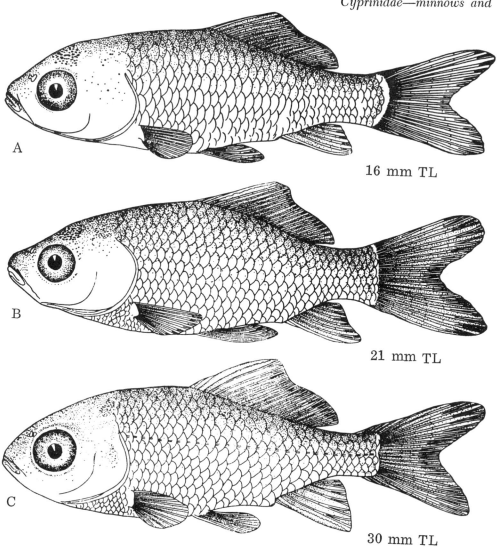

Fig. 57. Carassius auratus, goldfish. A. Juvenile, 16 mm TL. B. Juvenile, 21 mm TL. C. Juvenile, 30 mm TL. (*Dmitrieva, 1957: fig. 6.*)

7.9 mm; finfold discontinuous from dorsal to caudal at 10.0 mm, discontinuous from anal to caudal at 12 mm;[27] preanal finfold reduced at 11.6 mm.[1] Dorsal rays differentiated and spinous ray developing at 7.5 mm; caudal rays branching at 11.6 mm;[1] ventrals first evident as minute lateral buds at 9 mm, with incipient rays at 10.0[27]–11.6 mm.

Pigmentation: At 7.9 mm, melanophores of head region rounded, those of body stellate; a definite row of melanophores along lateral line; elongate melanophores in region of developing dorsal and anal fins; yellow pigmentation heavy; body iridescent. At 9.4–11.6 mm, opacity increased; ground color greenish-yellow to fawn.[1]

PREJUVENILES (Fig. 56 G)

Specimens described 12 mm TL.

Body nearing adult proportions; nasal opening elongate. Scales formed along lateral line with several rows of scales above and below lateral line on anterior 2/3 of body. Preanal finfold retained and extending beyond ventrals;[19] caudal rays segmented.[27]

Pigmentation: Scattered chromatophores over upper sides, back, and head.[19]

JUVENILES (Fig. 57 A-C)

Minimum size described ca. 15 mm TL.[6]

At 15.7 mm, body shape and form essentially as in adult.[1] Nostril single at 15 mm,[6] double at 21 mm.[19] Scalation complete at 15.7 mm in some populations,[1] apparently incomplete at 30 mm in others.[6]

At ca. 20 mm, dorsal soft-rays segmenting and branching,

spinous ray serrated. Serrations increase with age; 8 at ca. 35 mm, 12 at ca. 50, 12 with "four distal caps not yet fused to rest of spine" at 170 mm. Anal rays segmented at 14 mm, branched at 20 mm; 1st spinous ray serrated at 20 mm with serrations increasing with age. Caudal rays branched at 17 mm.[27] Ventral rays segmented at 17 mm, branched at 23 mm. Preanal finfold lost at ca. 15 mm.[27]

Pigmentation: Juvenile pigmentation variable, olive-gray [15] to gray-green,[13] becoming adult-like by loss of melanophores and increase in erythrophores and xantho-phores.[15] Time required for color change varies with individual [21,2] and never occurs in some specimens.[15] Juvenile pattern may be retained 3 [2] to 12 months,[28,13,21] or to a length of ca. 25 mm or more.[16]

Age and size at maturity: Usually 2 [2,8,21]–4 years; also reported at 8 months. Domestic varieties 3 inches long are reported to breed well.[29]

LITERATURE CITED

1. Battle, H. I., 1940:82–93.
2. Fearnow, E. C., 1925:454.
3. Khan, M. H., 1929:614–15.
4. Innes, W. T., 1936.
5. Carlander, K. D., 1953:322.
6. Okada, Y., 1959–1960:527–30.
7. Berg, L. S., 1949:827–30.
8. Nikolsky, G. V., 1954:250.
9. Trautmann, M. B., 1957:286.
10. Schwartz, F. J., 1964b:14.
11. Lockley, A. S., 1957:242.
12. Hubbs, C. L., and K. F. Lagler, 1958:77.
13. Sterba, G., 1962:257.
14. Black, V. S., 1951:56–7.
15. Rasquin, P., 1946:85.
16. Ryder, J. A., 1887:506–7.
17. Howarth, J. N., 1961:49.
18. Innes, W. T., 1949:77.
19. Dmitrieva, E. N., 1957:139.
20. Scott, W. B., 1954:45.
21. Smith, H. M., 1909:53–4, 59, 67, 78.
22. Watson, J. M., 1939:452.
23. Watase, S., 1887:266–7, Pl. 20.
24. Yamamoto, T., 1934:276.
25. Quast, T., 1929:4.
26. Scott, T. D., 1962:289–90.
27. Grimm, W. W., 1937:6–13, 18, 27.
28. Chen, S. C., 1926:294, 299.
29. Wolf, H. T., 1908:89–90, 101.
30. Slastenenko, E. P., 1958:184–85.
31. Affleck, R. J., 1950:353.
32. Tung, T. C., and Y. F. Y. Tung, 1944: Fig. 16b.

ADDITIONAL REFERENCES

Canagaratnum, P., 1959; Carbonnier, P., 1872, 1873; Brigidi, V., and A. Tafani, 1881; Bullen, G. E., 1909; Delaval, A., 1899; Fukuda, H., 1935; Heron, R., 1842; Ho, H. J., 1933; Kajishima, T., 1958; Kishita, M., 1933; Kubota, S., 1957; Laackmann, H., 1912a, 1912b; Leon-hardt, E. E., 1912; Revoil, C., 1891; Ryder, J. A., 1894; Stratton, H., 1833; Stromsten, F. A., 1931; Susuki, R., 1957; Yamamoto, Takaharu, 1937a; Yamamoto, Toki-o, 1934; Yoshizaki, M., 1957.

Carp

Cyprinus carpio Linnaeus

ADULT (Fig. 58 A)

D. III–IV, 15–23; [9,13] A. III, 4–6; [13] C. 19; [21] scales in lateral line 32–41; gill rakers on first arch 21–29; pharyngeal teeth 1,1,3–3,1,1; vertebrae 32–39.

Body typically about 1/3 as deep as long; back compressed behind head forming a crest. Mouth inferior; upper jaw with 2 fleshy barbels on each side.

Color variable,[13] typically slaty- or golden-olive above; lower sides golden yellow; venter yellowish-white; scales on sides and back with black basal spot.[4,32]

Maximum length ca. 1,219 mm.[32] Maximum recorded weight 90 pounds.[17,19]

DISTRIBUTION AND ECOLOGY

Range: Native to Asia, now widely introduced in North America and elsewhere.[20]

Area distribution: Tidal tributaries of Chesapeake Bay as far north as Havre de Grace, Maryland; [8,9] New Jersey.[11]

Habitat and movements: Adults—A schooling species found in moderately warm, generally shallow waters of rivers, lakes, and reservoirs, usually associated with aquatic vegetation; [4,32] also rocky shoal areas, protected bays over sand, clay, or mud bottoms [24] and, rarely, swift flowing water during spawning runs.[21] Move into lake shallows, stream tributaries, marshes, and drowned flood

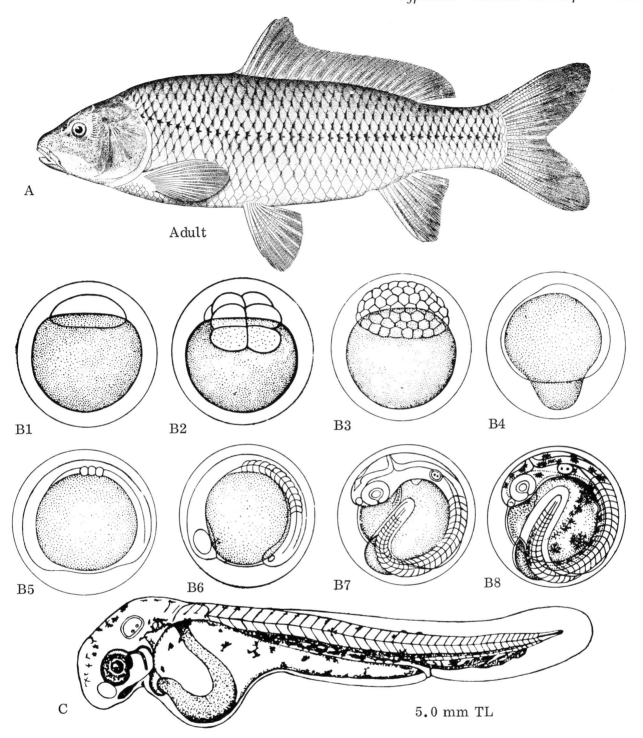

Fig. 58. *Cyprinus carpio*, carp. A. Adult. B. Development of egg at 12–25 C. Diameter ca. 2.0 mm. B1. Blastodisc, 1/2–1 hour. B2. Eight-cell stage, 5 1/3 hours. B3. Sixty-four-cell stage, 10 1/2 hours. B4. Late gastrula, 38 hours. B5. Early embryo, 65 hours. Three myomeres. B6. Tail-free embryo, 80 1/2 hours. Kupffer's vesicle drawn as small oval near end of tail; 13 myomeres formed. B7. Late embryo, 4 days. Melanophores on optic cup not illustrated; yolk elongated posteriorly. B8. Late embryo, 5 days, just before hatching. Circulation established. C. Late embryo removed from egg, 5.0 mm TL, 2 days. Developed at 23–24C; circulation pattern over yolk shown as shaded area. (A, *Smith, 1896: pl. 75.* B, *Okada, 1959–1960: pl. 39 (After Hikita, 1956).* C, *Kostomarov, 1955: 50B.*)

plains prior to spawning when temperature reaches ca. 10 C;[24] also known to make excursions of up to 674 miles.[21] Reported in salinity of 17.6 o/oo in Chesapeake Bay[1] and from salt water in Russia and Europe.[10,13,29] Maximum depth ca. 100 feet.[24,25]

Yolk-sac larvae—frequently in water 1–4 inches deep,[24] attached to or lying near submerged vegetation.

Larvae—at bottom among aquatic vegetation.[36]

Juveniles—at ca. 25 mm, begin to move into slightly deeper water.[14,21] Young less than 1 year old, non-schooling and found in vegetation in shallow water over sand, clay, or silt bottoms.[24]

SPAWNING

Location: Shallow, weedy areas of lakes, ponds, tributary streams, swamps, temporary flood plains and marshes in depths of 3 inches to ca. 6 feet.[16,17,36]

Season: June in Maryland;[5] April to August in North America;[6,17] possibly as late as September or October in Russia.[13] Intermittent spawning lasting several days to several weeks,[7] and possibly with 2 spawning peaks in some areas.[26]

Time: Day or night,[16,21] but most frequently in the morning.[17,34]

Temperature: Optimum 18–22 C, but recorded between 10[13] and 30 C. Reported to virtually cease in New York when temperature falls below ca. 14 C.[27]

Salinity: Usually in freshwater, but also reported in water exceeding 10 o/oo.[13]

Fecundity: 93,000[13]–2,059,750;[12] number of eggs discharged at primary spawning 50,000–620,000.[22]

EGGS (Fig. 58 B,C)

Description: Deposited in clusters of 500[21]–700[28] in an area about 6 feet in diameter[19] often on aquatic vegetation, twigs, and stones.[7]

Ripe eggs—diameter 0.9–1.2 mm;[35] extremely adhesive when first deposited.[31]

Fertilized eggs—ca. 2.0 mm in diameter[2,19,24,31] (reported as 1.0 mm in Canada[32] and averages of 1.26–1.71 mm in Russia).[35] Spherical; slightly adhesive;[24] variously described as colorless,[2] greyish-white,[19,24] yellowish, extremely translucent.[29,31] Perivitelline space ca. 1/5 egg radius;[2] yolk with numerous, small oil globules.[33]

Development: At temperatures varying from 12–25 C.

4 hours, 15 minutes—2-cell stage.
4 hours, 30 minutes—4-cell stage.

10 hours, 15 minutes—32-cell stage.
34 hours—morula.
38 hours—gastrula.
63 hours—embryo formed.
65 hours—3 somites.
80 hours, 30 minutes—7–13 somites; optic vesicles; Kupffer's vesicle.
95 hours—Kupffer's vesicle no longer visible; 25 somites; auditory vesicles and neural cord formed; embryonic movement noticeable.
101 hours, 10 minutes—tail free; lens, notochord, and otoliths formed; melanophores on optic cup.
123 hours, 30 minutes—30 somites; circulation established; melanophores on yolk and body.[2,3] "Eyed" embryos within 24 hours at ca. 21.6 C.[28]

Incubation: 3[14]–16 days,[9,29] depending on temperature; 3–5 days at 20 C; 5 days at 15 C.[2,14]

YOLK-SAC LARVAE (Fig. 59 A-D)

Hatching length ca. 3.0[24] to 6.41 mm TL; maximum length 7.0 mm;[18] duration of stage 4[21] to 10 days.[14]

Total myomeres 36; preanal myomeres 24. Yolk mass elongate, initially nearly round or oval anteriorly, cylindrical behind; head slightly deflected[2,3] or straight;[18] mouth open at hatching.[3] Jaws evident, nasal openings elongate at 5.7 mm;[18] gill rakers prominent at 6.0 mm. Gas bladder evident at hatching, enlarged by 3 days.[2]

Origin of dorsal finfold near 3rd myomere at hatching; preanal finfold narrow; pectorals with incipient rays at 5.5 mm.[30]

Pigmentation: At hatching, eyes black; melanophores on head and anterior half of dorsum, along dorsal surface of alimentary canal, above and below urostyle, over anterior half or all of yolk mass. At 6.3 mm, back of head and body light greenish-yellow; chromatophore pattern little changed.[2] At 7.0 mm, pigment increased in density especially over head, on dorsal surface of gas bladder, and in region of urostyle.[18]

LARVAE (Fig. 59 E-G; Fig. 60 A-C)

Size range described 6.5[2]–15.0 mm TL.[30]

D. 6 at 10 mm,[6] ca. 16 at 11.5 mm; A. ca. 4 at 11.5 mm; P. ca. 4 at 12.2 mm;[18] total myomeres 30–38; preanal myomeres 18–25; postanal myomeres 12–13.[2,6] Body stout. Head relatively small; mouth moderate,[6] suckerlike at 9.0–10.0 mm.[6,28] Gas bladder with 2 chambers at 11.5 mm TL.[18]

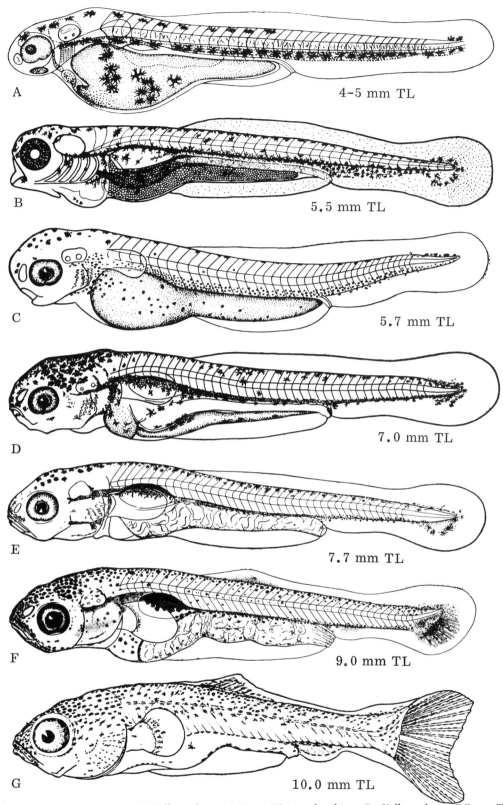

Fig. 59. Cyprinus carpio, carp. A. Yolk-sac larva, 4–5 mm TL, just hatching. B. Yolk-sac larva, 5.5 mm TL. C. Yolk-sac larva, 5.7 mm TL, 5.5 mm SL. Recently hatched. D. Yolk-sac larva, 7.0 mm TL, 6.6 mm SL. E. Larva, 7.7 mm TL, 7.1 mm SL. F. Larva, 9.0 mm TL, 8.6 mm SL. G. Larva, 10.0 mm TL, 8.4 mm SL. Preanal myomeres 18; postanal myomeres 12. (A, *Okada, 1959–1960: pl. 39.* B, *Smallwood and Smallwood, 1931: fig. 1.* C-F, *Bragensky, 1960: fig. 1–4.* G, *Fish, 1932: fig. 24.*)

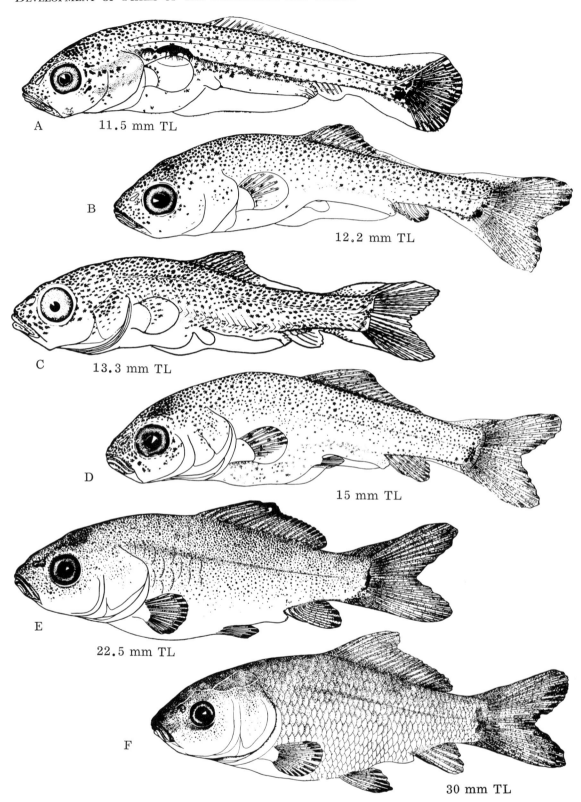

Fig. 60. Cyprinus carpio, carp. A. Larva, 11.5 mm TL, 10.5 mm SL. Gas bladder with two chambers; ventral buds formed. B. Larva, 12.2 mm TL, 10.25 mm SL. C. Larva, 13.3 mm TL, 11.1 mm SL. Preanal myomeres 21 (22); postanal myomeres 13. D. Prejuvenile, 15.0 mm TL, 12.5 mm SL. E. Juvenile, 22.5 mm TL, 18.0 mm SL. F. Juvenile, 30 mm TL, 22 mm SL. (A, B, D-F, *Bragensky, 1960:* fig. 5–9. C, *Fish, 1932:* fig. 25.)

Dorsal and anal with incipient rays at 9–11.5 mm.[2] First indication of caudal at 7.7 mm;[18] caudal with incipient rays at 8.2 mm, forked or forking at 10–10.5 mm,[2,6] with segmented rays at 12.2 mm.[18] Pectorals rounded, without rays at 10.0 mm;[6] ventrals first evident at 10.5 mm.[2] Urostyle tipped upward at 7–9 mm.[2,18]

Pigmentation: At 6.5–6.8 mm, melanophores posteriorly on head and along mid-dorsal line.[2] At 9.0 mm, pigmentation similar but with very dense concentration of chromatophores over gas bladder;[18] skin with a yellowish hue and a dark spot developing at base of tail.[28] At 10.0 mm, stellate chromatophores on both jaws, top of head, fins, dorsal aspects of head and body and, to a lesser extent, on sides to region of lateral line; subsurface chromatophores in double series along lateral line; ventrally to anus, on gills, and dorsal surface of intestine.[6] At 10.5 mm, pigment increased laterally and longitudinal rows of chromatophores developed on caudal base;[2] at 11.5 mm, density of pigment increased over entire body.[18]

PREJUVENILES (Fig. 60 D)

Specimen described 15.0 mm TL.

Body conspicuously deeper anteriorly. Finfolds still evident in some specimens.

Pigmentation: Pigment most dense over head and dorsum, less dense on sides and below.[18]

JUVENILES (Fig. 60 E,F)

Minimum size described 22.5 mm TL.[18]

At 30.75 mm, preanal myomeres 19; postanal myomeres 17. Body stout.[6] Nasal opening constricted at 22.5 mm, divided at 30.0 mm.[18] At 30.75 mm, a single barbel on each side of upper jaw.[6] Scales evident anteriorly on sides at 22.5 mm; scalation complete at 30.0 mm.[18]

Pigmentation: At 30.75 mm, chromatophores over head and dorsum at least to dorsal fin, dense to lateral line, scarcer below. Venter unmarked except for few chromatophores near vent and in subsurface series from vent to caudal. Chromatophores on upper lip, snout, and below eye; iris speckled.

Age and size at maturity: Females 2 to 5 years; males 1 to 4 years.[23] Minimum size of females ca. 310 mm,[13] males ca. 178.[15]

LITERATURE CITED

1. Schwartz, F. J., 1964b:14.
2. Okada, Y., 1959–1960:523, 525, Pls. 38, 39.
3. Hikita, T., 1956:81, 83.
4. Trautman, M. B., 1957:283, 285.
5. Schwartz, F. J., 1963:21.
6. Fish, M. P., 1932:322–3.
7. Bean, T. H., 1903:167–68.
8. Massmann, W. H., 1958:5.
9. Hildebrand, S. F., and W. C. Schroeder, 1928: 121–23.
10. Hessel, R., 1878:877.
11. Fowler, H. W., 1906:430.
12. Cole, L. J., 1905:574.
13. Berg, L. S., 1949:834, 839.
14. Nikolsky, G. V., 1954:251.
15. La Rivers, I., 1962:451.
16. Sigler, W. F., and R. R. Miller, 1963:67.
17. Adams, C. C., and T. L. Hankinson, 1928:321.
18. Bragensky, R. Y., 1960: Figs. 1–9.
19. Migdalski, E. C., 1962:281–82.
20. Briggs, J. C., 1958:260.
21. Sigler, W. F., 1958:7, 9, 23–4, 36.
22. Matsui, I., 1957:147.
23. Shields, J. T., 1958:26.
24. Sigler, W. F., 1955:97–104.
25. Cady, E. R., 1945:112.
26. Struthers, P. H., 1931:212.
27. Greeley, J. R., 1928:93.
28. Struthers, P. H., 1929:212–13.
29. Gill, T., 1907a:204–6.
30. Ehrenbaum, E., 1909:332–34.
31. Edwards, L. F., 1928:14.
32. Slastenenko, E. P., 1958:182.
33. Brinley, F. J., 1938:52.
34. Brinley, F. J., 1937:527.
35. Nikolsky, G. V., 1963:157, 173, 273.
36. Richardson, R. E., 1913a:399.

ADDITIONAL REFERENCES

Cole, L. J., 1906; English, T. S., 1952; Fukada, H., 1935; Halkett, A., 1907; Hamai, I., 1941; Hunt, W. T., 1912; Hutchins, D. E., 1906; Keene, J. H., 1879; Leach, G. C., 1919; Maejima, M., 1952; Matsubara, S., 1890; McGovern, H. D., 1882; Mottley, C. McC., 1938; Nusbaum, J., 1908; Sato, M., 1955; Smallwood, W. M., and M. L. Smallwood, 1931; Smallwood, W. M., and P. H. Struthers, 1928; Struthers, P. H., 1930; Takahashi, N., 1955.

ADULT (Fig. 61 A)

D. 7–8; A. 7–8; [12] C. 19; P. 15–16; V. 8; lateral line scales 31[8]–45; [13] predorsal scale rows 13–18; total vertebrae 36–37; precaudal vertebrae 20; [8] pharyngeal teeth 4–4.[10,12]

Proportions as percent SL: Body depth 20.1–27.2; head length 23.0–26.5; snout length 7.0–9.0; eye length 5.6–7.1.

Body subterete; [8] head rather sharp, profile evenly curved; lower jaw included (RJM); mouth small, terminal, somewhat oblique; [12] maxillary not quite reaching eye; lateral line complete, slightly decurved.[7] Breeding males with tubercles over top and sides of head, on chin, cheeks, opercles, apical edges of scales of back and sides, and sides of fins; tubercles on females confined to top of head and pectoral and ventral fins.[1]

Greenish above, silvery on sides, pale below; sometimes with a faint, plumbeous, lateral band posteriorly; fins pale, dorsal and caudal somewhat dusky; peritoneum black.[7] Breeding males light yellow along sides from eye to base of tail; mid-line of belly silvery; fins faint yellow.[12]

Maximum recorded length ca. 159 mm but possibly reaching ca. 178 mm or more.[12]

DISTRIBUTION AND ECOLOGY

Range: East of Rocky Mountains from Lake Ontario watershed to Gulf of Mexico.[9]

Area distribution: Tidal tributaries of Chesapeake Bay in Maryland [7] and Virginia.[4,5]

Habitat and movements: Adults—large, quiet rivers (RJM), lakes,[11] bayous, and stream pools; usually in slow, moderate,[8] or no current; [10] over mud, sand, and gravel bottoms; [8] also adaptable to pond culture.[6] Undertakes spring spawning migrations, concentrating in shallow water of tributary coves from mid-March to mid-May in New York.[1] Maximum salinity 8.3 o/oo.[3]

Yolk-sac larvae—near bottom.

Larvae—rise to surface following yolk absorption and concentrate in small schools near shore, usually among emergent vegetation.

Juveniles—some leave tributary nursery grounds and enter lakes by July 15 in New York; [1] "small fish" over bottom having much vegetation and humus.[11]

SPAWNING

Location: Usually in small coves,[12] over bottom ooze near base of newly sprouted grass in 2–6 inches of water,[1] or in ponds on silt bottom which may be partly covered with detritus and decaying vegetation.[6]

Season: Late April to May or possibly June in New York.[2,6]

Time: Daylight hours with peak activity between 12 noon and 2:00 P.M.

Temperature: 13–20.5 C.

Fecundity: 2,000–6,000 in specimens 60–90 mm SL.[1]

EGGS

Description: Diameter 1.0 mm. Scattered over decaying vegetation and bottom ooze, sometimes becoming buried to a depth of a few millimeters. Essentially non-adhesive, although occasionally attached to bits of bottom debris; somewhat milky when first deposited.

Incubation: Six to 7 days when daytime temperatures vary from 13.3–20.5 C.[1]

YOLK-SAC LARVAE (Fig. 61 B)

Mean size at hatching 5.5 mm SL, 6.0 mm TL.

Head not deflected; yolk comparatively small, elongate; anus posterior to mid-point of body. Finfold conspicuously constricted in area of future caudal peduncle.

Pigmentation: Eyes pigmented; chromatophores on cheek, yolk, along gut and venter, and in double series on dorsal surface terminating anteriorly in scattered group over head.[1]

LARVAE (Fig. 61 C,D; Fig. 62 A)

Specimens described 6.1–14.0 mm TL.

At 6.1 mm, total myomeres 35 (21+14); finfold reduced; incipient rays in caudal. At 7.85 mm, incipient rays in dorsal, anal, and pectoral; urostyle directed upward; gut highly convoluted (NSS). At 14.0 mm, preanal finfold still present.

Pigmentation: In largest specimen pigment more diffuse on dorsum and venter; conspicuous, roughly triangular blotch on top of head.[1]

PREJUVENILES (Fig. 62 B)

Specimen described 17.3 mm TL.

Preanal myomeres 23; postanal myomeres 13; preanal finfold absent; gas bladder constricted (NSS).

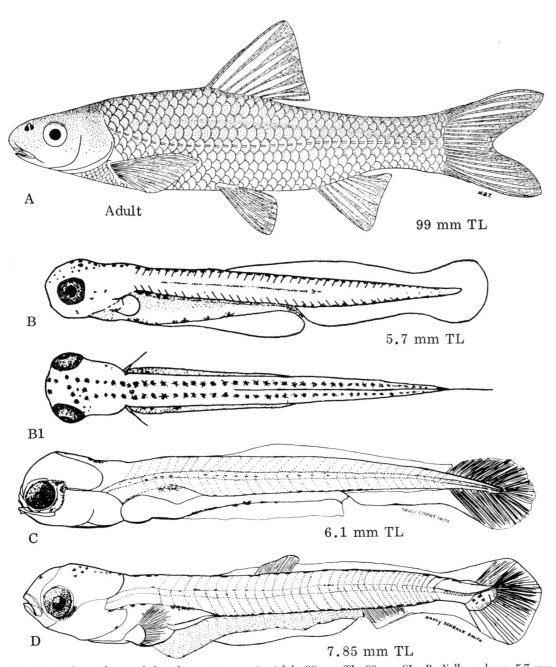

A   Adult   99 mm TL

B   5.7 mm TL

B1

C   6.1 mm TL

D   7.85 mm TL

Fig. 61. Hybognathus nuchalis, silvery minnow. A. Adult, 99 mm TL, 80 mm SL. B. Yolk-sac larva, 5.7 mm TL, newly hatched. B1. Dorsal view of same. C. Larva, 6.1 mm TL. Total myomeres 35; preanal myomeres 21; postanal myomeres 14. D. Larva, 7.85 mm TL. Total myomeres 35. (A, *reprinted from* THE FISHES OF OHIO *by Milton B. Trautman, Fig. 97. Copyright © 1957 by Ohio State University Press. Reprinted with the permission of the author and the publisher. B. Raney, 1939: fig. 2. C, D, original drawings, N. S. Smith.*)

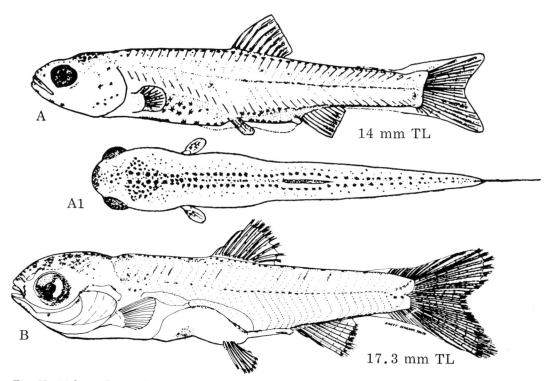

Fig. 62. *Hybognathus nuchalis*, silvery minnow. A. Larva, 14 mm TL, 12 mm SL. Scattered pigment over fins. A1. Dorsal view showing pigmentation pattern. B. Prejuvenile, 17.3 mm TL. Total myomeres 36; preanal myomeres 23; postanal myomeres 13. (A, *Raney, 1939: fig. 3.* B, *original drawing, N. S. Smith.*)

JUVENILES (Fig. 62 C)

Age and size at maturity: Some females apparently at 1 year; males probably at 2 years. Minimum size of females 50–55 mm SL.[1]

LITERATURE CITED

1. Raney, E. C., 1939:674–80.
2. Wright, A. H., and A. A. Allen, 1913:6.
3. Schwartz, F. J., 1964b:14.
4. Massmann, W. H., 1958:5.
5. Raney, E. C., and W. H. Massmann, 1953:428.
6. Raney, E. C., 1942b:215–18.
7. Hildebrand, S. F., and W. C. Schroeder, 1928:124.
8. Fingerman, S. W., and R. D. Suttkus, 1961:463–66.
9. Moore, G. A., 1957:135.
10. Trautman, M. B., 1957:396–7.
11. Adams, C. C., and T. L. Hankinson, 1928:365–66.
12. Slastenenko, E. P., 1958:236–37.
13. Smith, H. M., 1907:85–6.

ADULT (Fig. 63 A)

D. 7–8;[29] A. 8–19;[19] C. 19; P. 17; V. 9;[26] lateral line scales 40[22]–57;[21] scale rows in advance of dorsal 23–25;[1] average total vertebrae (excluding Weberian apparatus) 32.7–35.0, depending on locality;[9] gill rakers on first arch 5+16;[6] pharyngeal teeth 5–5.[8] Body depth 2.85–4.25 times in SL; eye ca. 2.6–4.1 times in HL.

Body deep, rather strongly compressed; back elevated; ventral outline strongly decurved. Head small, somewhat depressed above, scaleless; snout short, blunt; mouth strongly oblique;[1] maxillary reaching only to anterior nostril;[26] scales cycloid, rather deep; midline of belly naked from ventrals to anus;[1] lateral line decurved (ECR).

Dorsum golden underlaid with olive-green; sides more golden with silvery reflections; venter yellowish or yellow-silvery; fins light olive or yellow;[8] breeding males with crimson ventrals and orange, black-margined anal fin.[2]

Maximum length ca. 305 mm.[1,26]

DISTRIBUTION AND ECOLOGY

Range: From Nova Scotia and Manitoba[25] south to Florida and mouth of Rio Grande;[23] widely introduced westward.[8]

Area distribution: Tidal tributaries of Chesapeake Bay in Maryland[1] and Virginia.[4,32]

Habitat and movements: Adults—typically weedy lakes, ponds, and quiet streams;[3,18,28,30] also recorded from ditches,[2] canals, swamps, millponds (RJM), sloughs,[8] bayous, muddy holes,[16] and, rarely, rocky creeks;[10] able to live in waters of low oxygen content; recorded over both muddy[26] and clear bottom;[8] rarely in turbid water or water with little or no aquatic vegetation.[8,16] Maximum recorded salinity 14.4 o/oo.[1] Maximum depth unknown, but recorded from "deeper waters" of Delaware River.[6] Migratory during spawning season, with runs beginning in April in New York.[16]

Juveniles—recorded from brackish water and tidal freshwater of upper Chesapeake Bay among aquatic vegetation over various types of bottom;[1] found near periphery of ponds or in open water of shallows not far from vegetation.[24,33] In lakes with rock shores young remain in deeper water where vegetation may be found.[33]

SPAWNING

Location: Ponds, streams,[5] lakes, sloughs,[7] and sheltered bays;[4] in quiet water among plants,[17] over beds of submerged vegetation,[33] and frequently in nests of *Micropterus salmoides*.[7]

Season: Late March[11] to August,[13] possibly to late October[11] depending on locality; sometimes with 4 or 5 distinct spawning peaks per season.

Time: Early morning to noon.

Temperature: 20–27 C.[14]

Fecundity: Up to 200,000.[35]

EGGS

Description: Attached to filamentous algae, less frequently to rooted aquatic plants[13,26,27,28] or stones,[12] and rarely over bare sand bottom.[7]
      Ovarian eggs—single micropyle.[34]
      Fertilized eggs—diameter 1.0 mm;[27] adhesive;[5,26,28] lacking oil globules.[31,30]

Incubation: 4 days at ca. 24–27 C.[14]

LARVAE

Undescribed.

PREJUVENILES (Fig. 63 B,C)

Specimens described 18–24 mm TL.

Preanal myomeres 20–21; postanal myomeres 17; vertebrae 21+19 at 18 mm TL. Greatest body depth ca. 4.5 times in SL at 14.5 mm SL.

Body slender, elongate, somewhat compressed, especially in caudal region. Head short; snout pointed; mouth small, terminal, oblique, not quite reaching front of eye; nostril single at 18 mm,[3] double by ca. 20 mm.[20] Fully scaled at 24 mm TL.[3]

Dorsal fin higher than long, situated at mid-body; anal longer than dorsal.

Pigmentation: At 18 mm TL, melanophores on jaws, top of head, fins, dorsum, upper sides of body, and in a broad lateral band from head to caudal; in double ventral series from anus to caudal base; internally in abdominal

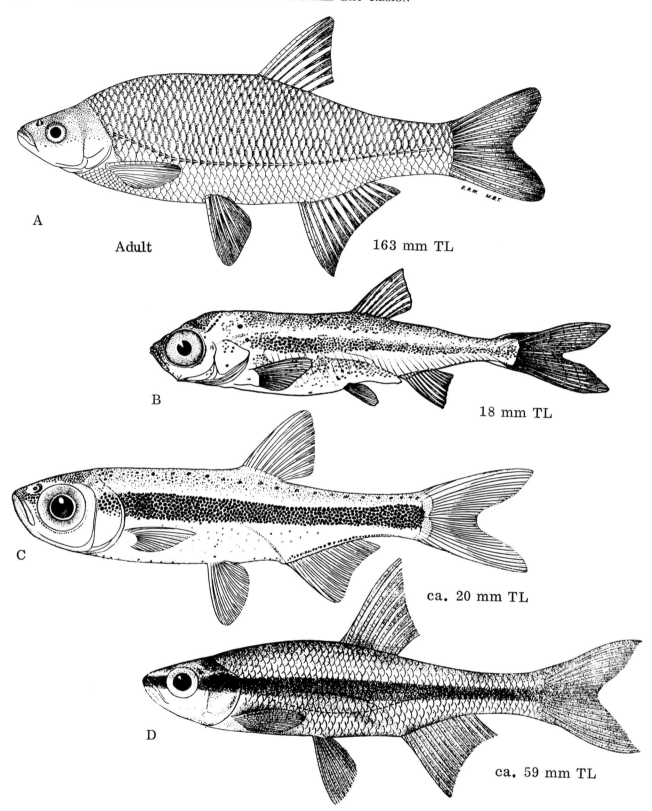

A

Adult   163 mm TL

B

18 mm TL

C

ca. 20 mm TL

D

ca. 59 mm TL

Fig. 63. *Notemigonus crysoleucas*, golden shiner. A. Adult, 163 mm TL. B. Prejuvenile, 18 mm TL, 14.5 mm SL. Preanal myomeres 20 (21); postanal myomeres 17. C. Prejuvenile, ca. 20 mm TL. D. Juvenile, ca. 59 mm TL. (A, *reprinted from* THE FISHES OF OHIO *by Milton B. Trautman, fig. 59. Copyright © 1957 by Ohio State University Press. Reprinted with the permission of the author and the publisher. B, Fish, 1932: fig. 52. C, Fowler, 1945: fig. 84. D, Fowler, 1906: 136.)*

region. Some specimens with brilliant golden tinge throughout, all with golden tinge about head, fins, and caudal peduncle.[3]

JUVENILE (Fig. 63 D)

Size limits of stage unknown.

Body less deep than in adult at ca. 59 mm TL.[6]

Pigmentation: A distinct lateral band from eye[1] or snout[6] to caudal base;[1] fins silvery; body silvery rather than golden.[8,25]

Age and size at maturity: 1[13]–3 years,[15] mostly in 2nd year;[14] 50–70 mm.[15]

LITERATURE CITED

1. Hildebrand, S. F., and W. C. Schroeder, 1928: 123–24.
2. Smith, H. M., 1907:88–9.
3. Fish, M. P., 1932:342–43.
4. Massmann, W. H., 1958:5.
5. Schwartz, F. J., 1963:26.
6. Fowler, H. W., 1906:136–37.
7. Kramer, R. H., and L. L. Smith, Jr., 1960:74.
8. Trautman, M. B., 1957:289–91.
9. Gosline, W. A., 1948:59.
10. Greeley, J. R., 1929:172.
11. Swingle, H. S., 1946:47.
12. Greeley, J. R., and C. W. Green, 1931–88.
13. Dobie, J., O. L. Meehean, and G. N. Washburn, 1948:99.
14. Dobie, J., O. L. Meehean, S. F. Snieszko, and G. N. Washburn, 1956:95–6, 98
15. Cooper, G. P., 1936:594.
16. Adams, C. C., and T. L. Hankinson, 1928:360, 363.
17. Wright, A. H., and A. A. Allen, 1913:6.
18. Smith, C. L., 1954:284.
19. Schultz, L. P., 1927:423.
20. Fowler, H. W., 1945: Fig. 84.
21. Hubbs, C. L., 1918:148.
22. Hart, J. S., 1952:77.
23. Miller, R. R., 1952:32.
24. Lewis, W. M., 1961:835.
25. Migdalski, E. C., 1962:275.
26. La Rivers, I., 1962:421–424.
27. Cooper, G. P., 1935:140.
28. Hubbs, C. L., and G. P. Cooper, 1936:68.
29. Frey, D. G., 1951:15.
30. Slastenenko, E. P., 1958:215–17.
31. Forbes, S. A., and R. E. Richardson, 1908:128.
32. Raney, E. C., and W. H. Massmann, 1953:428.
33. Webster, D. A., 1942:158.
34. Eigenmann, C. H., 1890:144.
35. North Carolina Wildlife Resources Commission, 1962:16.
36. Wallen, I. E., 1951:11.

ADDITIONAL REFERENCES

Brinley, F. J., 1937; Forney, J. L., 1957; Prather, E. E., 1957.

ADULT

D. 8;[1] A. 10–12; lateral line scales 36–40;[6] predorsal scales 18–30;[7] circumferential scales 25–31; caudal peduncle scales 13–15;[6] scales below lateral line to anal origin 3–4, to ventral origin 2–4;[7] pharyngeal teeth usually 2,4–4,2.[3]

Proportions as percent SL: Greatest body depth 18.3–23.5; HL 24.2–27.9; snout length 7.0–8.6; dorsal origin to base of tail 44.2–48.6.[6]

Body long, compressed, lower 2/3 of sides almost vertical;[5] mouth large, oblique; maxillary extending to margin of orbit; lateral line decurved;[1] dorsal well behind ventral insertion.[3]

Pale, translucent green above, side silvery; a plumbeous lateral band, poorly developed or lacking on anterior half of body;[4,5,8] lips dark; top of head with rather evenly distributed melanophores; mid-dorsal dark streak faint and diffuse behind dorsal.[5]

Maximum length ca. 102 mm.[1,4]

DISTRIBUTION AND ECOLOGY

Range: East of the Allegheny Mountains from central and southeastern New York to Cape Fear drainage, North Carolina[3,4] (ECR).

Area distribution: Tidal freshwater in Pamunky River, Virginia.[2]

Habitat: Adults—quieter waters of streams (ECR); usually in pools near moving water;[2] rarely in large rivers and canals (RJM).

SPAWNING

Season: Summer (ECR).

EGGS

Undescribed.

LARVAE

Undescribed.

JUVENILES (Fig. 64)

Size range unknown. Specimen 35.6 mm TL essentially adult-like.

LITERATURE CITED

1. Smith, H. M., 1907:99.
2. Raney, E. C., and W. H. Massmann, 1953:428.
3. Moore, G. A., 1957:125.
4. Eddy, S., 1957:128.
5. Raney, E. C., 1950:165–6.
6. Gilbert, C. R., 1961:454–55.
7. Ross, R. D., 1958:9.
8. Bean, T. H., 1903:151.

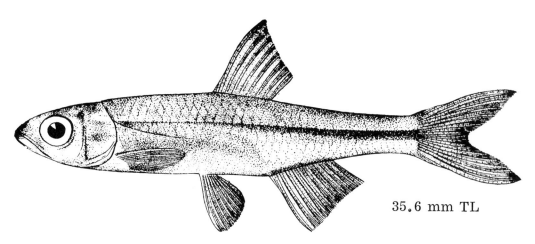

35.6 mm TL

Fig. 64. Notropis amoenus, comely shiner. Probable juvenile, 35.6 mm TL. Appearance essentially as adult, but anal fin more falcate. (*Fowler, 1906: 148.*)

ADULT (Fig. 65 A)

D. 8; [11] A. 7–10; P. 11–17; scales in lateral line 32–38; predorsal circumferential scales above lateral line 11–15; teeth 1,4–4,1. Body depth 22–30% SL; length of orbit 6–8% SL.

Head triangular; snout rather sharp; mouth terminal or sub-terminal; end of jaw to about anterior level of orbit. Body usually deep; lateral line slightly decurved from posterior margin of opercle to below middle of dorsal. Breeding males with scattered medium sized tubercles on top of head, snout, between eye and snout, and on rays of all fins. Scales large, appearing diamond-shaped.[5]

Silvery-blue above; [11] lateral band dark on posterior half of body, light anteriorly; a dark mid-dorsal stripe; belly immaculate; top of head and side of snout plubeous; both lips pigmented; dorsal at least moderately pigmented; ventrals immaculate; breeding males with iridescent bluish sheen, dark pigment near anal base, other fins milky.[5]

Maximum length ca. 102 mm.[9]

DISTRIBUTION AND ECOLOGY

Range: Atlantic coastal drainages from Mohawk-Hudson to Santee River, South Carolina; isolated populations in Great Lakes drainage.[5]

Area distribution: Tidal tributaries of Chesapeake Bay in Maryland (RJM) and Virginia.[2]

Habitat and movement: Adults—small to large streams; tidal portions of some large rivers; mountain and upper piedmont streams in the Carolinas; [5] also reservoirs.[1] Undertake spawning migrations to shallows.[8] Maximum salinity 2.0 o/oo (RJM).

Larvae—yolk-sac larvae mostly at bottom except for sporadic upward movements.[9]

SPAWNING

Location: Usually in slow moving water ca. 2 inches to 1 1/2 feet deep in shallow lakes and streams in association with submerged logs, sticks, or roots. Adults in spawning condition observed on riffles, but apparently not spawning there.[8]

Season: May to late August in Maryland.[4,7]

Time: 6:00 A.M.–5:30 P.M., most vigorous in direct sunlight.

Temperature: 18.3 [8]–30.0 C.[3]

Fecundity: 409–864.[8]

EGGS (Fig. 65 B)

Description: Deposited singly or in clusters of a few to several hundred in crevices or on underside of submerged branches, logs, sticks, stumps, or posts or between rocks and debris on bottom.[4,8,10]

Unfertilized eggs—ca. 1.0 mm in diameter when "nearly ripe." Micropyle prominent, funnel-shaped.

Fertilized eggs—mean diameter 1.5 mm when alive, 1.4 mm when preserved. Spherical; pale yellow. Egg capsule very adhesive, minutely papillose under magnification. Yolk somewhat opaque; oil globules small, dispersed throughout yolk.

Development: At mean temperatures of 19.8 C–20.4 C.

One hour—blastodisc prominent.
1 hour, 15 minutes—2-cell stage.
2 hours, 45 minutes—8-cell stage.
4 hours, 15 minutes—morula.
19 hours, 15 minutes—germ ring.
23 hours—early embryo; brain visible.
116 hours—eyes pigmented.

Incubation: 8–9 days at 20.5 C; 11 or more days at ca. 19.5–20.3 C.[8]

YOLK-SAC LARVAE (Fig. 66 A)

Size "just after hatching" 5.0 mm TL; duration of stage 1–1 1/2 days. Preanal myomeres 20; postanal myomeres 12+. At 5.0 mm TL, length to vent 3.03 mm; eye diameter 0.36 mm; body depth 6.7 times in SL. Body quite slender; mouth inferior; eyes large, oval; pectorals evident.

Pigmentation: Lacking except in eyes.[8]

LARVAE (Fig. 66 B)

Specimen described 6.7 mm TL.

Length to vent 4.0 mm; eye diameter 0.57 mm. Gas bladder 2-chambered. Incipient rays in dorsal and anal; ventrals scarcely evident.

Pigmentation: A double row of melanophores on dorsum, uniting anteriorly behind head and posteriorly just before caudal; a double row ventrally, uniting anteriorly near gills and posteriorly at anal fin; a single row from anal to caudal; a mid-lateral row of elongate melanophores from gas bladder to base of caudal; scattered melanophores on top of head, opercle, and base of caudal.[8]

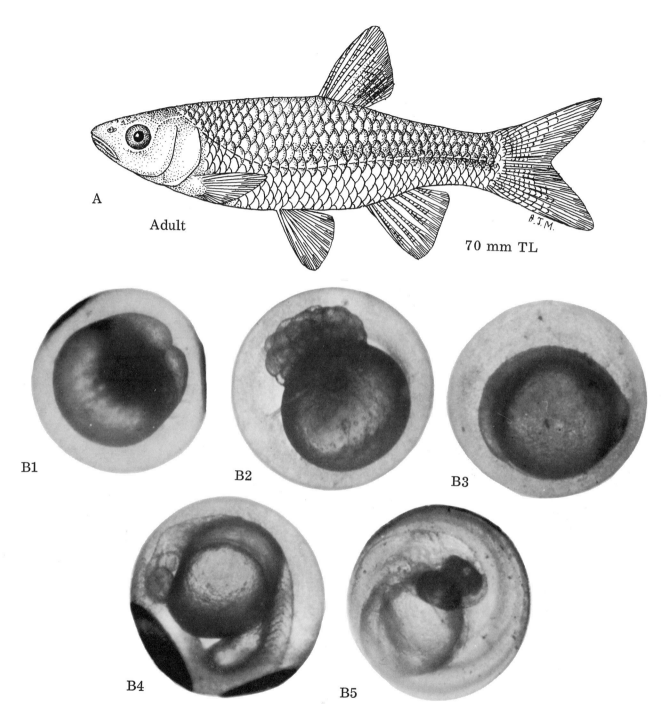

Fig. 65. *Notropis analostanus*, satinfin shiner. A. Adult, 70 mm TL, 55 mm SL. B. Development of egg at ca. 20 C. B1. Two-cell stage, 1 1/4 hours. B2. Morula, 4 1/4 hours. B3. Early embryo, 23 hours. B4. Tail-free embryo, 44 hours. B5. Embryo, 116 hours. Eyes darkly pigmented. (A, *original drawing, A. J. Mansueti.* B, *Stone, 1940: pl. 5, 6.*)

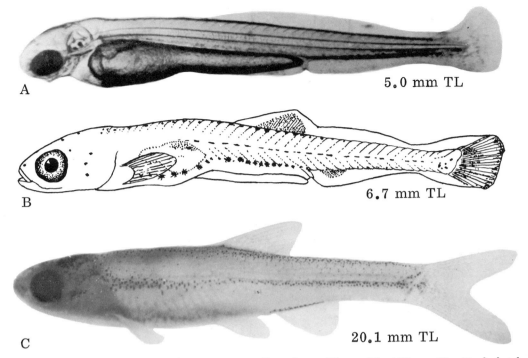

5.0 mm TL

6.7 mm TL

20.1 mm TL

Fig. 66. Notropis analostanus, satinfin shiner. A. Yolk-sac larva, 5.0 mm TL, 4.75 mm SL. Newly hatched; preanal myomeres 20; postanal myomeres 12+. B. Larva, 6.7 mm TL, 5.8 mm SL. C. Prejuvenile, 20.1 mm TL, 16.0 mm SL. D. 8; A. 9; scales present. (A, C, *Stone, 1940: pl. 6, 8.* B, *redrawn after Stone, 1940: pl. 7.*)

PREJUVENILES (Fig. 66 C)

Specimens described 12.6–20.1 mm TL.

Preanal myomeres 20; postanal myomeres 14. At 12.6 mm, length to vent 7.1 mm; at 20.1 mm, 10.3 mm. Scales present at 20.1 mm.

Pigmentation: At 12.6 mm, pigment similar to previous stage but with three irregular mid-dorsal rows of melanophores from head to dorsal origin and with melanophores developed on snout, cheek, and dorsal half of opercle. At 20.1 mm, pigment increased throughout; mid-dorsal band continued to caudal fin; chromatophores of anterior part of lateral stripes stellate, posterior ones round; ventral rows of chromatophores subsurface anterior to anus; a ring of small elongate melanophores around orbit; dense, triangular blotch of round melanophores on top of head behind eyes; dorsal and caudal with melanophores along rays; first 3 interradial membranes of dorsal with melanophores (diagnostic for species).[8]

JUVENILES

Specimen described, ca. 24 mm (identity questionable).

Body proportionately less deep; eye larger than in adult.[6]

Age and size at maturity (minimums): 2nd summer; males ca. 53 mm TL, females ca. 47 mm TL.[8]

LITERATURE CITED

1. Hubbs, C. L., and K. F. Lagler, 1958:83.
2. Massman, W. H., 1958:5.
3. Winn, H. E., and J. F. Stout, 1960:222.
4. Stout, J. F., and H. E. Winn, 1958:511.
5. Gibbs, R. H., Jr., 1963:513, 515, 520–23.
6. Fowler, H. W., 1945: Fig. 94.
7. Stout, J. F., 1959:643.
8. Stone, U. B., 1940:38–74.
9. Mansueti, R. J., 1957:14.
10. Stout, J. F., 1963:84.
11. Smith, H. M., 1907:93.

ADULT (Fig. 67 A)

D. 8; A. 6–7; predorsal scales 12–13; [1,5,16] scales in lateral series 33–36; [11] pharyngeal teeth in main row 4–4. [15]

Proportions as times in SL: Body depth 4.0–4.9; HL 3.7–4.25.

Body rather slender, compressed; [13] dorsal and ventral outlines about equally curved; dorsal contour of nape slightly concave or nearly straight; "snout very bluntly pointed, scarcely or not at all projecting beyond upper lip; mouth rather strongly oblique, rising anteriorly to above level from lower margin of pupil". [15] Lateral line somewhat decurved, [11] typically incomplete except at southern end of range. Breeding males with few scattered nuptial tubercles on head. [15]

Greenish-brown above, silvery below; [11] lateral band intense, much wider than pupil; a conspicuous, black, caudal spot conjoined with lateral band; mid-dorsal streak weak; upper lip blackish on exposed and concealed parts, except near edge of gape; entire region around anus conspicuously pigmented; [15] breeding males brassy-yellow below black lateral band. [9,13]

Maximum size ca. 62 mm TL; [5] possibly to ca. 75 mm. [16]

DISTRIBUTION AND ECOLOGY

Range: Southern Maine to Potomac River system, Virginia; also drainages of Lake Champlain, Lake Ontario, and St. Lawrence River. [1,6]

Area distribution: Tidal and brackish tributaries of Chesapeake Bay north to Havre de Grace, Maryland. [11,12]

Habitat and movements: Adults—shallow portions of ponds, lakes, streams and rivers in still or slowly flowing water over mud, silt or detritus in areas of moderate to abundant vegetation; [3,8] also along beaches in open, tidal rivers (RJM). Maximum recorded salinity 11.8 o/oo. [2]
  Yolk-sac larvae—lie on sides at bottom. [3]
  Larvae—Initially associated with beds of *Myriophyllum*; later also found in small schools in shallow, open water over barren bottom. [7]

SPAWNING

Location: Typically among aquatic vegetation in still, frequently turbid, water about 2 feet deep and 3–10 yards from shore; over relatively barren areas by end of spawning season.

Season: May to early August, depending on locality; [4,7,9] experimentally induced preseasonally by lengthened photoperiod. [10,13,14]

Time: 4:30 A.M. to 4:00 P.M., with strongest activity between 7:00 A.M., and 2:00 P.M.

Temperature: 14.4–26.7 C. [7]

Fecundity: 1,062–2,110 in specimens 34.0–44.0 mm long, with number increasing with size; possibly not all developing to maturity during one season. [4]

EGGS (Fig. 67 B)

Description: Demersal, [3] probably falling to bottom through aquatic vegetation. [7]
  Unfertilized eggs—adhesive; perfectly spherical; micropyle single; egg proper white, future perivitelline space pearly-grey. [3]
  Fertilized eggs—become non-adhesive; [7] pale golden; translucent; diameter 1.5 mm; perivitelline space ca. 1/3 egg radius; oil globules lacking.

Development: At mean temperature of 23.9 C.

17 minutes—outline somewhat asymmetrical; germinal disc prominent; pale yellow; moderately opaque.
1 hour, 10 minutes—first cleavage.
1 hour, 14 minutes—second cleavage.
1 hour, 42 minutes—3rd cleavage.
2 hours, 13 minutes—4th cleavage.
8 hours, 20 minutes—blastoderm extends to equator of yolk.
12 hours, 10 minutes—yolk completely invested with blastoderm.
15 hours, 40 minutes—embryo evident; keel of epiblast and shallow medullary groove present.
23 hours, 10 minutes—optic invaginations, Kupffer's vesicle, notochord, somites formed or forming.
28 hours, 15 minutes—tail free; yolk mass reduced; otoliths present; heart beat established.
32 hours, 20 minutes—eyes partially pigmented; lens formed; tail extended beyond auditory vesicles.

Incubation: 57–71 hours. [3]

YOLK-SAC LARVAE (Fig. 67 C)

Hatching length 4.1 mm TL. Duration of stage apparently ca. 2–3 days.

Body elongate; head not sharply deflected over yolk; yolk mass elongate, proportionally small at hatching, inconspicuous by 2nd day. Gills apparently developed by

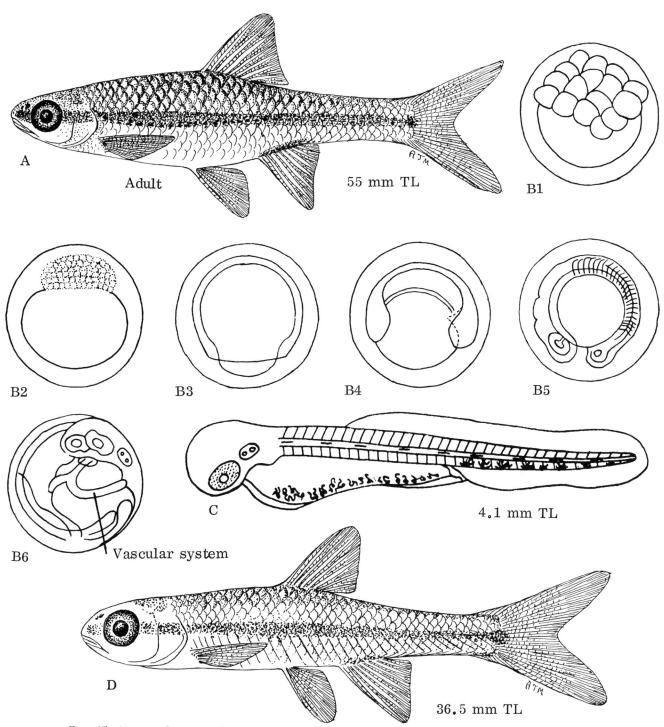

Fig. 67. *Notropis bifrenatus*, bridle shiner. A. Adult, 55 mm TL, 43.5 mm SL. B. Development of egg at ca. 24 C. Diameter 1.5 mm. B1. Sixteen-cell stage, 2 hours and 13 minutes. B2. Morula, 3 hours and 35 minutes. B3. Late gastrula, 9 hours and 40 minutes. B4. Embryonic axis, 15 hours and 40 minutes. B5. Early embryo, 23 hours and 10 minutes. Optic vesicles, Kupffer's vesicle, and some somites developed. B6. Pre-hatching embryo, 56 hours and 25 minutes. Vascular network over surface of yolk. C. Yolk-sac larva, 4.1 mm TL, newly hatched. A broken line of melanophores along side. D. Juvenile, 36.5 mm TL, 28 mm SL. Total myomeres 32; preanal myomeres 17; postanal myomeres 15. (A. D, *original drawings*, A. J. Mansueti, B, C, Harrington, 1947a: fig. 1.)

2nd day. A single, anterior, oval-shaped gas bladder by 3rd day. Finfold initially broad, originating ca. 1/3 TL from anterior end. Pectoral buds minute or absent at hatching; pectorals forming at 8 hours, conspicuous at 2 days. Notochord straight, reticulate.

Pigmentation: At hatching, eye pigmented; body transparent; melanophores along sides, over lower part of yolk-sac and ventrally from anus to tail; at 8 hours, a slight golden tinge; at 3 days, small chromatophores on head and dorsum.[3]

LARVAE

Size range described 7.0–13.0 mm TL (6.4–10.0 mm SL); age 9–28 days.

At ca. 7.0 mm, gas bladder 2–chambered; urostyle oblique; incipient rays in caudal; ventral buds evident at ca. 10.5 mm.

Pigmentation: At beginning of stage, black slender lateral band present. At ca. 10.5 mm, lateral band broad; caudal spot proportionately larger than in juveniles and adults.[3]

JUVENILES (Fig. 67 D)

Minimum size described 10.2 mm TL; age 43 days.[3]

Caudal peduncle longer, more slender in "young." [11]

At 36.5 mm, myomeres still visible; preanal myomeres 17, postanal myomeres 15. Dorsal and ventral outlines less curved; head and eye larger than in adult; lateral line not evident.

Pigmentation: Caudal spot larger than in adult; dorsal pigmentation light, extending halfway to lateral band (AJM). "Young" pale straw-color above.[7]

Age and size at maturity: Majority of males during 2nd summer, some females during 3rd summer;[4] specimens of unstated sex within 6 months of hatching.[13] Minimum size of males ca. 25.0 mm SL, females ca. 31.0 mm SL [3] (A 25 mm specimen contained 270 small eggs having some yolk, but was considered to be immature).[4]

LITERATURE CITED

1. Hubbs, C. L., and K. F. Lagler, 1958:76, 85.
2. Schwartz, F. J., 1964b:14.
3. Harrington, R. W., Jr., 1947a:97–102.
4. Harrington, R. W., Jr., 1948:86, 88.
5. Bailey, R. M., 1938:169.
6. Radforth, I., 1944:78.
7. Harrington, R. W., Jr., 1947b:189–91.
8. Adams, C. C., and T. L. Hankinson, 1928:343.
9. Webster, D. A., 1942:160.
10. Harrington, R. W., Jr., 1950:310.
11. Hildebrand, S. F., and W. C. Schroeder, 1928:126.
12. Massmann, W. H., 1958:5.
13. Harrington, R. W., Jr., 1957:555.
14. Harrington, R. W., Jr., 1959:653.
15. Hubbs, C. L., and E. C. Raney, 1947:4–10.
16. Slastenenko, E. P., 1958:234.

Ironcolor shiner   *Notropis chalybaeus* **(Cope)**

ADULT (Fig. 68 A)

D.7–8;[11] A. 7–9;[7] lateral line scales 32[4]–42; scales above lateral line 7–9, below 4–5; lateral line scales before dorsal 11–16; teeth 2,4–4,2.[11]

Proportions as percent SL at 40–50 mm SL: Greatest depth 21–23; length to vent ca. 60.6–67.4; greatest diameter of eye 8.3–9.7.[1]

Mouth moderately oblique; lower jaw included; snout rather blunt.[3] Lateral line usually incomplete,[7] decurved,[10] and with more than 10 unpored scales. Breeding males with nuptial tubercles well developed only on lower jaw and upper surface of pectoral.[7]

Dark above, pale yellow below; a broad, lustrous black, lateral band from snout to caudal base;[10] basicaudal spot scarcely or not at all wider and not darker than stripe on peduncle. Oral valves, floor and roof of mouth heavily pigmented.[7] Breeding males orange in dark water, rosy in clear water.[1]

Maximum size 51 mm SL.[7]

DISTRIBUTION AND ECOLOGY

Range: Atlantic coastal plain from Delaware River to central Florida and Texas; up Mississippi Valley into Illinois, Indiana, and Michigan.[3,9]

Area distribution: Reported from tidal fresh and slightly brackish water in Potomac River drainage, Maryland (FJS).

Habitat and movements: Adults—lakes [8,11] and slow, weedy streams in marshy or swampy areas of coastal

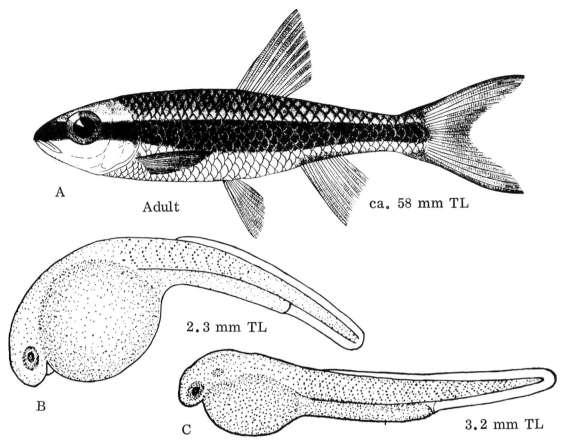

A
Adult

ca. 58 mm TL

2.3 mm TL

B

C

3.2 mm TL

Fig. 68. Notropis chalybaeus, ironcolor shiner. A. Adult, ca. 58.0 mm TL. B. Yolk-sac larva, 2.3 mm TL, 2.25 mm SL, newly hatched. C. Yolk-sac larva, 3.2 mm TL, 3.1 mm SL, one day. (A, *Fowler, 1906: 147*. B, C, *Marshall, 1947: fig. 3.*)

plain;[5] along edges of swift, deep rivers;[1] associated with sphagnum banks;[2] usually found over sandy bottom[1,8] in areas of abundant aquatic vegetation.[9] Maximum salinity apparently between 0.04 and 0.7 o/oo in Florida.[7]

Larvae—gregarious, frequently at surface in spawning area.[1]

SPAWNING

Area: Sand-bottomed pools.

Season: Early or mid-April to late September in Florida; probably somewhat shorter in northern localities.

Time: Throughout daylight hours at times of low, quiet water.

Temperature: Mean monthly air temperature during spawning season, 18.9–27.2 C.

Fecundity: Ca. 50 eggs recorded from a single stripping.[1]

EGGS

Description: Broadcast at random; demersal; adhesive shortly after deposition, becoming attached to sand grains and similar materials.

Freshly stripped eggs—diameter 0.8–0.9 mm; originally yellow, becoming pale cream.

Development: At air temperatures varying from 7.8 to 25.0 C (mean ca. 16.7 C).

Few minutes after fertilization—blastodisc contracted and forming white dome above yolk.
Ca. 1 hour, 30 minutes—4-cell stage.
Ca. 2 hours, 30 minutes—early morula; bastoderm a grey cap on top of lighter colored yolk.
Just before hatching—movements observable.

Incubation: 52–56 hours at mean temperature of ca. 16.7 C.[1]

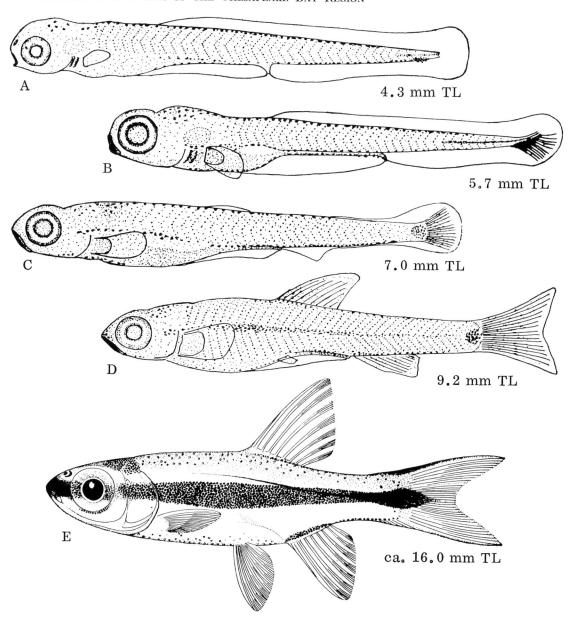

Fig. 69. *Notropis chalybaeus*, ironcolor shiner. A. Larva, 4.3 mm TL, 4.1 mm SL, 5 days. B. Larva, 5.7 mm TL, 5.4 mm SL, 19 days. C. Larva, 7.0 mm TL, 6.3 mm SL, 33 days. Caudal pigment spot noticeable. D. Larva, 9.2 mm TL, 7.4 mm SL, 47 days. Ventral buds present; preanal finfold retained. E. Juvenile, ca. 16.0 mm TL. (A-D, *Marshall, 1947: fig. 3, 4.* E, *Fowler, 1945: fig. 96.*)

YOLK-SAC LARVAE (Fig. 68 B,C)

Hatching length ca. 2.3 mm TL; length at end of stage ca. 4.0 mm.

Proportions as percent SL: Greatest depth 36.0 at 2.3 mm to 15.0 at 3.7 mm; length to vent 81.0 at 2.3 mm to 62.0 at 3.7 mm; eye diameter 5.0–8.0 throughout stage.

Myomeres indistinct; few, if any added after hatching. Dorsal outline arcuate at hatching. Head sharply deflected initially, less so at 3.2 mm. Yolk large, spherical at hatching; more than 1/2 reduced at 1 day; further

reduced and cylindrical at 3 days (3.9 mm). Eyes poorly developed at hatching, and remaining so at 3.2 mm. Pectoral buds evident at 3.9 mm.

Pigmentation: At 3.9 mm, melanophores present in mid-dorsal and posterior ventral regions; eye very slightly pigmented.[1]

LARVAE (Fig. 69 A-D)

Specimens described 4.3–9.2 mm TL. Duration of stage ca. 42 days.

Proportions as percent SL: Greatest depth 10.0–20.0; length to vent 60.0–68.0; eye diameter ca. 6.0–11.0; HL ca. 16.0–25.0.

Body noticeably more elongate at 4.6 mm; mouth functional, gills and gas bladder visible at 4.3 mm.

Caudal rays first evident at 5.7 mm, fin bifurcate at 9.2 mm. Dorsal and anal forming at 7.0 mm and with rays at 9.2 mm; ventral buds visible at 9.2 mm. Finfold very slightly constricted in caudal region at 4.3 mm. Urostyle turned obliquely upward at 5.7 mm, concealed at 6.2 mm.

Pigmentation: At 4.3 mm, melanophores along almost entire dorsal and ventral surfaces of body; at 5.7 mm, additional large blotch of melanophores over dorsal surface of head; at 6.2 mm, caudal spot developing; at 9.2 mm, a line of melanophores on mid-lateral surface from head to caudal spot.[1]

JUVENILES (Fig. 69 E)

Specimens described 14.8[1]–16.0 mm TL.[6] (The identity of the later specimen is questionable).

Proportions expressed as percent SL: Greatest depth 19.0; length to vent 63.0; diameter of eye 11.0.

Body adult-like.

Pigmentation: At 14.8 mm, pigmentation essentially same as at 9.2 mm;[1] at ca. 16.0 mm, lateral stripe extended to caudal fin; a dense patch of chromatophores along dorsum and venter, especially concentrated from origin of anal to caudal base and along dorsal margin of caudal fin.[6]

Age and size at maturity: Unknown.

LITERATURE CITED

1. Marshall, N., 1947:163–88.
2. Fowler, H. W., 1906:148.
3. Hubbs, C. L., and K. F. Lagler, 1958:75, 83.
4. Carr, A., and C. J. Goin, 1955:57.
5. Schwartz, F. J., 1963:28.
6. Fowler, H. W., 1945: Fig. 96.
7. Bailey, R. M., H. E. Winn, and C. L. Smith, 1954: 115, 127, 160–163.
8. Louder, D. E., 1962:71.
9. Gerking, S. D., 1947:90–91.
10. Smith, H. M., 1907:97.
11. Frey, D. G., 1951:16.

Spottail shiner | *Notropis hudsonius* (Clinton)

ADULT (Fig. 70 A)

D. 8; A. 7–8;[8] scales in lateral series 34[18]–41;[3] predorsal scales 14–23; scales from lateral line to lateral line across back 4–7, across belly 4–5;[18] pharyngeal teeth 2,4–4,2 or combinations to 0,4–4,0.[8]

Proportions as times in SL: Body depth 3.6–5.8;[3] head 3.7[18]–4.8.

Body rather slender, compressed; lateral line complete, somewhat decurved;[3] mouth moderately oblique, front of upper lip on level with bottom of pupil.[13] Breeding males with small turbercles on dorsal half of head and basal portion of anterior pectoral rays.[8]

Greenish above, sides silvery, venter pale; a black or silvery lateral band, usually terminating with a prominent black caudal spot; fins pale, translucent;[3,16] peritoneum silvery.[15]

Maximum size ca. 147 mm,[8] but possibly reaching ca. 152 mm.[19]

DISTRIBUTION AND ECOLOGY

Range: From Canada and Great Lakes region south to Georgia in the east, Kansas in the west.[6]

Area distribution: Tidal tributaries of Chesapeake Bay.[3]

Habitat and movements: Adults—usually large rivers, lakes, and reservoirs in clear, sandy, or rocky shallows,[8,9] or over grassy bottoms,[3] but apparently avoiding dense vegetation.[9,14] Maximum salinity 10.7 o/oo.[2] Maximum depth possibly 60 feet.[8]

Juveniles—"young" frequently in schools in shallow water with abundant vegetation.[9]

SPAWNING

Location: Gravelly riffles,[10] near mouths of brooks,[4,5] and sandy shoals[17] along shores of large lakes.[1]

Season: April (ECR)[10] to early July,[1] possibly delayed in years of high water level during late spring.[11]

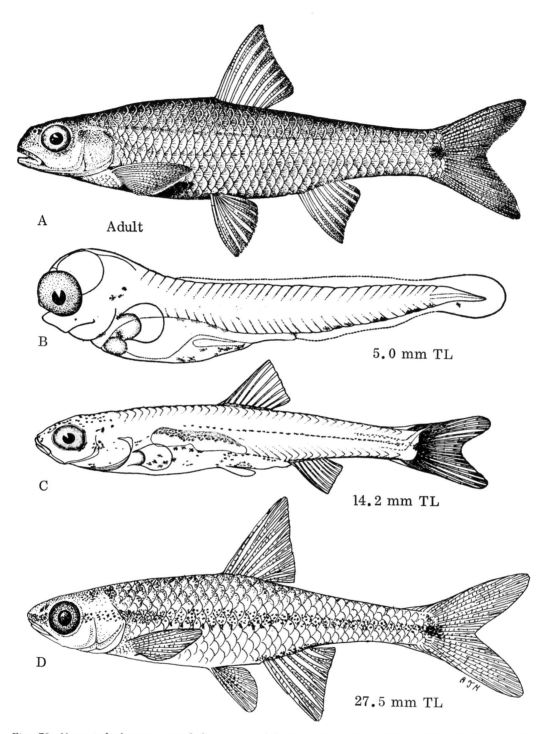

A   Adult

B   5.0 mm TL

C   14.2 mm TL

D   27.5 mm TL

Fig. 70. *Notropis hudsonius*, spottail shiner. A. Adult. B. Yolk-sac larva, 5.0 mm TL. C. Larva, 14.2 mm TL, 11.5 mm SL. Preanal myomeres 21 (22); postanal myomeres 16; dorsal and caudal pigmented. D. Juvenile, 27.5 mm TL, 22.0 mm SL. (A, *Truitt, Bean and Fowler, 1929: 40.* B, C, *Fish, 1932: fig. 39, 40.* D, *original drawing, A. J. Mansueti.*)

Time: Observed at dusk.[4]

Temperature: Unknown; ripe specimens observed in probable spawning areas at ca. 18.3 C.[5]

Fecundity: 100–2,600.[7]

EGGS

Demersal, scattered over clean sand or gravel in lakes and rivers.[4,15,17] Average diameter of ripe ovarian eggs 0.76 mm.[7]

PUTATIVE YOLK-SAC LARVAE (Fig. 70 B)

Specimen described 5.0 mm TL.

Preanal myomeres 17; postanal myomeres 15+; length to vent 2.75 mm.

Yolk mass elongate, with single large yellow oil globule anteriorly. Head very blunt, bulbous; mouth moderate, inferior; lower jaw included. Eye large; interorbital space wide; notochord bent slightly downward.

Pigmentation: Stellate melanophores along venter to anus; scattered chromatophores on sides of head, internally over stomach region, and along mid-ventral line from anus to caudal.[1]

LARVAE (Fig. 70 C)

Specimen described 14.25 mm TL.

D. 8; A. 9; preanal myomeres 21–22; postanal myomeres 16.

Body moderately elongate; head conical; snout blunt; mouth small, nearly horizontal; lower jaw slightly shorter than upper. Gas bladder two-chambered. Ventrals beneath dorsal origin; urostyle oblique; caudal forked.

Pigmentation. Chromatophores on opercle, beneath lower jaw, internally over gas bladder, in 3 rows along dorsum, in surface and subsurface series along future lateral line, in double series posterior to anus, and on dorsal and caudal fins. A prominent black spot at caudal base.[1]

JUVENILES (Fig. 70 D)

Minimum size described 18.0 mm TL.[7]

At 19.0 mm, preanal myomeres 22; postanal myomeres 18.[1] At ca. 27–30 mm, eye large; lateral line incomplete (AJM). Scales developing at 18–20 mm;[7,14] not fully formed in some specimens at ca. 24 mm;[12] fully formed in specimens 27.5 mm (AJM). In "young" origin of anal fin equidistant from caudal base to pectoral base, less than eyes diameter behind end of dorsal base; ventrals reaching to or a little beyond anal origin.[3]

Pigmentation: At 19.0 mm, head sparsely pigmented; 3 rows of chromatophores along dorsum to caudal; subsurface chromatophores along entire lateral line ending at caudal spot; small irregular chromatophores in dorsolateral region with few below lateral line.[1] At ca. 24.0–30.0 mm, lateral band and caudal spot well developed; dorsal scales with pigmented edges; pigment ventrally from anal origin to caudal base (AJM).[12]

Age and size at maturity: Some females by 1 year;[7] minimum size ca. 68 mm.[20]

LITERATURE CITED

1. Fish, M. P., 1932:334–35.
2. Mansueti, R. J., and R. S. Scheltema, 1953:3.
3. Hildebrand, S. F., and W. C. Schroeder, 1928:125–26.
4. Greeley, J. R., and C. W. Greene, 1931:87–8.
5. Greeley, J. R., 1930:80.
6. Moore, G. A., 1957:132.
7. McCann, J. A., 1959:337, 341.
8. Trautman, M. B., 1957:68, 361–63.
9. Adams, C. C., and T. L. Hankinson, 1928:346.
10. Wright, A. H., and A. A. Allen, 1913:7.
11. Keeton, D., 1963:3916.
12. Fowler, H. W., 1945: Fig. 93.
13. Bailey, R. M., 1956:360.
14. McCann, J. A., 1958:16–17, 45–6, 56.
15. Slastenenko, E. P., 1958:228–9.
16. Eddy, S., and T. Surber, 1960–161.
17. Hubbs, C. L., and G. P. Cooper, 1936:12, 28.
18. Ross, R. D., 1958:8.
19. Forbes, S. A., and R. E. Richardson, 1908:141–43.
20. Peer, D. L., 1966:456.

ADULT (Fig. 71 A)

D. 8; A. 8; [12] P. 18; V. 8; lateral line scales 45–50; [17] predorsal scales 18 [12]–23, [17] teeth 2,5–4,2.

Body oblong, robust, weakly compressed; head large, convex; snout bluntly conic; mouth large, terminal, somewhat oblique; a small barbel near corner of mouth; maxillary barely reaching front of orbit. [6]

Olive-brown to black, becoming silvery on sides and white ventrally; dark crescent-shaped or triangular bars at base of each scale along sides; [13] dorsal and caudal dusky, other fins plain; [9] breeding males with belly and lower fins rosy or crimson. [6]

Maximum length ca. 508 mm. [18]

DISTRIBUTION AND ECOLOGY

Range: James Bay region, northern St. Lawrence tributaries, Lake Ontario [4] and Lake Superior drainages; [5] south, east of the Appalachians, to Virginia. [4]

Area distribution: Tidal tributaries of lower Chesapeake Bay. [1,2]

Habitat and movements: Adults—clear streams and lakes, often near waterfalls or rapids, but also abundant in standing water. [14] Frequently in deep water, but also in small schools near shore line.

Larvae—"fry" apparently remain near nest for short period after hatching. [3]

Juveniles—specimens ca. 25 mm long from pools in small streams and along swampy shores; 50-mm individuals over sand and scattered stone in open spaces among bulrushes, also in small streams; large specimens in 3–5 feet of water. [14]

SPAWNING

Location: In pebble nest built by male [7] in fairly quiet water of pools, riffles, [15] or shallow margins of ponds and lakes. [14] Nest sometimes ca. 6.5 feet in diameter and up to 3 feet high, characterized by a keel-like crest which may lie crosswise or with the current.

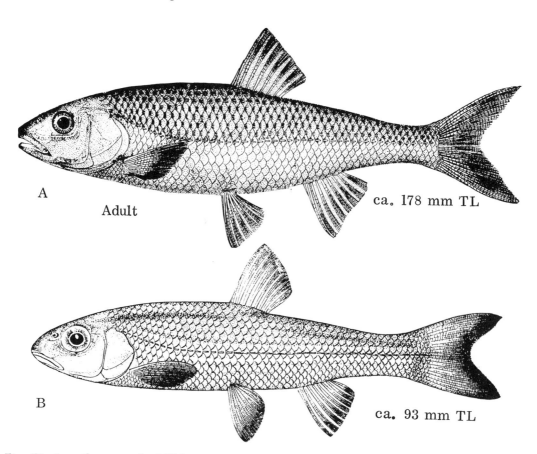

Fig. 71. Semotilus corporalis, fallfish. A. Adult, ca. 178 mm TL. B. Juvenile, ca. 93 mm TL. (A, *Goode, et al., 1884: pl. 228.* B, *Fowler, 1945: fig. 82.*)

Season: April to June in New York;[15] females in spawning condition in early April in Patuxent River, Maryland (RJM).

Fecundity: 1,000–4,000.[18]

EGGS

Described as both adhesive, sticking to stones in nest,[18] and non-adhesive.

Incubation: 7–9 days at average temperature of 15.5 C.[7]

LARVAE

Undescribed.

PREJUVENILE

Identity of specimen attributed to this species (ca. 16.5 mm TL)[10] questioned on basis of shape and position of mouth and presence of caudal spot.

JUVENILES (Fig. 71 B)

Specimen described ca. 93 mm TL.

Eye proportionately larger than in adult; scales fully formed.[10]

Size at maturity: Fowler[11] found females ca. 75 mm long with fully developed eggs, but found no tuberculated males under ca. 305 mm long; Kendall and Goldsborough[9] found that in small brooks fallfish reach maturity when "only a few inches" long.

LITERATURE CITED

1. Raney, E. C., and W. H. Massmann, 1953:428.
2. Massmann, W. H., 1958:5.
3. Webster, D. A., 1942:159.
4. Moore, G. A., 1957:104.
5. Dymond, J. R., 1964:14.
6. Jordon, D. S., and B. W. Evermann, 1896–221.
7. Atkins, C., 1905:189.
8. Wilson, A. W. G., 1907:323.
9. Kendall, W. C., and E. L. Goldsborough, 1908:26.
10. Fowler, H. W., 1945: Fig. 81.
11. Fowler, H. W., 1912:472.
12. Jordon, D. S., and B. W. Evermann, 1902:74.
13. Scott, W. B., 1954:48.
14. Adams, C. C., and T. L. Hankinson, 1928:337–39.
15. Raney, E. C., 1949:71, 74.
16. Raney, E. C., 1940:129.
17. Slastenenko, E. P., 1958:203.
18. Shoemaker, M. E., 1945:208–9.

Carpiodes cyprinus

Catostomus commersoni

Erimyzon oblongus

Moxostoma macrolepidotum

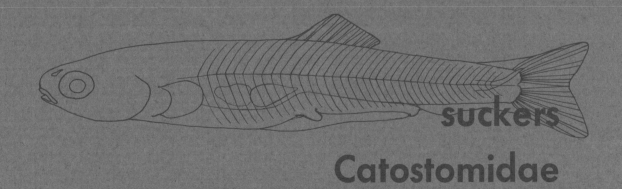

suckers
Catostomidae

Quillback   *Carpiodes cyprinus* (LeSueur)

ADULT (Fig. 72 A)

D. 22–30;[1] A. 7[11]–8; V. usually 10;[10] lateral line scales 33–42. Depth 2.2–3.4 times in SL;[1] HL 3.7–4.0 times in TL;[11] eye 4.0–8.8 times in HL.[1]

Body oblong, robust; head naked; jaws toothless; mouth small, inferior,[10] lacking barbels.[11] Anterior dorsal rays greatly elevated.[10]

Bronze-olive above, sides lighter; venter milk- or yellowish-white; tip of snout and lips often milk-white; anterior and distal edge of dorsal black;[1] paired fins edged with white.[11]

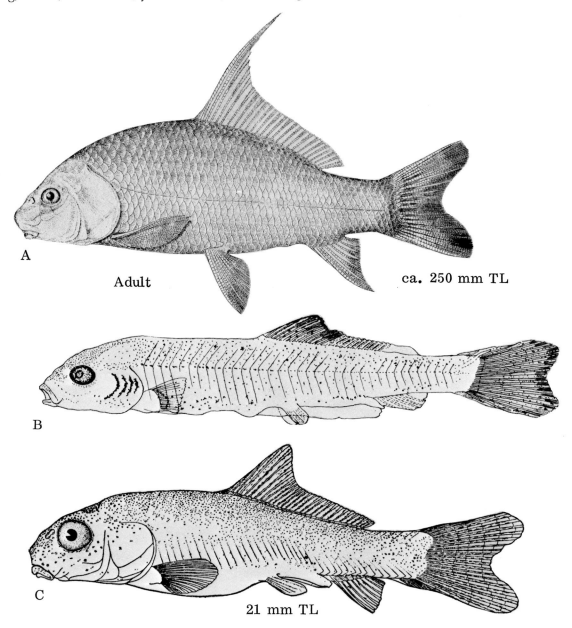

A

Adult   ca. 250 mm TL

B

C

21 mm TL

Fig. 72. Carpiodes cyprinus, quillback. A. Adult, ca. 250 mm TL. B. Larva, size unknown. C. Prejuvenile, 21 mm TL, 16.5 mm SL. D. 28; V. 10; preanal myomeres 25; postanal myomeres 12 +. (A, *Goode, et al., 1884: pl. 225.* B. *Howarth, 1961: fig. 15.* C, *Fish, 1932: fig. 18.*)

143

Maximum length possibly to ca. 660 mm.[1]

DISTRIBUTION AND ECOLOGY

Range: Southern Manitoba and Great Lakes to Kansas and western Florida;[3] on Atlantic coast from St. Lawrence River system to Roanoke River, Virginia.[2]

Area distribution: North to lower Susquehanna River in Chesapeake drainage (ECR); Delaware River.[6]

Habitat and movements: Generally lakes, creeks, and large rivers;[5,9] in Lake Erie over bottoms of sand, sandy gravel, silt, or clay;[1] shallow areas along shore in flooded, weedy places; on riffles in August;[4] migratory during spawning season.[5]

SPAWNING

Location: Over sand, silt, or mud in streams or overflow bayous.[5,11]

Season: Late April through May in Iowa.[5]

Fecundity: Unknown.

EGGS

Undescribed. Deposited at random.[5]

YOLK-SAC LARVAE

Undescribed.

LARVAE (Fig. 72 B)

Size range unknown.

Preanal finfold long, broad; urostyle oblique.

Pigmentation: Chromatophores concentrated above lateral line and over head, also developed in dorsal and caudal fin.[8]

PREJUVENILES (Fig. 72 C)

Specimen described 21 mm TL.

Preanal myomeres 25; postanal myomeres 12+.

Body oblong, dorsal outline slightly arched; snout becoming pointed; mouth inferior, small, horizontal; gas bladder 2-chambered.

Pigmentation: Chromatophores on upper jaws, sides and top of head, on dorsolateral aspects of body, in a double row along anal fin and beneath caudal peduncle, in a single mid-dorsal row to caudal, and on at least the dorsal and caudal fins.[7]

JUVENILES

Eye more than 4.5 times in HL in specimens less than ca. 100 mm long.[1]

Age and size at maturity: Unknown.

LITERATURE CITED

1. Trautman, M. B., 1957:232–34.
2. Moore, G. A., 1957:79.
3. Eddy, S., 1957:66.
4. Venicek, D., 1961:239.
5. Harlan, J. R., and E. B. Speaker, 1956:74.
6. Truitt, R. V., B. A. Bean, and H. W. Fowler, 1929:45.
7. Fish, M. P., 1932:316–17.
8. Howarth, J. N., 1961: Fig. 15.
9. Hubbs, C. L., and K. F. Lagler, 1947:50.
10. Jordon, D. S., and B. W. Evermann, 1896:165.
11. Slastenenko, E. P., 1958:156–67.

White sucker   *Catostomus commersoni* (Lacépède)

ADULT (Fig. 73 A)

D. 11[22]–15[3] (10–11 in subspecies *utawana*); A. 7–8; P. 15–17 (in *utawana*);[22] V. 9–10;[14] scales in lateral series 55–85;[11] predorsal scales 25–35 (30–35 in *utawana*);[22] total vertebrae 44–47; precaudal vertebrae 25–28.[8]

Proportions as times in SL: Body depth 4.45–4.82; head length 4.09–4.35.

Body elongate, little compressed;[3] head large, stout, convex above;[2] mouth inferior; lips papillose, lower one broader than upper.[3]

Olive- or brownish-slate above, scale margins darker; sides more or less silvery; venter white; dorsal and caudal light slate, other fins whiter. Breeding males black to olive above with lavender sheen; black (subspecies *commersoni*) to reddish (*utawana*) lateral band continued around snout and, above this, a band of whitish-yellow overcast with pink; lower fins light to faint yellow.[11,15]

Maximum length 635 mm TL,[4] but possibly reaching ca. 760 mm.[11]

DISTRIBUTION AND ECOLOGY

Range: East of Rocky Mountains; north to Mackenzie River and Hudson Bay drainage; south to Georgia, Arkansas, and northeastern Oklahoma;[12] introduced widely, especially in southwest.[11]

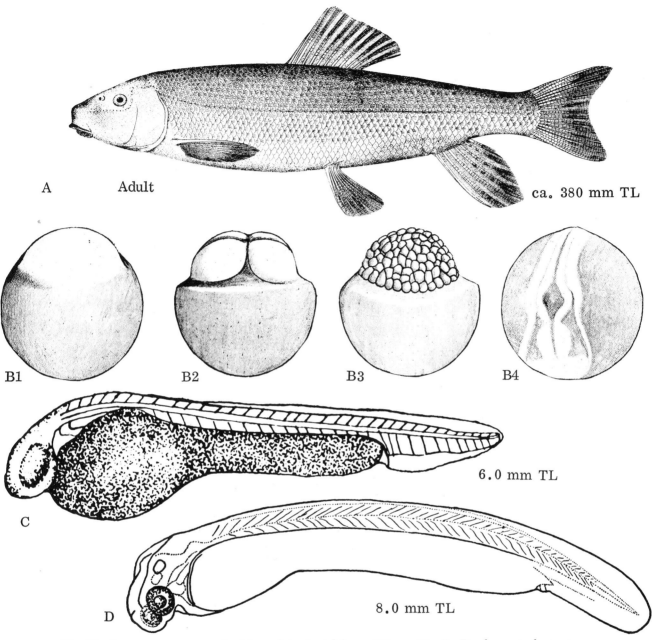

A Adult

ca. 380 mm TL

B1 B2 B3 B4

C

6.0 mm TL

D

8.0 mm TL

Fig. 73. Catostomus commersoni, white sucker. A. Adult, ca. 380 mm TL. B. Development of egg at mean temperature 10.3 C. Egg capsule removed. B1. Blastodisc, 2 1/2 hours. B2. Four-cell stage, 6 hours. B3. Morula, 2 1/2 hours. B4. Late embryo, 8 days. Tail reaches almost to head. C. Yolk-sac larva, 6.0 mm TL, newly hatched. D. Yolk-sac larva, 8.0 mm TL, newly hatched. (A, *Goode, et al., 1884: pl. 223.* B1-B4, D, *Stewart, 1926: fig. 2, 3, 6, 12, 20.* C, *Crawford, 1923: fig. 3.*)

Area distribution: Tidal tributaries of lower Chesapeake Bay [10] and slightly brackish water of upper Bay near Havre de Grace, Maryland.[3]

Habitat and movements: Adults—ubiquitious; winter in deeper water; [21,23,24,28] sometimes taken under moderately low oxygen conditions (RJM). Undertake spawning migrations, usually at night,[6,19,32] when water temperature reaches ca. 4–5 C or higher.[4,13,21] Maximum salinity ca.

2.0 o/oo (RJM). Maximum depth 45 [29] to possibly 80 feet.[30,31]

Yolk-sac larvae—on bottom.

Larvae—move to quiet waters.[34] Specimens 10–12 mm long in large schools over sand and pebble bottom in water ca. 8 inches deep.[25] Specimens 12–17 mm long near surface, usually in moderate current and frequently associated with *Elodea.*[2] "Youngest" seem to prefer shallow water over muddy bottom with little vegetation.[4]

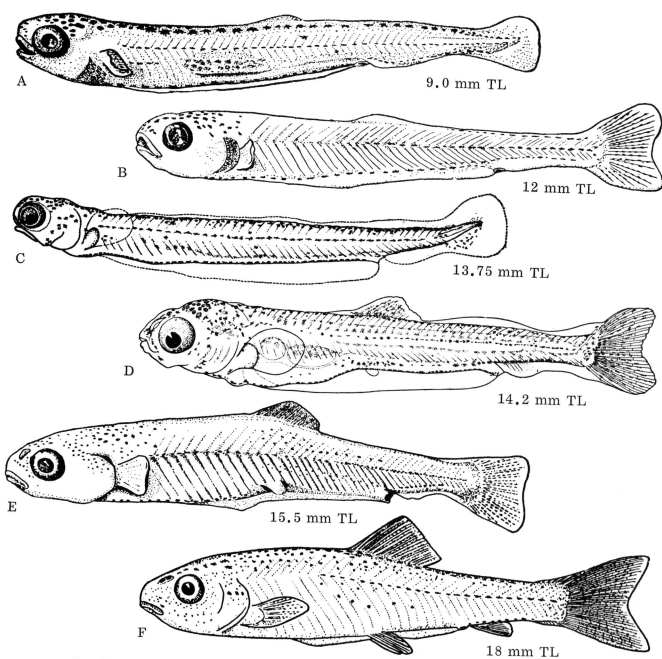

Fig. 74. Catostomus commersoni, white sucker. A. Larva, 9.0 mm TL. Gills exposed. B. Larva, 12 mm TL. Gas bladder one-chambered. C. Larva, 13.75 mm TL. Dorsal finfold retained. D. Larva, 14.2 mm TL. Gas bladder two-chambered; ventral buds formed. E. Larva, 15.5 mm TL. Mouth becoming inferior. F. Prejuvenile 18 mm TL. Mouth inferior, entirely below eye. (A, B, E, F, *Stewart, 1926: fig. 21–23, 25,* C, D, *Fish, 1932: fig. 19, 20.*)

Juveniles—bottom feeders at ca. 16–18 mm.[2] At 17–58 mm, in bayous with abundant pond weed, rushes and other aquatic plants, and over sandy river bottoms among *Potamogeton*.[36] "Fry" and "immature" in shallow muddy sloughs among weeds and along shores of lakes and ponds.[35]

SPAWNING

Location: In streams of all sizes,[11] usually in moderately swift water of riffles,[15,32] or over sand or gravel bottom,[6,15,17,20] sometimes at a depth of only 2 inches;[21,24,35] also in still pools,[15] lakes, and impoundments.[11,17,18] (The subspecies *utawana* spawns in swift, cold, mountain streams[26] and shows an affinity for shady, sheltered areas).[21,24]

Season: March[5] to early July, depending on locality.[4,5]

Time: Usually at night, but also during daylight hours.[4,6,15,21,24]

Temperature: Ca. 6.0–23 C.[11]

Fecundity: Varies according to length and subspecies; 775 at ca. 121 mm (in *utawana*) to 111,000 at ca. 483–508 mm;[16] maximum ca. 140,000.[9]

EGGS (Fig. 73 B)

Description: Demersal; deposited singly or in small groups.[15]
  Unfertilized eggs—diameter 2.0[2]–2.82 mm. Round, white[1] or pale yellow,[2] lacking oil globules; finely granular and slightly adhesive. Micropyle single.
  Fertilized eggs—diameter ca. 2.0 (in *utawana*)[22] to 3.0 mm. Non-adhesive after water-hardening.[2] Lacking large oil globules, but with numerous, clear droplets of minute size in yolk, and along edge of blastodisc.

Development: At mean temperature of 10.3 C.

2 hours, 30 minutes—blastodisc fully differentiated.
6 hours—4-cell stage.
8 hours—"eighteen-celled stage."
10 hours, 30 minutes—36-cell stage.
21 hours, 30 minutes—morula.
ca. 44 hours—blastoderm flattened on top.
54 hours—blastoderm nearly to equator of egg.
92 hours—yolk entirely invested by blastoderm.
149 hours—body of embryo visible as a straight white ridge, narrow and rather high, nearly encircling egg and terminating at anterior end as a flat rounded expansion.
174 hours—brain and optic evaginations visible.
198 hours—lateral boundaries of head and body

visible; tail almost around to anterior limit of head.
224 hours—yolk no longer spherical, but divided into a posterior cylindrical region and a spherical anterior region; notochord visible.
246 hours—length of embryo greater than circumference of yolk; eyes pigmented.[2]

Incubation: 4 days at 21.1 C; 7 days at 15.6 C;[6] 12 days at average of 11.7 C;[7] 12–21 days at average of 10.3 C.[2]

YOLK-SAC LARVAE (Fig. 73 C,D)

Size at hatching 6.0[5]–8.0 mm TL; maximum size at end of stage ca. 12.0 mm.

Body depth 1/6 TL at hatching. Body slender; head decurved; olfactory placodes evident as circular thickenings of epidermis; mouth incomplete at hatching, open at 9.0 mm; eye large, slightly elliptical; auditory vesicles simple ovoid sacs at hatching; branchial apparatus complete at 9.0 mm. Yolk sac initially cylindrical throughout[2] or spherical anteriorly.[5] Heart S-shaped; pericardial cavity a dome-shaped bulge at anterior end of yolk sac.

At hatching, pectoral buds present; caudal with or without incipient rays; finfold originating near mid-point of dorsum and terminating at vent.

Pigmentation: Body "whitish"; retina pigmented at hatching.[2]

LARVAE (Fig. 74 A-E)

Specimens described ca. 9.0[2]–ca. 16.0 mm TL.[5]

At 14.2 mm, preanal myomeres 33; postanal myomeres 10+.[1] Eyes very large, 3 times in HL at 9.0 mm. Mouth initially horseshoe-shaped, nearly vertical; at 14.0 mm, mouth opening on level with lower rim of eyes; at 16.0 mm, opening entirely below eyes. First loop of intestine formed at 16–17 mm; length of digestive tract equal to length of fish. Gas bladder first visible at 11.0 mm, connected to gut up to 14.0 mm,[2] and 2-chambered in a specimen 14.2 mm.[1] Liver first visible at 11.0 mm.

Incipient dorsal and anal at 9.0 mm; caudal rounded at 10.9 mm,[33] 2-lobed at 12.0 mm;[2] ventrals developing at 14[1] to 15 mm; dorsal finfold lost by 9.0 mm[2] or retained to ca. 14.2 mm;[1] preanal finfold long, wide at 14.0 mm; urostyle oblique at 14.0 mm.

Pigmentation: At 9.0 mm, a double row of large chromatophores along mid-dorsal region and ca. 30 smaller ones on top of head; a row of small chromatophores along mid-lateral line and a double row along venter. At 12.0 mm, chromatophores along caudal rays.[2]

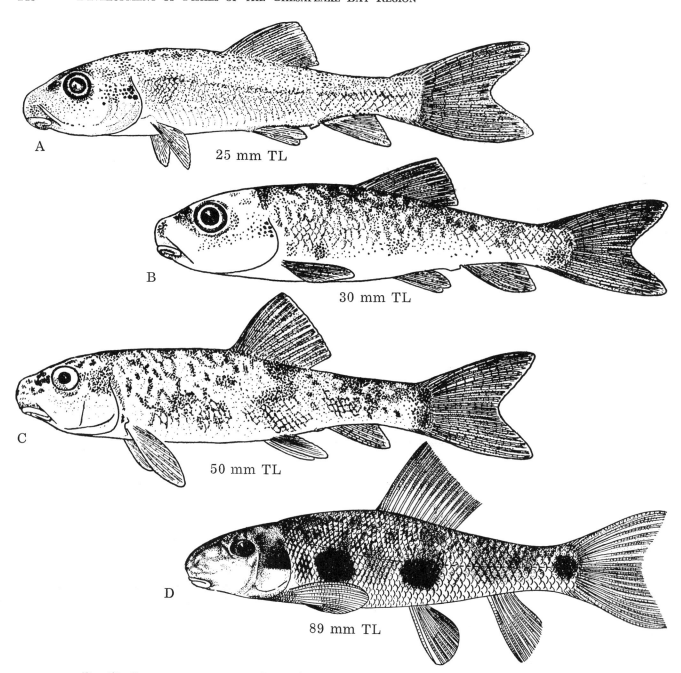

Fig. 75. *Catostomus commersoni*, white sucker. A. Juvenile, 25 mm TL. Scalation complete. B. Juvenile, 30 mm TL. C. Juvenile, 50 mm TL. Eye high; papillae on lips. D. Juvenile, 89 mm TL. Sides and back characteristically mottled. (A-C, *Stewart, 1926: fig. 26–28.* D, *Fowler, 1906: 156.*)

At 13.75 mm, eyes silvery, edged with black; 3 rows of chromatophores along dorsum and in a single mid-lateral series; a predominately subsurface series starting behind head, concentrated over dorsal surface of gas bladder and continuing in massed line to vent; ca. 57–60 large, rounded stellate chromatophores along ventral ridge from behind head to vent and continuing as massed line to end of body; small pepper-like chromatophores near caudal base.[1] At 14.0 mm, chromatophores along dorsal rays.[2] A 14.2 mm specimen has pigmentation essentially as in earlier stages, but with series of subsurface chromatophores above and below vertebral column connected laterally at myoseptums, along ventral aspect of notochord, and along margins of gill arches.[1] At 16.0 mm, large yellow and black chromatophores scattered over body.[5]

PREJUVENILES (Fig. 74 F)

Specimen described 18.0 mm TL.

Nostril apparently divided; preanal finfold retained; scattered chromatophores on dorso-lateral surfaces and operculum.[2]

JUVENILES (Fig. 75 A-D)

Minimum size described 20.0 mm TL.[2]

HL 3.5–4.25 times in body length in "young."[14]

Scale formation first evident at ca. 22.0 mm, complete by 25.0 mm. Papillae present on lips at 43.0 mm. Gut nearly twice length of fish at 24.0 mm.

Pigmentation: At 20.0 mm, all fins pigmented; scattered chromatophores over entire body. At 25.0 mm, scale margins becoming outlined with pigment; several spots or blotches of dark pigment on sides; sides with distinct golden iridescence.[2] "Young" mottled and blotched with black, the blotches sometimes more or less confluent.[3]

Age and size at maturity: Possible 3[20] to 8 years,[23] depending on subspecies and locality. Minimum size ca. 76 mm.[25,27]

LITERATURE CITED

1. Fish, M. P., 1932:317–18.
2. Stewart, N. H., 1926:147–84.
3. Hildebrand, S. F., and W. C. Schroeder, 1928:119.
4. Webster, D. A., 1942:150, 216.
5. Crawford, D. R., 1923:151, Fig. 3.
6. Raney, E. C., and D. A. Webster, 1942:140.
7. Carbine, W. F., 1943:49.
8. Snyder, R. C., 1949:63.
9. Eddy, S., and T. Surber, 1947:129.
10. Massmann, W. H., 1958:4.
11. Trautman, M. B., 1957:269–71.
12. Moore, G. A., 1957:88.
13. Tramblay, L., 1962:125–26.
14. Jordon, D. S., and B. W. Evermann, 1896:173.
15. Raney, E. C., 1943:256.
16. Carlander, K. D., 1953:84.
17. Scott, W. B., 1954:38.
18. Harlan, J. R., and E. B. Speaker, 1956:79.
19. Small, H. B., 1883:38.
20. Dence, W. A., 1940:224–25, 230.
21. Dence, W. A., 1948:115–16, 122, 134.
22. Slastenenko, E. P., 1958:162–65.
23. Migdalski, E. C., 1962:288–90.
24. Greeley, J. R., and C. W. Greene, 1931:84.
25. Spoor, W. A., 1938:496.
26. Kendall, W. C., and W. A. Dence, 1929:287.
27. Fowler, H. W., 1912:474.
28. Kendall, W. C., and E. L. Goldsborough, 1908:23–4.
29. Odell, T. T., 1932:333.
30. Hankinson, T. L., 1910:197.
31. Hankinson, T. L., 1908:207.
32. Stewart, N. H., 1922:8.
33. Mohrhardt, D. E., 1961:53.
34. Hubbs, C. L., and C. W. Creaser, 1924:372, 375.
35. Dence, W. A., 1937:622–23.
36. Bigelow, N. K., 1923:85, 89.

ADDITIONAL REFERENCES

Bassett, H. M., 1958; Langlois, T. H., 1945; Vessel, M. F., and S. Eddy, 1941.

Creek chubsucker

Erimyzon oblongus (Mitchill)

ADULT (Fig. 76 A)

D. 9 [3]–14;[5] A. 7–8; V. 8–10; scale rows to end of hypural 39–45;[13] scales in transverse series 13–14;[3] gill rakers on lower limb of first arch 7–10.

Proportions as times in SL: Body depth 2.75–4.2; head length 3.45–4.2.[13]

Body oblong, compressed; head short; scales large, closely overlapping;[3] lateral line lacking.[15] Breeding males usually with three large tubercles on each side of snout;[2] pearl organs along dorsal, anal, and caudal rays.[14]

Brownish-olive with coppery lustre above, pale beneath; fins more or less dusky, sometimes reddish.[3]

Maximum size ca. 457 mm.[10]

DISTRIBUTION AND ECOLOGY

Range: Minnesota east to Atlantic coast; reported from New Brunswick and Nova Scotia,[8] but records are possibly erroneous;[19] south on Atlantic coastal plain to Waccamaw River drainage in North Carolina;[17,25] in Mississippi drainage south to Texas and Florida.[8]

Area distribution: Tidal tributaries of Chesapeake Bay to Havre de Grace, Maryland,[3] Virginia,[11] New Jersey.[12]

Habitat and movements: Adults—a bottom species[2,20] inhabiting clear, rapid to slow-moving streams, frequently

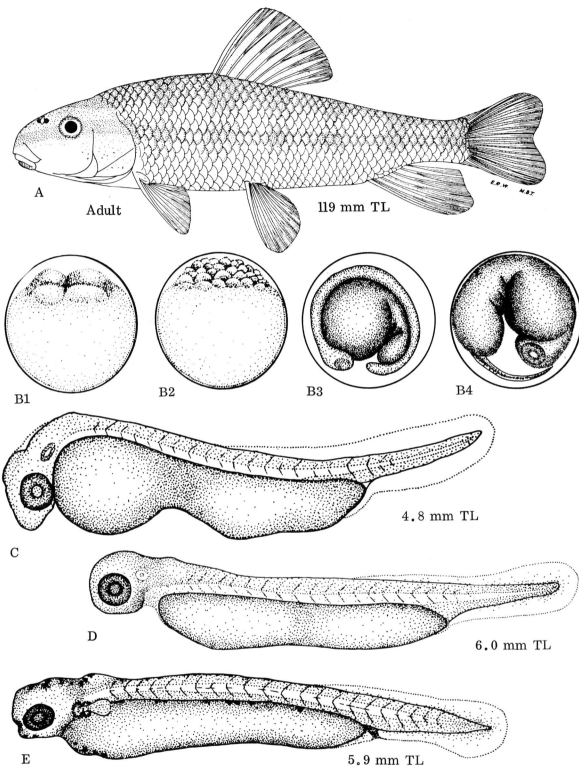

Fig. 76. Erimyzon oblongus, creek chubsucker. A. Adult, 119 mm TL, 98 mm SL. B. Development of egg at 20 C. B1. Four-cell stage, 2 hours. B2. Morula, 3 hours. B3. Tail-free embryo, 50 hours. B4. Embryo, 74 hours. C. Yolk-sac larva, 4.8 mm TL, just hatched. Yolk sac 3.05 mm long; pectoral buds present but not shown. D. Yolk-sac larva, 6.0 mm TL, ca. 2.2 days. E. Yolk-sac larva, 5.9 mm TL, ca. 3.9 days. A, *reprinted from* THE FISHES OF OHIO *by Milton B. Trautman, fig. 56. Copyright © 1957 by the Ohio State University Press. Used by permission of the author and the publisher. B-E, Carnes, 1958: pl. 2, fig. 3, 5; pl. 3–7.)*

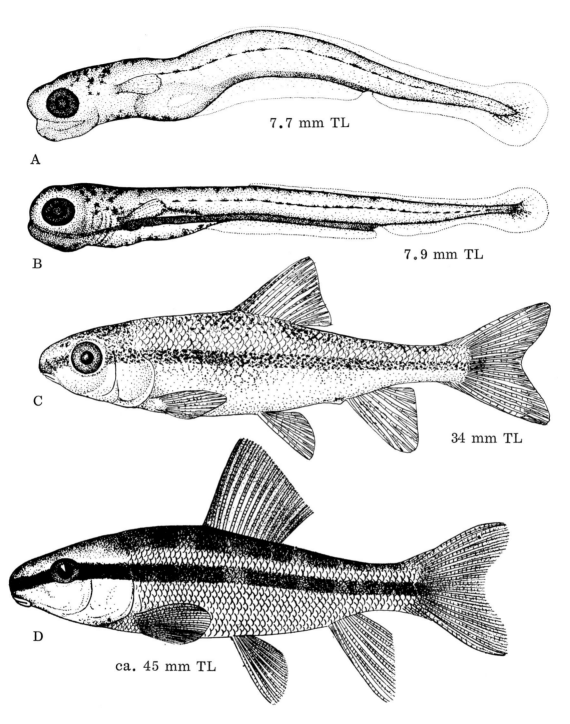

Fig. 77. Erimyzon oblongus, creek chubsucker. A. Larva, 7.7 mm TL, ca. 7.4 days. B. Larva 7.9 mm TL, ca. 20.4 days. C. Juvenile, 34 mm TL, 28 mm SL. D. Juvenile, ca. 45 mm TL. (A, B, *Carnes, 1958: pl. 8, 9.* C, *original drawing, A. J. Mansueti.* D, *Fowler, 1906:160.)*

in areas of thick vegetation; also lakes [1,16,22] and mill-ponds (RJM). Apparently some undertake spawning migrations to headwaters of streams in fall, winter, and spring [3,7,16,23] and move downstream to larger creeks following spawning.[4] Maximum salinity 2.17 o/oo.[18]

Juveniles—in small schools over vegetation along lake shores; [1,21] also in quiet pools of small streams.[6]

SPAWNING

Location: Presumably head waters of small creeks over sand and gravel,[4,14] also in ponds over muck bottoms.[26]

Season: March and April in North Carolina, with movements chiefly during evening hours.

Minimum temperature: Ca. 11.0 C.[14]

Fecundity: 7,500 [9]–83,013.[14]

EGGS (Fig. 76 B)

Description: Demersal; adhesive, attached to objects on bottom and to each other.

Ripe eggs—1.84 mm in diameter; spherical; light to deep, golden yellow; perivitelline space very narrow; oil globules lacking.

Development: At ca. 20 C (fluctuating from 17–23 C):

One hour—blastodisc formed; first cleavage evident.
2 hours—4-cell stage.
2 hours, 35 minutes—8-cell stage.
3 hours—morula.
24 hours—some eggs with incipient neural crest.
50 hours—embryo completely surrounds yolk, tail tip free; eyes barely distinguishable.
74 hours—tail completely free; yolk mass oval anteriorly, tubular behind; movement established.

Incubation: 96 hours at ca. 20 C (fluctuating from 17–23 C).[14]

YOLK-SAC LARVAE (Fig. 76 C-E)

Hatching at 4.8 mm TL; maximum size described 6.0 mm.

Head initially deflected over yolk, free at 6.0 mm; mouth poorly developed at 5.9 mm. Auditory vesicles small, elongate at hatching, no longer visible at end of stage. Yolk sac spherical anteriorly and elongate posteriorly at hatching, reduced to slender tube at 5.9 mm.

Pectoral buds present at hatching; preanal finfold extended forward toward head as yolk is absorbed.

Pigmentation: At 6.0 mm (ca. 2 days old), chromatophores apparently formed in finfold; at 5.9 mm (ca. 4 days old), chromatophores on head above and below eye, along anterior half of dorsal surface, and anterio-ventral surface of yolk.[14]

LARVAE (Fig. 77 A-B)

Specimens described 7.7–7.9 mm TL.

Mouth clearly visible and gas bladder formed at 7.7 mm; gill arches forming at 7.9 mm.

At 7.7 mm, pectorals well developed; incipient rays in caudal.

Pigmentation: At 7.7 mm, chromatophores throughout body with single row along vertebral column. At 7.9 mm, pigmentation more pronounced, with distinct, broken, dark line laterally.[14]

JUVENILES (Fig. 77 C,D)

Minimum size described 34 mm TL.

Eye larger than in adult. Scalation incomplete at 34 mm (AJM), apparently complete at ca. 45 mm.[12]

Pigmentation: A distinct dark lateral band [3] of widely spaced chromatophores evident at 34 mm (AJM), later broken into blotches forming transverse bands; [3,15] caudal amber.[8,24]

Size at maturity: Smallest males possibly ca. 61 mm, based on presence of breeding tubercles.[4]

LITERATURE CITED

1. Webster, D. A., 1942:151.
2. Forbes, S. A., and R. E. Richardson, 1920:81–2.
3. Hildebrand, S. F., and W. C. Schroeder, 1928: 117–18.
4. Trautman, M. B., 1957:280–82.
5. Schwartz, F. J., 1962b:23.
6. Surber, E. W., and D. D. Friddle, 1946:315–16.
7. Smith, H. M., and B. A. Bean, 1899:181.
8. Moore, G. A., 1957:86.
9. Wagner, C. C., and E. L. Cooper, 1963:355.
10. Mansueti, R. J., 1957:9.
11. Massmann, W. H., 1958:4.
12. Fowler, H. W., 1906:161–62.
13. Hubbs, C. L., 1930:37–40.
14. Carnes, W. C., Jr., 1958:10, 47–53.
15. Jordon, D. S., and B. W. Evermann, 1896:185.
16. Adams, C. C., and T. L. Hankinson, 1928:314.
17. Frey, D. G., 1951:14.
18. Keup, L., and J. Bayless, 1964:121.
19. Scott, W. B., 1954:37.
20. Eddy, S., and T. Surber, 1960:133.
21. Richardson, R. E., 1913b:410.
22. Hankinson, T. L., 1908:207.
23. Hankinson, T. L., 1919:135.
24. Hubbs, C. L., 1930:34.
25. Louder, D. E., 1962:69.
26. Underhill, A. H., 1940:253.

ADULT (Fig. 78 A)

D. 11–15;[2] A. 7[17]–8;[9] V. 8–10;[14] lateral line scales 40[2]–48.[18]

Proportions as times in SL: Body depth 3.2[19]–4.3;[2] HL 4.2[19]–5.4.

Body elongate, compressed; head small; mouth inferior; lips plicate; lower lip with straight, posterior margin; breeding tubercles of males confined to anal and caudal fins.

Olive-yellow above, shading ventrally to milk-white or yellowish; dorsal, caudal, and anal red; ventrals and pectorals yellowish-pink, sometimes flushed with crimson.

Maximum length ca. 620 mm.[2]

DISTRIBUTION AND ECOLOGY

Range: Central Canada, Great Lakes region and St. Lawrence drainages south to Hudson River and tributaries of Chesapeake and Delaware Bays.[14] In Mississippi basin from Montana to Ohio south to Red River of Oklahoma and Texas.[14,16,21]

Area distribution: In Chesapeake drainage north to Havre de Grace, Maryland;[1] Virginia,[16] Delaware Bay,[14] and New Jersey.[15]

Habitat and movements: Adult—primarily in larger, clear streams,[12] rivers[15] and lakes;[24] also large lakes over bottoms of sand, gravel, or bedrock; less frequently in turbid water over heavily silted bottom.[2,3] Introduced in millponds and reservoirs (RJM). Migratory, ascending streams to spawn.[4,6,9] Maximum salinity, 3.0 o/oo (RJM).

Juveniles—fast water[3] in small streams.[6]

SPAWNING

Location: Riffles or gravelly rapids in streams 30–40 feet wide;[7,8,11] also over sand bottoms (RJM).

Season: April to June in Maryland (RJM).

Time: "Night";[6] also 10.00 A.M. to 4:00 P.M. (ECR).

Temperature: Ca. 11 C.

Fecundity: 13,500–27,150.[3]

EGGS

Undescribed. Scattered in small lots,[11] buried in the bottom by vigorous spawning[11] (ECR).

PUTATIVE LARVAE (Fig. 78 B)

Specimen described 7.5 mm TL (7.1 mm SL).

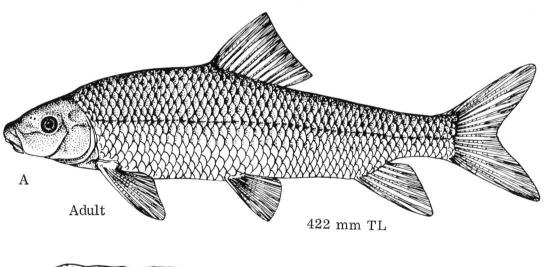

A

Adult   422 mm TL

B   7.5 mm TL

Fig. 78. *Moxostoma macrolepidotum,* northern redhorse. A. Adult female, 422 mm TL. B. Putative larva, 7.5 mm TL, 7.1 mm SL. (A, *redrawn from colored plate, Greeley, 1930: pl. 8.* B, *Fish, 1932: fig. 22.*)

Preanal myomeres 24; postanal myomeres 13. Mouth moderate, terminal; upper jaw somewhat projected, suckerlike. Gas bladder large, one-chambered. Origin of dorsal finfold over 10th myomere; future dorsal fin indicated by concentration of cells at anterior end of dorsal finfold.

Pigmentation: Small black chromatophores over head; ca. 26–35 large stellate chromatophores in a double, uneven line on dorsum; a subsurface line of small chromatophores passing from mid-line of eye behind head, merging over top of gas bladder as black patch and continuing along dorsal surface of gut to caudal region; venter with double series of small chromatophores from vent to caudal; subsurface chromatophores from behind eye to anterior margin of gas bladder.[5]

JUVENILES

Minimum size unknown. Head 3.5–4.0 times in SL in "young" less than ca. 75 mm long.[2]

Age at maturity (minimum): Age group III.[3]

LITERATURE CITED

1. Hildebrand, S. F., and W. C. Schroeder, 1928:119.
2. Trautman, M. B., 1957:253–54.
3. Meyer, W. H., 1962:418.
4. Luce, W. M., 1933:102.
5. Fish, M. P., 1932:320.
6. Adams, C. C., and T. L. Hankinson, 1928:316.
7. Wright, A. H., and A. A. Allen, 1913:6.
8. Forbes, S. A., and R. E. Richardson, 1908:91.
9. Nash, C. W., 1908:32.
10. McCormick, L. M., 1892:15.
11. Reighard, J., 1920:15–18.
12. Shelford, V. E., 1937:119.
13. Hubbs, C. L., and Lagler, K. F., 1947:52.
14. Moore, G. A., 1957:84.
15. Fowler, H. W., 1906:163.
16. Massmann, W. H., 1958:4.
17. Jordan, D. S., and B. W. Evermann, 1896:188.
18. Harlan, J. R., and E. B. Speaker, 1956:78.
19. Hubbs, C. L., 1930:32.
20. Meek, S. E., and S. F. Hildebrand, 1910:254.
21. Riggs, C. D., and G. A. Moore, 1963:421–22.

Bagre marinus

Galeichthys felis

sea catfishes

Ariidae

Gafftopsail catfish

Bagre marinus **(Mitchill)**

ADULT Fig. 79 A)

D. I, 7; A. 22–28; P. I, 11–14; V. 6; vertebrae 20+30 (WRT).[6,10]

Body robust; head depressed; teeth villiform, in bands on jaws and palate; two pairs of barbels, one pair on lower jaw; maxillary barbels long, flattened, sometimes reaching nearly to base of ventrals. Dorsal and pectoral spines with extended filaments;[6] anal with a prominent V-shaped indentation on posterior margin.[2]

Dorsum steel blue, sides silvery, venter white; dorsal and anal white or bluish; caudal dusky or grey.

Maximum length ca. 571 mm.[6]

DISTRIBUTION AND ECOLOGY

Range: Cape Cod to northern South America.[3,7,12]

Area distribution: Chesapeake drainage north to Rock Point, Potomac River, Maryland.[6]

Habitat and movements: Adults—a bottom species of coastal waters and estuaries;[1] recorded from freshwater,[11] but most abundant between 5 and 30 o/oo;[4] leaves estuaries in fall, returns in spring.[4,9]

Larvae—retained in mouth of male parent; if removed demersal but sometimes hanging at surface.[1]

SPAWNING

Location: Probably mud flats.[1]

Season: May and June,[2] with spawning rarely lasting over 10 days.[4,5]

Fecundity: Ca. 20[2]–68.[5]

EGGS (Fig. 79 B)

Description: Carried in mouth of male, sometimes in spaces between branchial arches; number of eggs per male 2–55.

Ripe, ovarian eggs—longest diameter 15.0[1]–21.5[8] mm. Fertilized eggs—golden yellow;[8] oval or elliptical, rarely round;[2,5] longest diameter 15–26 mm; average longest diameter of 327 eggs, 19.5 mm.[5]

Development: At unspecified temperature. When embryo is 17 mm long, eye pigmented; tail free. At 20–25 mm, embryo sunken into egg; head twisted to side with only one eye visible; yolk vascular system well developed; caudal fin rays formed; pigment along dorsum.[1] Prior to hatching, 2 barbels on lower jaw differentiated; filaments of pectoral and dorsal fins formed.[2]

Incubation: Unknown.

YOLK-SAC LARVAE (Fig. 79 C-E)

Length at hatching ca. 45 mm TL.[5] Length at end of stage 78[4]–100 mm.[5]

Apparently larvae are retained in mouth of male parent until yolk is absorbed. Time period in mouth, beginning with fertilization, 42[2]–70 days. At 57 mm TL, choroid fissure faintly visible; dorsal spine ca. 1/4 TL.

Pigmentation: Black stippling on head, along dorsum, and in distinct lines along myomeres.[1]

JUVENILES

Minimum size ca. 80–100 mm TL.[5]

At time of yolk absorption, all adult characteristics visible.

Size at maturity (minimum): Females, 265 mm.[2]

LITERATURE CITED

1. Gudger, E. W., 1916:131–56.
2. Merriman, D., 1940:222, 238–41.
3. Briggs, J. C., 1956:18.
4. Gunter, G., 1945:36–7.
5. Gudger, E. W., 1918:31–46.
6. Hildebrand, S. F., and W. C. Schroeder, 1928:127, 129.
7. Fowler, H. W., 1953:51.
8. Gudger, E. W., 1919:122.
9. Gunter, G., 1938b:339.
10. Jordon, D. S., and B. W. Evermann, 1896:118.
11. Gunter, G., 1942:314.
12. Schultz, L. P., 1944:183.

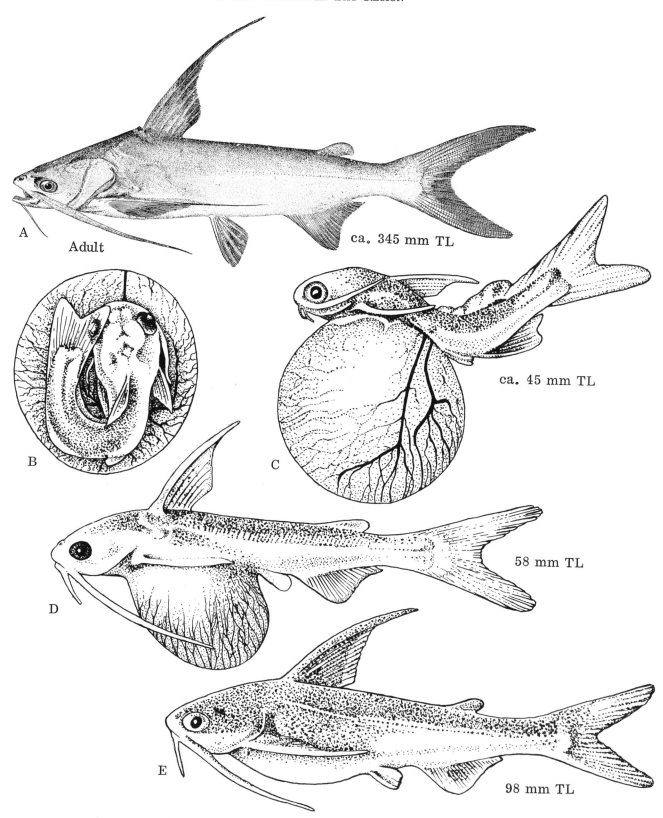

Fig. 79. *Bagre marinus,* gafftopsail catfish. A. Adult, ca. 345 mm TL. B. Egg just before hatching. Diameter 18.5 mm; head sunk into yolk; yolk with extensive vascular system. C. Yolk-sac larva, ca. 45 mm TL, recently hatched. D. Yolk-sac larva, 58 mm TL. E. Yolk-sac larva, 98 mm TL. (A, *Goode, et al., 1884: pl. 235. B-E, redrawn from Gudger, 1918: figs. 9–12.*)

ADULT (Fig. 80 A)

D. I, 7;[17] A. 19–20; P. I, 6–10 (WRT); V. 6.[18]

Body rather elongate, tapering to slender tail; head depressed, flattened above; 3 pairs of barbels, 2 pairs on lower jaw (WRT); maxillary barbels nearly as long as head;[17] posterior margin of anal not deeply indented.[6]

Steel-blue above, sides and belly silvery; lower fins plain.[17]

Maximum length ca. 610 mm.[2]

DISTRIBUTION AND ECOLOGY

Range: Cape Cod to Yucatan, Mexico[20] (records from Panama[9] are apparently in error. WRT).

Area distribution: Lower Chesapeake Bay.[5]

Habitat and movements: Adults—shallow, coastal water over sand or mud bottom during summer;[1] sometimes in schools.[13] Recorded from freshwater;[8,14,19] common in salinities up to 45 o/oo; maximum salinity 60 o/oo.[12] Maximum depth 90 feet.[1] In Texas found in bays in spring, departing to Gulf of Mexico in fall.[10]

Larvae—carried in mouth of male parent.[1,2]

Juveniles—apparently more numerous than adults in water of low salinity.[10,11]

SPAWNING

Location: In Gulf of Mexico area, back bays in water as shallow as 2–4 feet; probable salinity 13–30 o/oo.[3]

Season: Males observed with young in mouths from first of May to first week in August.[4,6,15]

Fecundity: Ca. 20–64 mature ova produced each season.[6]

EGGS (Fig. 80 B)

Description: Carried in mouth of male parent.[1] It has been suggested that (1) eggs are deposited initially in sandy depressions from which they are picked up by male parent,[6] and (2) females use flap-like modifications on ventral fins to assist in placing eggs directly in mouth of male.[1] Demersal when dropped by parent.[3]

Ripe, ovarian eggs—diameter 12–19 mm;[6] greenish;[4] micropyle single, stellate; ca. 0.5 mm in diameter.[3]

Fertilized eggs—maximum diameter 14–18 mm;[4] somewhat oval or elliptical, rarely round;[6] egg capsule with thin, colorless adhesive film; adhesiveness lost as development proceeds.[3]

Development: At 29.5–30.5 C.

4 hours—2-cell stage.
7 hours—4-cell stage.
9 hours—8-cell stage.
11 hours—16-cell stage.
20 hours—blastula.
29 hours—gastrula.

Development of embryos of unknown age:

5–7 mm—body straight; brain divisions, optic vesicles, and olfactory placodes visible; blood circulation established; movement in tail.
9–15 mm—embryo embedded in yolk; pectoral fins leaf-like; ventral buds formed; 3 gill buds present; vitelline vessels over 1/2 yolk; pigment lacking except in retina.
18–24 mm—pigment in pectoral region.
23–25 mm—6 barbels, olfactory bulbs, cerebral hemispheres, optic lobes, and 4 branchial arteries differentiated; light pigmentation developed.
38–45 mm—opercular cartilage and membrane formed; all external features developed; dorsal region of head, body, and tail pigmented.[4]

Just prior to hatching, membrane covering head becomes increasingly transparent.[18]

Incubation: Possibly ca. 30 days to hatching with larvae retained in parent's mouth an additional 2–4 weeks.[6]

YOLK-SAC LARVAE (Fig. 80 C)

Hatching size apparently ca. 29[1]–45 mm.[4] Size range described 29[1]–ca. 52 mm.[7,10] Duration of stage, up to ca. 55 days under laboratory conditions.

Yolk sac large, round; rays developed or developing in all fins except pectorals; eyes large.[6]

JUVENILES

Adult-like features apparently acquired at time of yolk absorption or shortly thereafter.

Size at maturity: Smallest mature female 126 mm; smallest brood male 142 mm.[1]

LITERATURE CITED

1. Lee, G., 1937:50–6.
2. Smith, H. M., 1907:63–4.

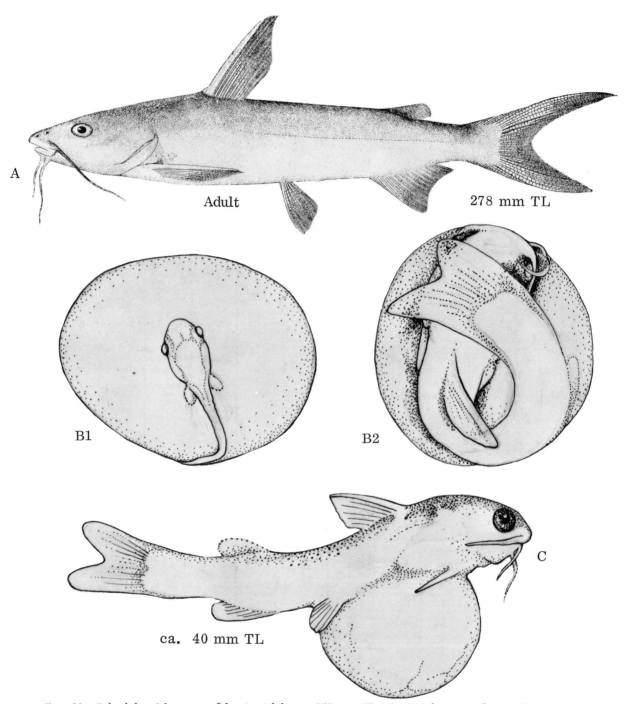

Fig. 80. *Galeichthys felis*, sea catfish. A. Adult, ca. 278 mm TL. B. Development of egg. Diameter ca. 14–17 mm; capsule removed. B1. Embryo. Tail coiling around yolk; most myomeres formed. B2. Late embryo. Barbels and fins present; dorsal pigmentation and well-developed hypural plate not illustrated. C. Yolk-sac larva, ca. 40 mm TL. (A, *Goode, et al., 1884: pl. 236. B, C, redrawn from photographs in Merriman, 1940: pl. 2.*)

3. Gunter, G., 1947:218–20.

4. Ward, J. W., 1957:296–97.

5. Massmann, W. H., 1958:5.

6. Merriman, D., 1940:239–45.

7. Atz, J. W., 1958:185.

8. Moore, G. A., 1957:138.

9. Briggs. J. C., 1958:259.

10. Gunter, G., 1945:38–40, 136.

11. Springer, V. G., and K. D. Woodburn, 1960:22.

12. Simmons, E. G., 1957:181.

13. Gunter, G., 1938b:339.

14. Henshall, J. A., 1895:211.

15. Lee, G., 1931:60.

16. Fowler, E., 1942:81.

17. Jordon, D. S., and B. W. Evermann, 1896:128.

18. Breder, C. M., Jr., 1948:45.

19. Gunter, G., 1942:314.

20. Hubbs, C. L., 1936:179.

Ictalurus catus

Ictalurus natalis

Ictalurus nebulosus

Ictalurus punctatus

Noturus gyrinus

Noturus insignis

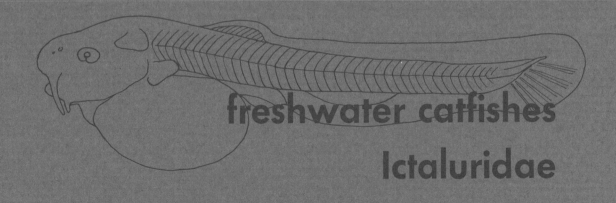

freshwater catfishes

Ictaluridae

Ictaluridae—freshwater catfishes

ADULT (Fig. 81 A)

D. I, 5 [8]–7; [19] A. 18–24; [4] P. I, 8–9; V. 8.[19] Body depth 3.5–4.75 times in TL; eye 6.9–7.84 times in HL; pectoral spine 2.22–2.41 times in HL.

Body rather robust, somewhat compressed; head depressed, broad; mouth very broad; lower jaw slightly included; teeth villiform, in bands on jaws; 4 pairs of barbels; pectoral spine stout, not as long as longest soft ray; caudal moderately forked.

Grayish above and on sides, white below; head olive-gray; anal whitish, edged with gray; [2,3] no distinct dark spots on body; breeding individuals bluish-black to dusky-blue above, whitish blue below.[4]

Maximum length ca. 610 mm.[2]

DISTRIBUTION AND ECOLOGY

Range: Coastal streams from Pennsylvania,[4] New York,[7] and Massachusetts [15] south to Lake Okeechobee, Florida,[3] and west along the Gulf coast to Escambia drainage system [22] (records from Texas [14,15] are apparently in error, WRT); introduced on Pacific Coast,[21] in Nevada,[7] and Lake Erie.[11]

Area distribution: Tidal tributaries of Chesapeake Bay north at least to Patapsco River.[2,10]

Habitat and movements: Adults—river channels [2] and streams in sluggish current; [4] also lakes,[6] ponds and bayous frequently over heavily silted bottom; [4] capable of extensive movement away from tagging sites, but with no apparent migratory tendencies.[18] Maximum salinity 14.5 o/oo.[9]

Juveniles—initially guarded by parents; remain in schools until end of first summer.[20]

SPAWNING

Location: Still or running water [8] in nests usually built near sand or gravel banks; nest large, up to 36 inches across and 18 inches deep.

Season: Late May to early June in Pennsylvania, lasting about 1 week; [12] probably in early July in California; [6] mid-July in captivity.[1]

Time: Eggs deposited sometime prior to 10:00 A.M. in one case reported.[16]

Temperature: Ca. 21 C.[8]

Fecundity: 1,000 [8]–3,500.[5]

EGGS (Fig. 81 B)

Description: Demersal,[1] sometimes covered with 5–6 inches of gravel; [12] deposited in masses, one of which measured 8 inches long, 4 inches wide, 1/2 to 3/4 inches thick, and contained ca. 2,000 eggs. Egg masses guarded and aerated chiefly by male parent.[1,12]

Ripe eggs—diameter 4.0–4.5 mm.[5]

Fertilized eggs—diameter ca. 4.2 mm; [16] spherical; [1] yellowish-white; [12] adhesive; yolk granular,[1] ca. 3.2 mm in diameter; [16] egg capsule double,[1] with adhesive, non-gelatinous and highly elastic outer envelope.[1,16] Ryder [1] mentions minute "corpuscles" within the perivitelline space.

Development: At unspecified temperature.

Second day—tail-free stage; rudimentary branchial arches and clefts, nasal pits, maxillary barbels and finfold developing; mouth not open.

Third day—tail with movement; vascular system, pectoral buds, and anlage of operculum present; finfold complete; mouth open; maxillary barbels developing as flat lobes at angle of mouth.

Fourth day—barbels of lower jaw forming.

Fifth day—incipient anterior dorsal fin and caudal rays evident.[1,16]

Incubation: 2–6 days at unspecified temperature.[1,12]

YOLK-SAC LARVAE (Fig. 81 C; Fig. 82 A–E)

Hatching length 9.0–9.75 mm TL. Specimens 1–4 days old vary randomly from 9.0–10.0 mm in length, while a specimen 5 days old is 13.6 mm in length.

Yolk oval at hatching. Nostril divided by 1st day. Choroid fissure no longer visible by 2nd day. Urostyle oblique at hatching. Four barbels evident on 1st day; nasal barbels first evident on 4th day. Heart prolonged downward over anterior pole of yolk at hatching; gas bladder evident by 4th day.

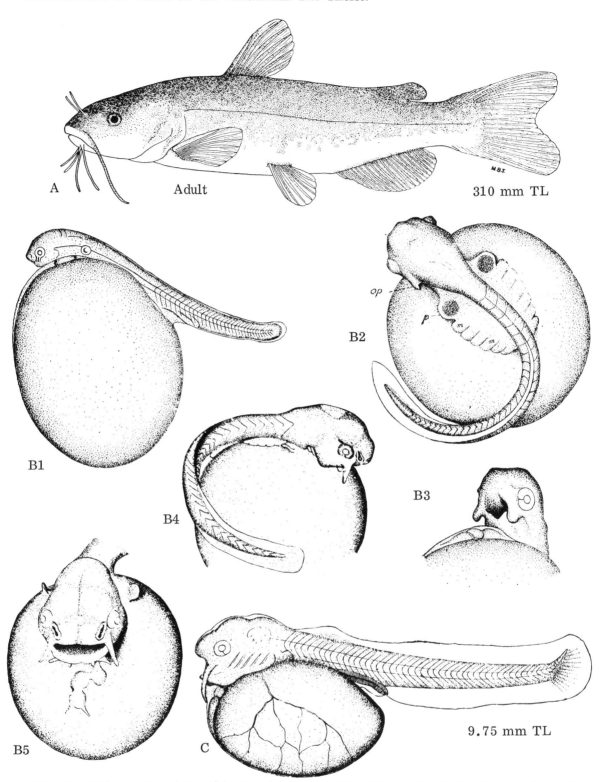

Fig. 81. *Ictalurus catus*, white catfish. A. Adult, 310 mm TL, 253 mm SL. B. Development of egg at unspecified temperature. Capsule diameter ca. 4.2 mm; yolk diameter ca. 3.2 mm; capsule removed. B1. Tail-free embryo, 2 days. Mouth closed. B2. Embryo, 3 days. Operculum (op), pectoral buds (p) and myomeres (m) developed. B3. Head of embryo, 3 days. Maxillary barbels at corners of open mouth; heart developed. B4. Embryo, 4 days. Mandibular barbels forming. B5. Late embryo, 5 days. View of head region. C. Yolk-sac larva, 9.75 mm TL, just hatched. (A, *reprinted from* THE FISHES OF OHIO, *by Milton B. Trautman, fig. 105. Copyrighted © 1957 by the Ohio State University Press. Used by permission of the author and the publisher.* B-C, *Ryder, 1887: fig. 155, 156, 159, 161–3.*)

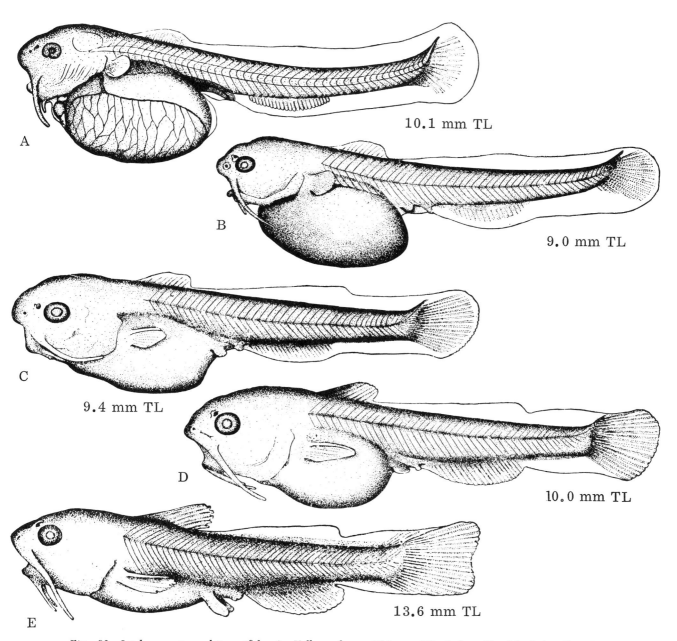

10.1 mm TL

9.0 mm TL

9.4 mm TL

10.0 mm TL

13.6 mm TL

Fig. 82. Ictalurus catus, white catfish. A. Yolk-sac larva, 10.1 mm TL, 1 day. Nasal barbel evident just anterior to posterior nares; internal structures illustrated. B. Yolk-sac larva, 9.0 mm TL, 2 days. C. Yolk-sac larva, 9.4 mm TL, 3 days. Ventral buds developed. D. Yolk-sac larva, ca. 10 mm TL, 4 days. E. Yolk-sac larva, 13.6 mm TL, 5 days. Nasal barbels elongating. *(Ryder, 1887: fig. 164–8.)*

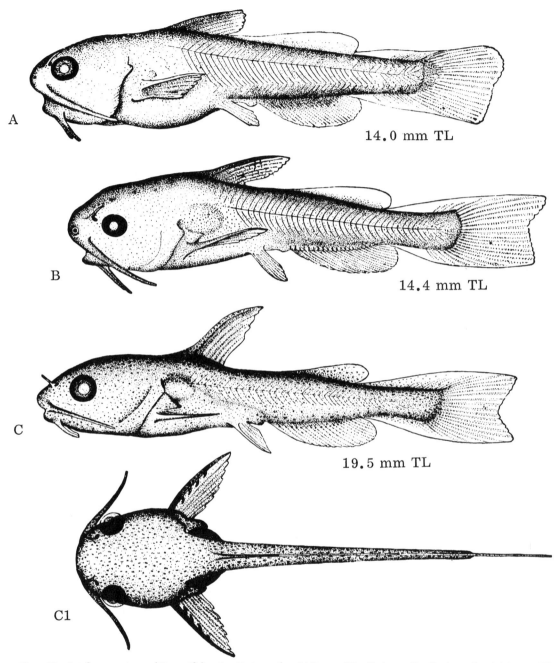

14.0 mm TL

14.4 mm TL

19.5 mm TL

Fig. 83. Ictalurus catus, white catfish. A. Prejuvenile, 14.0 mm TL, 9 days. B. Prejuvenile, 14.4 mm TL, 14 days. Gas bladder evident. C. Prejuvenile, 19.5 mm TL, 82 days. C1. Dorsal view of same. (*Ryder, 1887: fig. 169–72.*)

Incipient rays in caudal at hatching, in dorsal and anal by 1st day, and in pectorals by 2nd day; rays fully formed except in ventrals by 13.6 mm (5th day). Ventral buds evident on 2nd day. Finfold somewhat widened in region of incipient adipose by 2nd day, and with definite notch at posterior margin of developing adipose by 3rd day.[1]

PREJUVENILES (Fig. 83 A-C)

Specimens described ca. 14.0–19.5 mm TL.[1]

Eye 4.25–4.8 times in SL in "young."[2] Body tadpole-like; postscapular process evident at 19.5 mm. At ca. 14.0 mm, teeth present. Posterior end of gas bladder with indication of 2 lobes at 14.4 mm, evident externally as rounded prominence behind shoulder girdle at 19.5 mm. At ca. 14.0 mm, lower lobe of caudal shorter than upper. At 14.4 mm, lower lobe of caudal longer than upper; pectoral spine nearly horizontal; adipose free.

Pigmentation: Adult-like at 19.4 mm.[1]

JUVENILE

Minimum size described 24.9 mm SL.

Proportions as percent of SL in specimens 24.9–57.0 mm SL; Body depth 24.5–26.1; head length 26.8–29.1; anal length 24.6–26.4; predorsal length 32.9–35.6; pectoral spine 15.9–20.5; dorsal spine 17.5–20.5.[19] Ventrals inserted a little nearer tip of snout than base of caudal in "young."[2] Lateral line incomplete anteriorly at ca. 80 mm.[17]

Age and size at maturity (minimums): 1–2 years;[13] ca. 152[8]–211 mm FL.[6]

LITERATURE CITED

1. Ryder, J. A., 1887:534–6, 538–40.
2. Hildebrand, S. F., and W. C. Schroeder, 1928:129–30.
3. Carr, A., and C. J. Goin, 1955:62.
4. Trautman, M. B., 1957:418.
5. Menzel, R. W., 1945:366.
6. Murphy, G. I., 1951:467–68.
7. Moore, G. A., 1957:141.
8. La Rivers, I., 1962:487–88.
9. Schwartz, F. J., 1964b:14.
10. Massmann, W. H., 1958:5.
11. Hubbs, C. L., and K. F. Lagler, 1958:90.
12. Fowler, H. W., 1917b:33.
13. Sneed, K. E., and H. P. Clemens, 1963:608.
14. Eddy, S., 1957:148.
15. Briggs, J. C., 1958:260.
16. Ryder, J. A., 1883:226.
17. Fowler, H. W., 1935: Fig. 33.
18. McCammon, G. W., and C. M. Seeley, 1961:246.
19. Frey, D. G., 1951:18.
20. Migdalski, E. C., 1962:302.
21. Shapovalov, L., and W. A. Dill, 1950:386.
22. Bailey, R. M., H. E. Winn, and C. L. Smith, 1954: 130.

Yellow bullhead

Ictalurus natalis (LeSueur)

ADULT (Fig. 84 A)

D. I–6–7 [12] (WRT); A. 23–28,[12,16] possibly to 31;[11] P. I–8; V. 8.[12] Body depth 3.5–4.0 times in length. Head broad; mouth wide;[5] jaws nearly equal; four pairs of barbels (WRT). Posterior edge of pectoral spine with sharp serrations; caudal square or slightly rounded; adipose free posteriorly.

Yellow-olive, brown, brownish-black or slate-black above; sides yellowish, sometimes mottled; bright yellow, yellow-white or milk-white below;[7] mental barbels usually white, somewhat dusky;[1] fin membranes weakly pigmented;[13] anal fin usually with dark horizontal median band and dusky or black margin.[7]

Maximum length 465 mm.[14]

DISTRIBUTION AND ECOLOGY

Range: North Dakota to Great Lakes and St. Lawrence drainage, south to Gulf Coast, and southwest to eastern Oklahoma and northeastern Mexico;[7] introduced in Pacific states[8] and elsewhere.[7]

Area distribution: Tidal tributaries of Chesapeake Bay in Virginia.[4,15]

Habitat and movements: Adults—shallow water in lakes, ponds, streams, and swamps over gravel, sand, peat, or muck bottoms.[7]

Larvae and juveniles—guarded by parent fish until late July or August[6] or until young are ca. 50 mm long.[16]

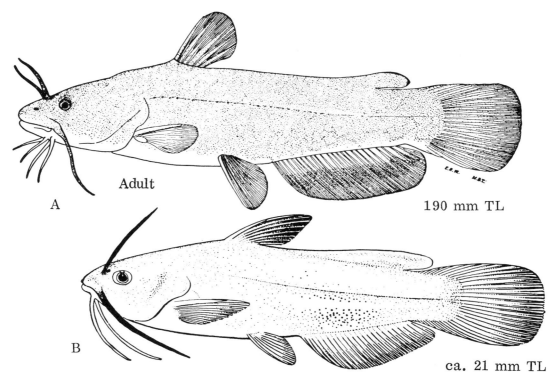

Fig. 84. *Ictalurus natalis*, yellow bullhead. A. Adult, 190 mm TL, 160 mm SL. B. Juvenile, ca. 21 mm TL. (A, *reprinted from* The Fishes of Ohio *by Milton B. Trautman, fig. 106. Copyrighted © 1957 by the Ohio State University Press. Used by permission of the author and the publisher.* B, *Fowler, 1935: fig. 34.*)

SPAWNING

Location: Depths of 18 inches to 4 feet [6] with eggs deposited in shallow, saucer-shaped nest [9,14] which is somewhat larger than fish itself [2] and usually located beside or beneath a bank, log, or tree root; [9] also in inclined burrows as much as 2 feet deep.

Season: Mid-May to early June,[1,2,6] and lasting ca. 2 weeks.[2]

Fecundity: 1,650 [3]–7,000.[6,14]

EGGS

Yellowish-white; adhesive, sometimes attached to roots in nest; number of eggs per nest ca. 300–700.[2]

Incubation: 5–10 days at unspecified temperature.[6]

LARVAE

Undescribed.

JUVENILES (Fig. 84 B)

Specimens described 17 [1]–21 mm TL.[10]

Preanal vertebrae 15; postanal vertebrae 27. Maxillary barbel equal to HL at 17 mm. Dorsal and pectoral spines well developed and caudal fin rounded at 17 mm.

Pigmentation: At 17 mm, small, round, closely set chromatophores on head, body, and fins; underside of head and body from lower jaw to vent colorless; chin barbels white.[1] Specimens less than ca. 50 mm long often entirely black above.[7]

Age at maturity: During 3rd year.[6]

LITERATURE CITED

1. Fish, M. P., 1932:350–51.
2. Fowler, H. W., 1917b:33.
3. Ulrey, L., C. Risk, and W. Scott, 1938:76.
4. Massmann, W. H., 1958:1.
5. Carr, A., and C. J. Goin, 1955:63–4.
6. Harlan, J. R., and E. B. Speaker, 1956:112.
7. Trautman, M. B., 1957:421, 423.
8. Moore, G. A., 1957:141.
9. Scott, W. B., 1954:65.
10. Fowler, H. W., 1935: Fig. 34.
11. Frey, D. G., 1951:18–20.
12. Sterba, G., 1959:280.
13. Forbes, S. A., and R. E. Richardson, 1920: 185–86.
14. Migdalski, E. C., 1962:307.
15. Raney, E. C., and W. H. Massmann, 1953:426, 428.
16. Eddy, S., and T. Surber, 1960:178.
17. Pearson, J. F. W., and E. M. Miller, 1935:123–4.

ADDITIONAL REFERENCES

Jenkins, R. M., E. M. Leonard, and G. E. Hall, 1952; Schaffman, R. J., 1955; Smith, H. M., and L. G. Harron, 1904; Vessel, M. F., and S. Eddy, 1941.

ADULT (Fig. 85 A)

D. I, 6;[20] A. 19–26;[22] P. I, 8[29]–9 (WRT); V. 8.[21] Body depth 3.5–4.3 times in "length;"[20] HL 3.2–3.6 times in "body";[23] pectoral spine 6.44–8.76 times in SL.[22]

Head somewhat narrow, depressed;[20] 4 pairs of barbels; jaws nearly equal (WRT). Caudal slightly emarginate; posterior end of adipose free from back;[10] pectoral spine with sharp teeth along posterior margin.

Light to dark brownish-yellow above, with or without an overlaid mottling of darker coloring; lighter on sides; white-gray or pinkish below;[20] mental barbels brownish (WRT).

Maximum length ca. 508 mm.[20]

DISTRIBUTION OF ECOLOGY

Range: Southern Canada through eastern United States to Gulf States and southern Florida;[13,27,28] widely introduced on Pacific coast of North America, in Europe, parts of USSR,[10] and Canada.[11]

Area distribution: Tidal tributaries of Chesapeake Bay in Virginia[7] and Maryland (RJM).

Habitat and movements: Adults—a schooling, bottom species,[25] sometimes forming dense aggregations.[15] Found over mud or among aquatic vegetation in ponds and sluggish rivers;[19] also reservoirs, swamps, ponds, and stagnant water; occasionally in clear, clean water (RJM); largely nocturnal in habits.[12] Maximum salinity 7.6 o/oo[1] (observed dying at 14.0 o/oo).[14]

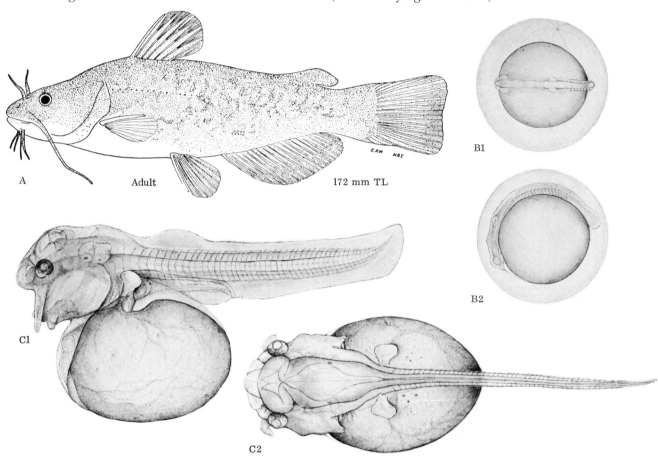

Fig. 85. Ictalurus nebulosus, brown bullhead. A. Adult, 172 mm TL, 142 mm SL. B. Egg, 2 days. Diameter ca. 3.0 mm; ca. 17 somites. B1. Dorsal view; stellate structure with micropyle in center frequently retained on egg capsule. B2. Lateral view. C. Embryo, 7 days. Egg capsule removed; tail bent over dorsum of head when egg intact. C1. Lateral view. C2. Dorsal view. (A, *reprinted from* THE FISHES OF OHIO, *by Milton B. Trautman, fig. 107. Copyright © 1957 by the Ohio State University Press. Used by permission of the author and the publisher. B, C, reprinted from* STAGES IN THE DEVELOPMENT OF *ICTALURUS NEBULOSUS, by Philip B. Armstrong, figs. 26, 40. Copyright © 1962 by the Syracuse University Press. Used by permission of the author and the publisher.*)

Larvae—in tight mass on bottom for 6 [24]–16 days, thereafter herded about in schools for some weeks.[2,16,23,25,33]

Juveniles—sometimes in schools throughout first summer among vegetation or near other suitable cover over more or less muddy bottoms.[12]

SPAWNING

Location: Sluggish, weedy, muddy streams and lakes [30] usually at depths of several inches to several feet.[2] In nests consisting of open excavations in sand, gravel, or, rarely, mud, and often in shelter of logs, rocks or vegetation; [12,27,32] in burrows up to 3 feet long excavated under roots of aquatic plants; [27] occasionally in cavities of old stumps, stovepipes, old pails,[19] and terra cotta pots.[18]

Season: Late spring in Maryland (RJM), early April to August or later throughout range,[2,3,4] and possibly occurring twice yearly.[2]

Time: Early morning [33] to 2:00 P.M.[2]

Temperature: Ca. 21–25 C.[2]

Fecundity: Ca. 2,000–13,800.[26]

EGGS (Fig. 85 B,C)

Description: Adhesive; [2] 50 [6]–10,000 or more per nest; [25] deposited in clusters (similar to masses of frog eggs) [23] as much as 4 inches long and 2.5 inches wide.[16] One or both parents usually attend clusters, often with oral agitation.[2,12,31]

Unfertilized eggs—single micropyle.[27]

Fertilized eggs—pale cream[2] pale yellow,[16] or light orange; [33] nearly transparent. Diameter ca. 3.0 mm,[2]

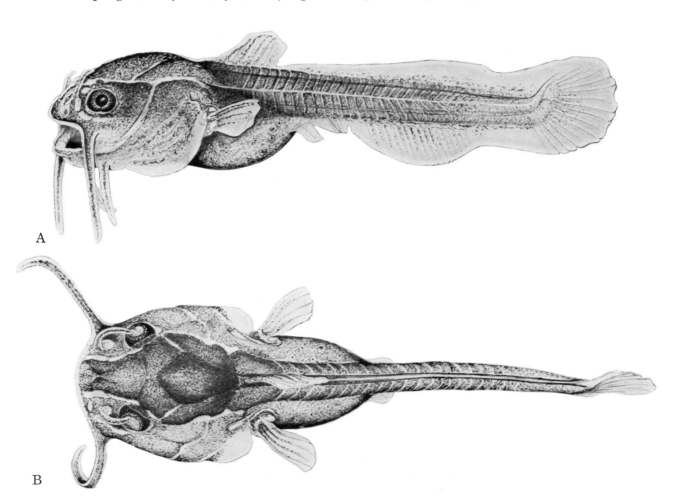

Fig. 86. *Ictalurus nebulosus,* brown bullhead. Yolk-sac larva, ca. 13–14 days from fertilization. A. Lateral view. B. Dorsal view. (*Reprinted from* STAGES IN THE DEVELOPMENT OF *ICTALURUS NEBULOSUS, by Philip B. Armstrong, fig. 51. Copyright © 1962 by the Syracuse University Press. Used by permission of the author and the publisher.*)

but varying in size from nest to nest often with a size difference of 1.0 mm.[29] Egg capsule transparent, thin; perivitelline space ca. 1/3 egg diameter.

Development: At 20–21 C.

1 hour, 12 minutes—blastodisc evident.
1 hour, 36 minutes—first cleavage.
3 hours—3rd cleavage.
6 hours—morula; blastoderm conspicuously high and dome-shaped.
1 day—embryonic shield evident.
2 days—ca. 14 somites, tail bud well defined; blastopore closed; brain division discernible but ventricles not evident; some movement established; anlagen of otoliths sometimes present.
5 days—pigment developing in eye; pectoral buds and barbels developing.
6 days—dorsal finfold elevated in region of future dorsal fin.[27]

Incubation: 5 days at 25 C;[32] 8 days at 20–21 C[27] (a report of "less than 20 hours" at ca. 25.0–25.0 C[33] is probably in error).

YOLK-SAC LARVAE (Fig. 86 A,B)

Hatching length 4.0[32]–8.0 mm.[19]

Caudal with incipient rays at hatching.[27] Barbels and spines developed by 3rd day.[16] On ca. 10th day, anterior edge of maxillary barbel serrated; incipient rays in dorsal, anal, and pectoral.

Pigmentation: Transparent and yellowish[16] or cream-white at hatching[2] with few chromatophores on head, yolk mass, and body;[27] by 2nd day, dorsal surface darkened; by 4th day, upper parts uniform bluish-black, under parts whitish.[16]

LARVAE

Undescribed except that "young" (possibly juveniles) are coal-black when they leave the nest.[17]

JUVENILES

Specimens described 22 mm TL.

At 22 mm, vertebrae 14+26; length to vent 9.9 mm; greatest depth 4.5 mm; maxillary barbel about as long as head.[8] "Young" with 6–10 well developed teeth on posterior edge of pectoral spine.[23]

Pigmentation: At 22 mm, top and sides of head, dorsal aspects of body, fins, and barbels covered with small, close set chromatophores; belly light.[8] "Young" jet-black.[12]

Age at maturity: 3 years.[9]

LITERATURE CITED

1. Schwartz, F. J., 1964b:14.
2. Breder, C. M., Jr., 1935:145–73.
3. Kendall, W. C., 1910:18.
4. Hildebrand, S. F., and I. L. Towers, 1929:121.
5. Kendall, W. C., 1904:408–9.
6. Fowler, H. W., 1917b:34.
7. Massmann, W. H., 1958:5.
8. Fish, M. P., 1932:350.
9. Nash, C. W., 1908:23.
10. Berg, L. S., 1949:920.
11. Atton, F. M., and R. P. Johnson, 1955:84.
12. Webster, D. A., 1942:162–3.
13. Briggs, J. C., 1958:260.
14. Springer, V. G., and K. D. Woodburn, 1960:23.
15. McAtee, W. L., and A. C. Weed, 1915:9.
16. Smith, H. M., and L. G. Harron, 1904:152–53.
17. Breder, C. M., Jr., 1932:131.
18. Breder, C. M., Jr., 1939a:368.
19. Eycleshymer, A. C., 1901:911–15.
20. La Rivers, I., 1962:492–93.
21. Sterba, G., 1962:384.
22. Hart, J. S., 1952:76, 78.
23. Forbes, S. A., and R. E. Richardson, 1920:187, 189.
24. Adams, C. C., and T. L. Hankinson, 1928:373.
25. Harlan, J. R., and E. B. Speaker, 1956:110.
26. Carlander, K. D., 1953:107.
27. Armstrong, P. B., 1962:1–8, Figs. 26, 40, 51.
28. Livingstone, D. A., 1951:51, 57.
29. Bachmann, F. M., 1914:356.
30. Wright, A. H., and A. A. Allen, 1913:16.
31. Gill, T., 1907b:446.
32. Smith, H. M., 1903:243.
33. Stranahan, J. J., 1910:29.

ADDITIONAL REFERENCES

Menzel, R. W., 1945; Titcomb, J. W., 1920; Vessel, M. F., and S. Eddy, 1941.

ADULT

D. I, 6; [27] A. 24–30; [5] P. I, 9; V. 8.

Body elongate, compressed posteriorly; [27] head slender, subconic, [6] with 4 pairs of barbels; [4] upper jaw longer than lower; eyes located in dorsal half of head. Anal fin base usually contained 3.2–4.0 times in SL; caudal fin deeply forked.

Silver-blue to dark steel-blue above, yellowish to milk-white ventrally; often with scattered, dark spots on body except in larger individuals.

Maximum length ca. 1168 mm. [5]

DISTRIBUTION AND ECOLOGY

Range: Prairie provinces of Canada and Hudson Bay region south to Florida and northern Mexico; [23] widely introduced in Atlantic and Pacific coast drainages. [17]

Area distribution: Pamunkey River, Virginia [9] and tidal freshwater in Susquehanna River, Maryland. [10]

Habitat and movements: Adults—chiefly in channels of large rivers (RJM) and lakes; [23] also ponds, bayous, [33] stagnant pools, [25] and swift, clear streams with gravelly shoals and riffles; [33] sometimes near waterfalls [23] or in pools below dams; [33] seldom in dense vegetation. Some populations apparently undertake spawning migrations in small streams [5] and individuals may make excursions of up to 180 miles in Mississippi River. [35] Maximum salinity 15.1 o/oo. [1]

Larvae—apparently guarded by male; [3,16] initially in mass on bottom, [3] later making excursions to surface. [12] Travel in schools for several days or weeks.

Juveniles—after dispersal, feed singly in quiet, shallow water over sand bars, around drift piles, and among rocks; [6] some winter under boulders in rather swiftly flowing water. [5]

SPAWNING

Location: Weedy places near lake shores, [2] under rock ledges [6] or in tunnels in submerged turf; [3] also small streams, [5] sometimes in very swift water; [21] in ponds, spawn in tin cans, nail kegs, and terra-cotta pots. [14,20]

Season: Early April [27] through July, [8,12] possibly to September, [26] sometimes with 2 spawning peaks per season. [24]

Time: 12:30–7:30 A.M. and 3:30–5:30 P.M., 8:50 P.M. under laboratory conditions.

Temperature: Ca. 21–29 C, optimum ca. 27 C. [12]

Fecundity: 1,600 [7]–70,000. [35]

EGGS (Fig. 87 B)

Description: Demersal; adhesive; deposited in large gelatinous masses [19] of 2,500–20,000. [29] Initially light [19] or golden yellow [11] becoming brownish-yellow with age. [31]

Fertilized egg—diameter, 3.53 mm; [16] average diameter with capsule removed, 3.2 mm; [19] egg capsule tough. [11]

Development: At 24.7–26.8 C.

50 minutes—blastodisc rounded, well-defined, raised moderately from yolk surface.

2 hours, 30 minutes to 3 hours, 15 minutes—2-cell stage.

3 hours to 4 hours, 30 minutes—8-cell stage.

5–7 hours—morula.

10 hours—early gastrula.

11–16 hours—germ ring formed; embryonic shield barely evident.

21 hours—blastoderm over 2/5 yolk; embryonic shield forward from dorsal lip region.

23 hours—embryonic shield elongate; incipient neural tube and notochord evident.

25 hours—blastoderm over 3/4 yolk; large yolk plug formed; embryonic keel, neural groove, and anlage of forebrain evident.

26 hours—anlage of optic vesicles, 3–5 somites.

ca. 27 hours—blastopore small; 10–11 somites, brain region evident; optic vesicles and auditory placodes visible.

ca. 30 hours—blastopore closed, 15–16 somites, optic cup, and lens formed, heart a straight tube; anlage of pectoral fin evident; Kupffer's vesicle formed.

34 hours—ca. 24 somites, heart 2-chambered; auditory vesicles large; Kupffer's vesicle nearly obliterated. [19]

ca. 48 hours (temperature unrecorded)—movement established; eyes "fairly well-formed". [25]

Incubation: 5–10 days at various temperatures; [13] ca. 7–10 days at ca. 24–26 C; 6–9 days at ca. 27–28 C. [12,14]

YOLK-SAC LARVAE (Fig. 87 C)

Minimum hatching size ca. 6.4 mm. [28] Duration of stage 3–6 days. [11] Specimens described 12.2–15.0 mm TL. [3]

Body slender at hatching. [16] Yolk mass conspicuously elongate, bluntly pointed posteriorly at ca. 13 mm, shorter and less pointed at 14.5 mm. Mouth well formed and with barbels at ca. 13 mm. [3]

Spines developed, [15] but not necessarily visible at or shortly after hatching. At ca. 13 mm, incipient rays in

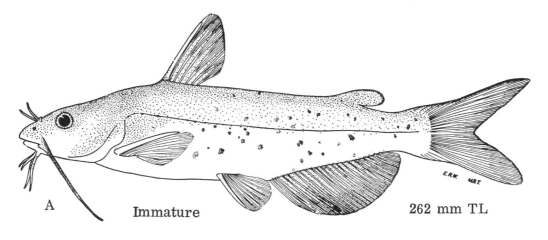

A   Immature   262 mm TL

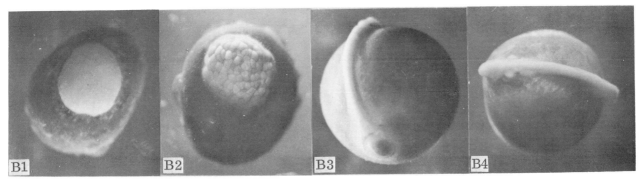

B1   B2   B3   B4

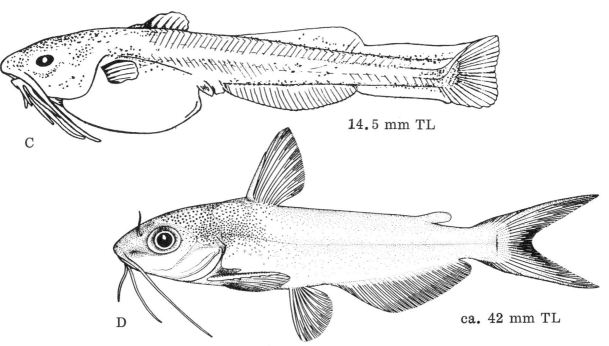

14.5 mm TL

C

D   ca. 42 mm TL

Fig. 87. *Ictalurus punctatus,* channel catfish. A. Immature, ca. 262 mm TL, 198 mm SL. B. Development of egg at 24.7–26.8 C. Diameter ca. 3.5 mm; capsule removed. B1. Blastodisc, 50 minutes. B2. Morula, 5 hours. B3. Early embryo, 27 hours. Just before closure of blastopore. B4. Tail-free embryo, 3.5 mm long, 34 hours. Pectoral buds pesent; ca. 24 somites formed. C. Yolk-sac larva, 14.5 mm TL. D. Juvenile, ca. 42 mm TL. (A, *reprinted from* THE FISHES OF OHIO *by Milton B. Trautman, fig. 104. Copyright © 1957 by the Ohio State University Press. Used by permission of the author and publisher. B, Saksena, Yamamoto and Riggs, 1961: fig. 1, 6, 11, 15, 19. C, Greeley and Bishop, 1932: fig. 3. D, Fowler, 1945: fig. 144.*)

dorsal; pectoral short, squarely truncate; ventrals present as short rounded lobes; anlagen of anal and adipose evident. Ventrals elongate at ca. 14.5 mm.[3]

Pigmentation: At hatching, body golden,[11,15] transparent;[21] yolk sac pink[14] or light amber.[16] At ca. 13 mm, body bright golden; chromatophores in triangular patch on head, in an ill-defined line on either side of mid-dorsal line to caudal base, and sometimes in a broken line along trunk and anal base. At ca. 14.5 mm, pigment present over most of snout and sides of head, in a line from head to caudal base, at all fin bases, and to some extent on fins.[3]

LARVAE

Apparently blue immediately after yolk absorption.[28]

JUVENILES (Fig. 87 A)

Minimum size described 32.6 mm TL. Maximum size attained at least 257 mm TL.[5]

At 32.6 mm, 16 preanal vertebrae; 28 postanal vertebrae. Body slender; head slightly convex above; maxillary barbels longer than head; pectoral spine ca. 2/3 HL; caudal forked; posterior margin of adipose free.

Pigmentation: Body nearly white with sparsely distributed melanophores; subsurface spots pronounced over stomach; chromatophores on all fins.[2] Young with or without spots at ca. 50–75 mm.[6]

Age and size at maturity: 2nd to 5th year;[11] minimum size ca. 178 mm.[18]

LITERATURE CITED

1. Schwartz, F. J., 1964b:14.
2. Fish, M. P., 1932:349.
3. Greeley, J. R., and S. C. Bishop, 1932:64–6, 68–9.
4. Carr, A., and C. J. Goin, 1955:61.
5. Trautman, M. B., 1957:415–17.
6. Harlan, J. R., and E. B. Speaker, 1956:106–7.
7. Dill, W. A., 1944:157.
8. Doze, J. B., 1925a:173.
9. Raney, E. C., and W. H. Massmann, 1953:426.
10. Howarth, J. N., 1961:49.
11. Davis, J., 1959:8–10.
12. Clemens, H. P., and K. E. Sneed, 1957:6, 7, 9.
13. Toole, M., 1951:7.
14. Canfield, H. L., 1947:28–9.
15. Lenz, G., 1947a:232.
16. Shira, A. F., 1917a:81, 83.
17. Moore, G. A., 1957:141.
18. Davis, J. T., and L. E. Posey, Jr., 1959:73.
19. Saksena, V. P., K. Yamamoto, and C. D. Riggs, 1961: 156–60.
20. Geibel, G. E., and P. J. Murray, 1961:101.
21. Surber, T., 1920:83.
22. Hay, O. P., 1895a:181.
23. Hubbs, C. L., and K. F. Lagler, 1949:72.
24. Marzolf, R. C., 1957:28.
25. Doze, J. B., 1925b:6, 12, 14.
26. Kendall, W. C., 1904:406.
27. Jordan, D. S., and B. W. Evermann, 1902:16.
28. McClellan, W. G., 1954:14.
29. Plosila, D. S., 1961:59–60.
30. Lenz, G., 1947b:4–6.
31. Brown, L., 1942:312.
32. Shira, A. F., 1917b:46.
33. Henshall, J. A., 1920:246.
34. Harrison, H. M., 1954:642.
35. Carlander, K. D., 1953:105.

ADDITIONAL REFERENCES

Adams, C. C., and T. L. Hankinson, 1928; Greenback, J., and M. A. Munson, 1949; Langlois, T. H., 1939; Murphree, J. M., 1940.

Tadpole madtom   *Noturus gyrinus* (Mitchill)

ADULT (Fig. 88)

D. I, 4–7; A. 12–18; C. 50–66 (total count); P. I, 5–9; V. 5–10; total vertebrae 32–37; precaudal vertebrae 8–9; gill rakers on first arch 5–10; branchiostegals 8–10.

Body variable, usually short and chubby, sometimes elongate.[11] Head short, deep, broad;[8] band of teeth on premaxillary with rounded edges; 4 pairs of barbels; jaw sub-terminal.[11] Adipose high; shallow notch between adipose and caudal often inconspicuous;[2] pectoral spine deeply grooved, non-serrate.[11]

Light-yellow to chocolate-brown or olive-gray above, sides lighter, venter yellow-white or white;[2,11] sides usually with a narrow, dark, lateral streak; vertical fins not dark-edged.[8]

Maximum length ca. 127.[4]

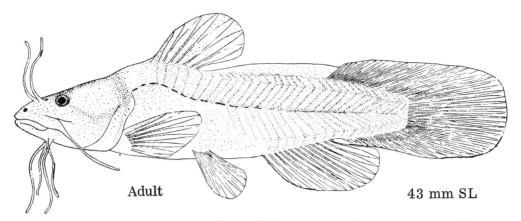

Adult   43 mm SL

Fig. 88. *Noturus gyrinus,* tadpole madtom. Adult, 43 mm SL. (*Trautman, 1948: pl. 1, fig. 3.*)

DISTRIBUTION AND ECOLOGY

Range: Manitoba to Texas in the west, east to Atlantic coast and north to New York and St. Lawrence River; [11] isolated populations may occur in the Appalachians; [2] introduced in New Hampshire, Massachusetts, Idaho, and Oregon.[5,11]

Area distribution: Tidal portions of Virginia rivers.[1,9]

Habitat: Adults—usually clear water in base- or low-gradient streams, springs, marshes, potholes, and lakes with soft bottom and abundant aquatic vegetation; [2,11] sometimes under sticks and stones.[3] Maximum salinity: 0.98 o/oo.[12]

SPAWNING

Location: Low- or base-gradient portions of streams, oxbows, glacial pothole lakes or artificial impoundments over bottoms of muck, mud, or organic debris; [6] recorded in water 3 feet deep.[10]

Season: May to July in northern localities.[4,6,7]

Fecundity: Ca. 50–93; [3] maximum eggs per nest 117.[13]

EGGS

Description: Deposited in clusters beneath boards or logs, in crawfish burrows, holes in mud, under roots,[6] and in old tin cans.[14]

Fertilized eggs: Average diameter ca. 3.5 mm.[13] Adhesive; in discrete clusters surrounded by a gelatinous matrix; yolk light-yellow.

LARVAE

Undescribed.

JUVENILES

Essentially adult-like at ca. 25 mm TL (WRT).

Age and size at maturity: Unknown.

LITERATURE CITED

1. Raney, E. C., and W. H. Massmann, 1953:427.
2. Trautman, M. B., 1957:443–45.
3. Evermann, B. W., and H. W. Clark, 1920:331–32.
4. Forbes, S. R., and R. E. Richardson, 1920:197–98.
5. Bisbee, L., 1955:56.
6. Trautman, M. B., 1948:172.
7. Wright, A. H., and A. A. Allen, 1913:6.
8. Mansueti, R. J., 1950:9.
9. Massmann, W. H., 1958:5.
10. Hankinson, T. L., 1908:208.
11. Taylor, W. R., 1956:115–17.
12. Keup, L., and J. Bayless, 1964:121.
13. Bailey, R. M., 1938:172.

ADULT (Fig. 89 A)

D. I, 5–7; A. 15–21; C. 56–67 (total count); P. I, 7–10; V. 8–10; precaudal vertebrae 9–11; caudal vertebrae 28–30.[8] Head 3.75–4.50 times in length.[3] Head depressed, lower jaw included; four pairs of barbels. Posterior serrae present on pectoral spine; caudal rounded or truncate.

Yellowish to slate-gray, lighter below with a narrow bridge of pigment in front of ventrals; fins lightly pigmented, especially near their bases; pectoral, anal, dorsal, and caudal fins frequently with dark margins.[8]

Maximum length ca. 178 mm.[9]

DISTRIBUTION AND ECOLOGY

Range: Lake Ontario drainage; Atlantic coastal streams from New York to Georgia; apparently introduced in New Hampshire and Tennessee River basin of Virginia.[8]

Area distribution: Tidal tributaries of Chesapeake Bay in Virginia.[6]

Habitat and movements: Adult—usually on riffles (WRT) of clear, rocky streams in water 6–18 inches or more deep. Beneath stones,[2] and planks,[1] occasionally in quiet water (WRT) and in muddy areas and deep holes, or among aquatic vegetation.[2,9] Apparently gregarious during winter.[1]
   Juveniles—among masses of *Potamogeton* and *Elodea*.[2]

SPAWNING

Location: Shallow excavations under stones, usually in quiet water above and below riffles.[1,4]

Season: Probably late June to early July in New York.

Fecundity: 53–223.[2]

EGGS (Fig. 89 B)

Description: Adhesive; deposited in compact masses 40–60 mm across, each containing 54[1]–200 eggs.[4]
   Ovarian eggs—orange, ca. 4.0 mm in diameter;[5] micropyle single.[1]
   Fertilized eggs—Diameter ca. 3.0[4]–6.0 mm;[1] very pale cream to yellowish-white[4] or yellow with orange tinge.

Development: At 19.8–25.7 C. At time of first caudal movement, egg capsule grayish, yolk whitish-yellow, and body pigment lacking. One day later, embryo 9.0 mm long, pectoral fins developing, and eye pigmented.[1]

YOLK-SAC LARVAE (Fig. 89 C-F; Fig. 90 A)

Hatching length 10 mm TL. Largest specimen described 17 mm.

Total myomeres at hatching 38; 9 myomeres to posterior base of dorsal; 29 myomeres behind dorsal.

Head rounded, mouth sub-terminal, all barbels developed at hatching. Yolk mass initially more or less round, becoming smaller and pear-shaped by 13 mm. Branchiostegals and operculum well developed at 17 mm.

Urostyle oblique; origin of dorsal finfold over 1st myomere at hatching; finfold notched posterior to incipient dorsal at 13 mm.

Pigmentation: Stellate chromatophores on dorsal surface of head and at base of maxillary barbel at hatching. At 13 mm, pigment developed on snout and continuous to anterior margin of incipient dorsal. At 13.25 mm, melanophores spread to origin of finfold and upper surface of yolk sac. At 17 mm, body entirely pigmented with exception of lower parts of head, ventral aspect of yolk sac, and 3 lowest pairs of barbels. By time of yolk absorption, juvenile characteristics essentially developed.[1]

LARVAE

Undescribed.

JUVENILES (Fig. 90 B)

Size range described 21[1]–30 mm TL.[7]

At 21 mm, dorsal surface pigmented. All upper barbels and proximal 1/4 of lower pairs pigmented. Unpigmented circular areas around eyes and above gill covers.[1] By ca. 30 mm, body adult-like, but head somewhat deeper.[7]

Age and size at maturity: Females 24 months; males possibly 12 months.[5]

LITERATURE CITED

1. Bowman, H. B., 1936:31–63.
2. Bowman, H. B., 1932:5–30.
3. Swain, J., and G. B. Kalb, 1883:640.
4. Fowler, H. W., 1917b:35.
5. Clugston, J. P., and E. L. Cooper, 1960:11.
6. Massmann, W. H., 1958:5.
7. Fowler, H. W., 1945: Fig. 163.
8. Taylor, W. R., 1956:189, 191.
9. Raney, E. C., 1950:171–72.

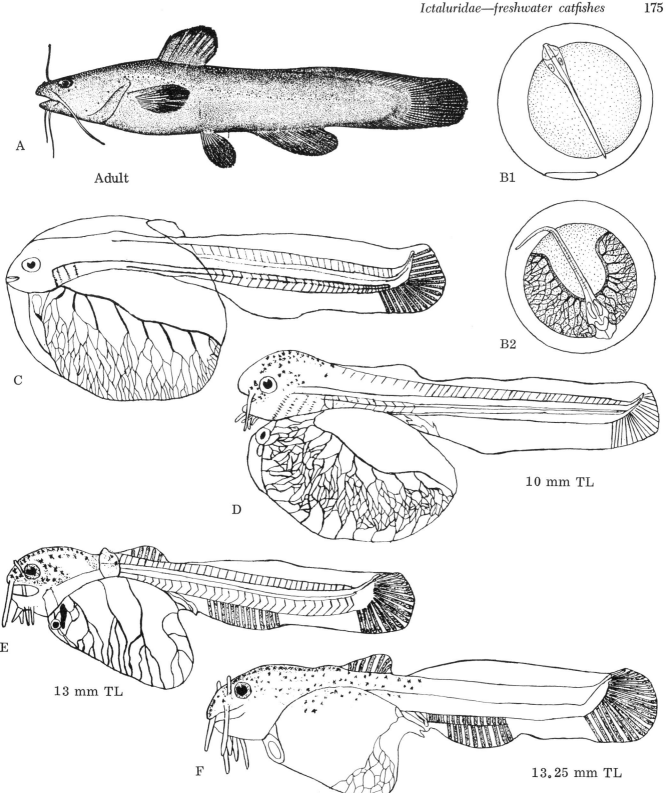

Fig. 89. Noturus insignis, margined madtom. A. Adult. B. Development of egg. Diameter 5–6 mm. B1. Early embryo, no pigmentation. B2. Embryo one day older. Eye pigmented; pectorals developed; embryo 9.0 mm long; yolk diameter 4 mm. C. Yolk-sac larva emerging from egg capsule. D. Yolk-sac larva, 10 mm TL, newly hatched. E. Yolk-sac larva, 13 mm TL, 2 days. F. Yolk-sac larva, 13.25 mm TL, 4 days. (A, *Truitt, Bean, and Fowler, 1929: fig. 6.* B, *redrawn from Bowman, 1936: pl. 11.* C-F, *Bowman, 1963: pl. 12–14.*)

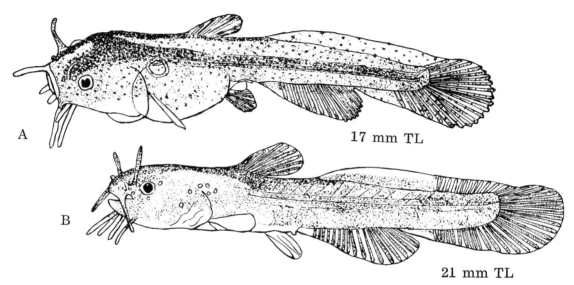

Fig. 90. *Noturus insignis*, margined madtom. A. Yolk-sac larva, 17 mm TL, 8 days. B. Juvenile, 21 mm TL. 16 days. (*Bowman, 1936: pls. 15–16.*)

BIBLIOGRAPHY

Abbott, Charles C. 1861. Description of a new species of *Chatoessus,* Cuv., from New Jersey. Acad. Nat. Sci. Phil., Proc. 12:365–6.

Adams, Charles C., and T. L. Hankinson. 1928. The ecology and economics of Oneida Lake fishes. Roosevelt Wild Life Annals 1(3/4):235–548, 244 figs.

Affleck, Robert J. 1950. Some points in the function, development and evolution of the tail in fishes. Zool. Soc. London, Proc. 120(Part 2):349–68.

Agassiz, Alexander. 1878a. On the young stages of some osseus fishes. Amer. Acad. Arts and Sci., Proc. 13(4):117–26, 2 figs., 2 pls.

———. 1878b. Embryology of the gar-pike. Science News 1(2):19–20.

———. 1879. The development of *Lepisosteus.* Part I. Amer. Acad. Arts and Sci., Proc. 14(4):65–76, 5 pls.

Ahlstrom, Elvert H., and Robert C. Counts. 1955. Eggs and larvae of the Pacific hake, *Merluccius productus.* U. S. Fish and Wildl. Serv., Fish. Bull. 56(99):295–329, 25 figs., 9 tables.

Alexander, Elizabeth C. 1961. A contribution to the life history, biology and geographical distribution of the bonefish, *Albula vulpes* (Linnaeus). Dana-Report No. 53, 51 p., 16 figs., 12 tables.

Alikunhi, K. H., and S. N. Rao. 1951. Notes on the metamorphosis of *Elops saurus* Linn. and *Megalops cyprinoides* (Broussonet) with observations on their growth. J. Zool. Soc. India 3:99–109, 2 figs.

Allen, B. M. 1909. The origin of sex-cells of *Amia* and *Lepidosteus.* Anat. Rec. 3(4):229–32.

———. 1911. The origin of sex-cells of *Amia* and *Lepidosteus.* J. Morphol. 22(1):1–36, 1 fig., 3 pls., 5 tables.

Allis, Edward Phelps. 1889. The anatomy and development of the lateral line system in *Amia calva.* J. Morphol. 2(3):463–566, 10 figs., Pls. 30–42.

———. 1899. On certain homologies of the squamosal, intercalar, exoccipitale and extrascapular bones of *Amia calva.* Anat. Anz., Jena, 12:49–72.

Alperin, Irwin M., and Richard H. Schaefer. 1964. Juvenile bonefish (*Albula vulpes*) in Great South Bay, New York. N. Y. Fish and Game J. 11(1):1–12, 2 figs., 4 tables.

American Fisheries Society. 1960. A list of common and scientific names of fishes from the United States and Canada. Second Edition. Report of the Committee on Names of Fishes, presented at the 89th Annual Meeting. Amer. Fish. Soc., Spec. Pub. No. 2, 102 p.

Anderson, William W., Jack W. Gehringer, and Frederick H. Berry. 1966. Family Synodontidae: Lizardfishes, p. 30–102, Fig. 8–35. *In* Fishes of the Western North Atlantic. Sears Found. for Mar. Res., Mem. 1(Part 5).

Anokhina, L. E. 1959. On the relationship between fecundity and the fat content of *Clupea harengus membras* L. C. R. Acad. Sci., U.S.S.R. 129(6):1417–20. (In Russian, Transl. Mar. Lab., Aberdeen, Transl. No. 735).

Aquatic Life. 1918. Breeding habits of the American mud minnow. Aquatic Life 4:12–3, 1 fig.

Armstrong, Philip B. 1962. Stages in the development of *Ictalurus nebulosus.* Syracuse University Press, Syracuse, New York, 8 p., 53 figs.

Atkins, Charles G. 1887. The river fishes of Maine, p. 673–728. *In* George B. Goode and Associates, History and methods of the fisheries. The fisheries and fishery industry of the United States. Vol. I (Section 5). U. S. Comm. Fish and Fisheries, Washington, D. C.

———. 1905. Culture of the fallfish or chub. Amer. Fish Cult. 2:189.

Atton, F. M., and R. P. Johnson. 1955. First records of eight species of fishes in Saskatchewan. Can. Field Natur. 69(3):82–4, 1 fig.

Atz, James W. 1958. A mouthful of babies. Animal Kingdom 61(6):182–6.

Babcock. Louis L. 1936. The tarpon. 4th Edition. Privately printed, Buffalo, N. Y., 174 + vii p.

Bachmann, Freda M. 1914. The migration of the germ cells in *Amiurus nebulosus.* Biol. Bull. 26(6):351–66, 2 pls.

Bade, Ernst. 1898. Der amerikanische Schlammfisch (*Amia calva* L.). Blätt. Aquar. Terr. Freun. 9:273–4, 1 pl.

———. 1902. Der Schlammfisch. Blätt. Aquar.-Terrar. Kunde 13:16–8, Figs. 2–4.

Bailey, Reeve M. 1938. The fishes of the Merrimack watershed. p. 149–85, 1 fig., 2 pls., 2 tables. *In* A biological survey of the Merrimack watershed. New Hampshire Fish and Game Dept., Surv. Rept. 3.

———. 1956. A revised list of the fishes of Iowa, with keys for identification. p. 325–77, 10 figs. *In* James R. Harlan and Everett B. Speaker, Iowa fish and fishing. 3rd Edition. Iowa State Conserv. Comm., Iowa.

———, Howard E. Winn, and C. Lavett Smith. 1954. Fishes of the Escambia River, Alabama and Florida, with ecological and taxonomic notes. Acad. Nat. Sci. Phila., Proc. 106:109–64, 3 tables.

Balfour, F. M., and W. K. Parker. 1881. On the structure and development of *Lepidosteus.* Roy. Soc. London, Proc. 33:112–9.

———, and ———. 1882. On the structure and development of *Lepidosteus.* Roy. Soc. London, Philos. Trans. 173:359–442, Pls. 21–39.

Balls, Ronald. 1951. Environmental changes in herring behavior: A theory of light avoidance as suggested by echo-sounding observations in the North Sea. J. Cons. Int. Explor. Mer. 17:274–98, 2 figs., 2 pls.

Bamford, T. W. 1941. The lateral line and related bones of the herring (*Clupea harengus* L.) Ann. Mag. Nat. Hist. (Ser. 2) 8:414–38, 13 figs., 1 pl.

Bassett, Howard M. 1958. Further life history studies of suckers in Shadow Mountain Reservoir, Grand County, Colorado. Abstract of Thesis. Colorado Coop. Fish. Resource Unit 4:28–30.

Battle, Helen I. 1940. The embryology and larval development of the goldfish (*Carassius auratus* L.) from Lake Erie. Ohio J. Sci. 40(2):82–93. 21 figs., 1 table.

Baxter, I. G. 1959. Fecundities of winter-spring and summer-autumn herring spawners. J. Cons. Int. Explor. Mer 25:73–80, 5 figs.

Bean, Tarleton H. 1892a. The fishes of Pennsylvania, with descriptions of the species and notes on their common names, distribution, habits, reproduction, rate of growth and mode of capture. E. K. Meyers Printing House, Harrisburg, Penn., viii + 149 p., 35 pls.

———. 1892b. Observations upon fishes and fish-culture. U. S. Fish. Comm., Bull. 10:49–61.

———. 1902. Food and game fishes of New York. N. Y. Forest, Fish and Game Comm., Rept. 7:251–460.

———. 1903. Catalogue of the fishes of New York. N. Y. State Mus. Bull.60 (Zool. 9):1–784.

Beard, J. 1889. "On the early development of *Lepidosteus osseus*. Preliminary notice." Roy. Soc. London, Proc. 46:108–18.

———. 1896. The yolk-sac, yolk and merocytes in *Scyllium* and *Lepidosteus*. Anat. Anz., Jena 12:334–47.

Beaven, G. Francis. 1960. Temperature and salinity of surface water at Solomons, Maryland. Chesapeake Sci. 1(1):2–11, 6 figs., 1 table.

Beckwith, Cora J. 1907. The early development of the lateral line system of *Amia calva*. Biol. Bull. 14(1):23–34, 3 pls.

Beebe, William. 1927. A tarpon nursery in Haiti. N. Y. Zool. Soc., Bull. 30(5):141–5.

———, and Gloria Hollister. 1935. The fishes of Union Island, Grenadines, British West Indies, with the description of a new species of star-gazer. Zoologica, New York, 19(6):209–24, Fig. 26–7.

———, and J. Tee-Van. 1928. The fishes of Port-au-Prince Bay, Haiti. Zoologica, New York, 10:1–279.

———, and ———. 1933. Field book of shore fishes of Bermuda. G. P. Putnam's Sons, N. Y., xiv + 337 p.

Berg, L. S. 1949. Freshwater fishes of the U. S. S. R. and adjacent countries. Vol. 2, 4th edition. Guide to the fauna of the U. S. S. R., No. 29:477–1328, Fig. 288–946. Acad. Sci. U. S. S. R., Zool. Inst. (Transl. from Russian, Israel Program for Sci. Transl., Jerusalem, 1964, vii + 496 p.)

Berry, Frederick H. 1959. Young jack crevalles (*Caranx* sp.) off the southeastern Atlantic coast of the United States. U. S. Fish and Wildl. Serv., Fishery Bull. 59(152):417–535, 99 figs.

———. 1964. Review and emendation of: Family Clupeidae, pp. 257–454. By Samuel F. Hildebrand, with emendations by others, and sections on *Harengula* by Luis R. Rivas and on *Dorosoma* by Robert R. Miller. (In) Fishes of the Western North Atlantic. Sears Foundation for Marine Research, New Haven, Connecticut, Memoir I, Part 3, 630 pp., Figs. 1–139 . . . Copeia 1964(4):720–30.

———, and Izadore Barrett. 1963. Gillraker analysis and speciation in thread herring, Genus *Opisthonema*. Inter-Amer. Trop. Tuna Comm. 7(2):113–90, 14 figs., 3 tables.

Bezrukova, E. A. 1938. Plodovitost' belomorshikh sel'dey. Zool. Zh. 17(1):17.

Bhattacharyya, R. N. 1957. The food and feeding habits of larval and post-larval herring in the northern North Sea. Scot. Home Dept., Mar. Res. 1957, No. 3, 14 p., append., 2 fig.

Bigelow, Henry B., and William C. Schroeder. 1940. Notes on New England fishes. Copeia 1940(2):139.

———, and ———. 1953. Fishes of the Gulf of Maine. U. S. Fish and Wildl. Serv., Fish. Bull. 53(74):vii + 577, 288 figs.

———, and W. Welsh. 1925. Fishes of the Gulf of Maine. U. S. Bur. Fish., Bull. (1924) 40(Part 1):1–567, 278 figs.

Bigelow, N. K. 1923. The food of young suckers (*Catostomus commersonii*) in Lake Nipigon. Univ. Toronto Stud., Biol. Ser., No. 24:81–115, 1 fig.

Bisbee, Lawrence. 1955. Records of the tadpole madtom, *Schilbeodes mollis*, and the black bullhead, *Ameiurus melas*, from Oregon and Idaho. Copeia 1955 (1):56.

Bishai, H. M. 1961. The effect of salinity on the survival and distribution of larvae and young fish. J. Cons. Int. Explor. Mer 26 (2):166–79, 4 figs.

Black, Virginia Stafford. 1951. II. Osmotic regulations in teleost fishes, p. 53–89, 2 tables. *In* W. S. Hoar, V. S. Black, and E. C. Black, Some aspects of the physiology of fish. Univ. Toronto, Biol. Ser. No. 59.

Blaxter, J. H. S. 1956. Herring rearing—II. The effect of temperature and other factors on development. Scot. Home Dept., Mar. Res., 1956, No. 5, 19 p., 4 figs., 11 tables.

———. 1957. Herring rearing—III. The effect of temperature and other factors on myotome count. Ibid. 1957, No. 1, 16 p., 5 figs., 8 tables.

———. 1960. The effect of extremes of temperature on herring larvae. J. Marine Biol. Ass. U. K. 39:605–8, 1 fig.

———. 1962. Herring rearing—IV. Rearing beyond the yolk-sac stage. Dept. Agr. and Fish. for Scot., Mar. Res. (1962), No. 1, 18 p., 10 figs., 2 tables.

———, and G. Hempel. 1961. Biologische Beobachtungen bei der Aufzucht von Herringsbrut. Helgoländer Wiss. Meeresunters. 7:260–83, 6 figs., 5 tables.

———, and ———. 1963. The influence of egg size on herring larvae (*Clupea harengus* L.). J. Cons. Int. Explor. Mer 28(2): 211–40, 19 figs., 2 tables.

———, and ———. 1966. Utilization of yolk by herring larvae. J. Marine Biol. Ass. U. K. 46:219–34, 4 figs., 3 tables.

———, and F. G. T. Holliday. 1963. The behavior and physiology of herring and other clupeids, p. 261–393, 24 figs., 11 tables. *In* F. S. Russell, Editor. Advances in marine biology. Vol. 1. Academic Press, New York.

Bodola, Anthony. 1955. The life history of the gizzard shad, *Dorosoma cepedianum* (LeSueur), in western Lake Erie. PhD Thesis, Ohio State Univ., xi + 130 p., 44 figs.

———. 1966. Life history of the gizzard shad, *Dorosoma cepedianum* (LeSueur), in Western Lake Erie. U. S. Fish and Wildl. Serv., Fish. Bull. 65(2):391–425, 15 figs.

Bolster, G. C., and J. P. Bridger. 1957. Nature of the spawning area of herrings. Nature, London, 179(4560):638.

Borodin, N. 1925. Biological observations on the Atlantic sturgeon (*Acipenser sturio*). Amer. Fish. Soc., Trans. 55:184–90.

Bowers, A. B., and F. G. T. Holliday. 1961. Histological changes in the gonad associated with the reproductive cycle of the herring (*Clupea harengus* L.) Dept. of Agr. and Fish. for Scot., Mar. Res. (1961), No. 5, 16 p., 2 figs., 16 plates.

———, and D. I. Williamson. 1951. Food of larval and early post-larval stages of autumn spawned herring in Manx waters. Mar. Biol. Sta. Pt. Erin, Rep. 63:17–26.

Bowman, Harvey Bird. 1932. A description and ecologic study of the margined mad tom, *Rabida insignis* (Richardson). MS Thesis, Cornell Univ., 41 p., 9 figs.

———. 1936. Further notes on the margined mad tom, *Rabida insignis* (Richardson), and notes on a kindred species, *Noturus flavus* (Rafinesque). PhD Thesis, Cornell Univ., vii + 99 p., 17 figs., 1 chart.

Boyar, H. C. 1965. Age, length and state of maturity of adult herring in subarea 5. Int. Comm. Northwestern Atlantic Fish., Doc. 40, 5 p.

Brachet, A. 1912. Recherches sur la gastrulation et l'origine de l'hypoblaste du tube digestif chez *Amia calva*. Zool. Jahrb. (Suppl. 15) 2:425–56, 1 pl.

Bragensky, R. Y. 1960. Early development of the carp. p. 129–49, 9 figs. *In* C. G. Krevanovski. Works on the early development of bony fishes (In Russian). Stud. A. N. Stevertsova Inst. Anim. Morphol., Soviet Acad. Sci., No. 28.

Brawn, Vivien M. 1960a. Seasonal and diurnal vertical distribution of herring (*Clupea harengus* L.) in Passamaquoddy Bay, N. B. J. Fish. Res. Bd. Canada 17(5):699–711, 5 figs., 3 tables.

———. 1960b. Survival of herring (*Clupea harengus* L.) in water of low salinity. Ibid. 17(5):725–6, 1 table.

———. 1960c. Temperature tolerance of unacclimated herring (*Clupea harengus* L.). Ibid. 17(5):721–3, 1 table.

Breder, Charles M., Jr. 1932. The breeding of bullheads in the aquarium. New York Zool. Soc., Bull. 35(4):128–31, 2 figs.

———. 1933a. Young tarpon on Andros Island. Ibid. 42(4):99–110.

———. 1933b. The development of the urostyle in *Umbra pygmaea* (DeKay). Amer. Mus. Novitates, No. 610, 5 p., 2 figs.

———. 1935. The reproductive habits of the common catfish, *Ameiurus nebulosus* (Le Sueur), with a discussion of their significance in ontogeny and phylogeny. Zoologica, New York, 19(4):143–85, 23 figs., 4 tables.

———. 1939a. Variations in the nesting habits of *Ameiurus nebulosus* (Le Sueur). Ibid. 24(25):367–77, 3 figs., 2 tables.

———. 1930b. The tiniest of tarpon now at the aquarium. New York Zool. Soc., Bull. 42(4):154–5.

———. 1944a. The metamorphosis of *Synodus foetens* (Linnaeus). Zoologica, New York 29(3):13–5, 1 fig.

———. 1944b. Materials for the study of the life history of *Tarpon atlantica*. Ibid. 29(19):217–52, 9 figs., 17 tables.

———. 1948. Field book of marine fishes of the Atlantic coast from Labrador to Texas. Revised Edition. G. P. Putnam's Sons, N. Y. xxxvii + 332 p., 16 pls.

———. 1962. On the significance of transparency in osteichthid fish eggs and larvae. Copeia 1962(3):561–7.

———, and R. F. Nigrelli. 1936. The winter movement of the land-locked alewife, *Pomolobus pseudoharengus* (Wilson). Zoologica, New York 21(13):165–75.

Brice, John J. 1898. A manual of fish-culture based on the methods of the United States Commission of Fish and Fisheries, with chapters on the cultivation of oysters and frogs. U. S. Comm. Fish., Rept. (1897), Appendix, 340 p.

Bridger, J. P. 1961. On the fecundity and larval abundance of Downs herring. Fish. Invest. London (Ser. 2) 23(3):1:30.

Brigidi, V., and A. Tafani. 1881. Embrologia del *Cyprinus auratus*. R. Inst. Stud. Sup. Prat. Perfez. Pubbl., Firenze. 1(Ser. 9):115–92.

Briggs, John C. 1956. The fishes of Florida and their distribution. Florida State Mus., Gainesville, Florida. 80 p. (mimeo).

———. 1958. A list of Florida fishes and their distribution. Florida State Mus., Bull. 2(8):223–318, 3 figs., 5 tables.

———. 1960. Fishes of worldwide (circumtropical) distribution. Copeia 1960(3):171–80.

Brimley, C. S. 1896. On the mud minnow (*Umbra pygmaea*) as an air breather. Amer. Nat. 30(359):944.

Brinley, Floyd J. 1937. Eggs of fresh-water fishes suitable for laboratory studies. Science 85(2213):527–8.

———. 1938. Eggs of fishes. Tabulae Biol. 16(1):51–9, 1 table.

Brook, George. 1885. On the development of the herring. Part 1. Fish. Bd. Scot., 3rd Ann. Rep. (1884), Append. F:32–51, 2 pls.

———. 1886a. The spawning period of British food-fishes. Ibid., 4th Ann. Rep. (1885), Append. F:242–54.

———. 1886b. On the development of the herring. Part II. Ibid. Append. F:31–43, 2 pls.

———. 1886c. Report on the herring of Loch Fyne and the adjacent districts during 1885. 4th Ann. Rept., Fish. Bd. Scotland, Appendix, pp. 41–61, 4 pls.

Brown, Leo. 1942. Propagation of the spotted channel catfish (*Ictalurus Lacustris Punctatus*). Kansas Acad. Sci., Trans. 45:311–14.

Bückman, A. 1950. Die Untersuchungen der Biologischen Anstalt über die ökologie der Heringsbrut in der südlichen Nordsee. II. Helgoland Wiss. Meeresunters. 2:171–205, 7 figs., 22 tables.

———, W. Harder, and G. Hempel. 1953. Unsere Beobachtungen am Hering, *Clupea harengus* L. (English summary). Kurz. mitt. Inst. Fischereibiol., Hamburg 3:22–42.

Bullen, G. E. 1909. Notes on the post-larval development of the German or Crucian carp (*Carassius vulgaris*). Hertfordshire Nat. Hist. Soc., Trans. 14:15–8.

Cable, L. 1948. Recent decline of shad in Hudson River due to failure of reproduction, not to overfishing, seek cause through science. U. S. Fish and Wildl. Serv., 4 p. (mimeo).

Cady, Earl R. 1945. Fish distribution, Norris Reservoir, Tennessee, 1943. I. Depth distribution of fish in Norris Reservoir. J. Tenn. Acad. Sci. 20(1):103–14, 5 figs., 2 tables.

Caldwell, David K. 1962. Development and distribution of the short bigeye, *Pseudopriacanthus altus* (Gill) in the Western North Atlantic. U. S. Fish and Wildl. Serv., Fish. Bull. 62 (203):103–49, 32 figs.

Canagaratnam, P. 1959. Growth of fishes in different salinities. J. Fish. Res. Bd. Canada 16(1):121–30, 1 fig.

Canfield, H. L. 1947. Artificial propagation of those channel cats. Progr. Fish. Cult. 9(1):27–30.

Carbine, W. F. 1943. The artificial propagation and growth of the common white sucker, *Catostomus c. commersonii,* and its value as a bait and forage fish. Copeia 1943(1):48–9.

Carbonnier, M. P. 1874. Le fondule (*Fundula cyprinodonta,* Cuv.). Mensuel de la Soc. D'acclimation, Paris, Bull. 3(1):665–71.

Carbonnier, P. 1872. Sur la reproduction et la development du poisson telescope (*Cyprinus macrophthalmus*), originaire dec la Chine. Hebd. Ass. Sci., Bull. France, 11:180–2; also C. R. Acad. Sci., Paris, 75:1127–9; and Soc. Acclim., Paris, Bull. (Series 9) 2:789–90.

———. 1873. On the reproduction and development of the telescope fish of China. Ann. Mag. Nat. Hist. 4 (Series 11): 76–7.

Carlander, Kenneth D. 1953. Handbook of freshwater fishery biology with the first supplement. Wm. C. Brown Co., Dubuque, Iowa, 429 p.

Carnes, W. C., Jr. 1958. Contributions to the biology of the eastern creek chubsucker, *Erimyzon oblongus* (Mitchill). MS Thesis, North Carolina State College, viii + 69 p., 9 pls.

Carr, Archie, and Coleman J. Goin. 1955. Guide to the reptiles, amphibians and freshwater fishes of Florida. Univ. Florida Press lx + 341 p., 30 figs., 67 pls.

Carufel, Louis H., and Arthur Witt. 1963. Range extension of the gizzard shad, *Dorosoma cepedianum,* into North Dakota. Copeia 1963(1):178.

Chen, Shisan C. 1926. The development of the goldfish, *Carassius auratus,* as affected by being out of water, in distilled water, and in solutions of alcohol. China J. Sci. and Arts 4(6):294–303, 3 figs.

Clark, F. N. 1885. Notes on experiments in penning shad and taking eggs at Battery Station, Havre de Grace, Maryland in 1883. U. S. Fish. Comm., Rep. (1883)11:1045–50.

Clemens, Howard P., and Kermit E. Sneed. 1957. The spawning behavior of the channel catfish *Ictalurus punctatus.* Fish and Wildl. Serv., Spec. Sci. Rep.-Fish. No. 219, iii + 11 p., 3 tables.

Clugston, James P., and Edwin L. Cooper. 1960. Growth of the common eastern mad tom, *Noturus insignis* in central Pennsylvania. Copeia 1960(1):9–16, 5 figs., 4 tables.

Coker, R. E. 1921. A record of young tarpon. Copeia No. 93: 25–6.

Cole, Leon J. 1905. The German carp in the United States. U. S. Bur. Fish., Rep. (1904):523–641, 3 pl.

———. 1906. The status of the carp in America. Amer. Fish. Soc., Trans. (1905):201–6.

Coleman, N. 1872. Another note on the same. Change of temperature in water containing recently fertilized shad eggs. Amer. Nat. 6:493.

Collins, A. S. 1871. Shad eggs. Amer. Nat. 5:441.

Colton, John B., Jr., Kenneth A. Honey, and Robert F. Temple. 1961. The effectiveness of sampling methods used to study the distribution of larval herring in the Gulf of Maine. J. Cons. Int. Explor. Mer 26(2):180–90, 8 figs., 2 tables.

———, and R. F. Temple. 1961. The enigma of Georges Bank spawning. Limnol. and Oceanogr. 6(3):280–91.

Cooper, Gerald P. 1935. Some results of forage fish investigations in Michigan. Amer. Fish. Soc., Trans. 65:132–42, 3 figs., 2 tables.

———. 1936. Age and growth of the golden shiner (*Notemigonus crysoleucas auratus*) and its suitability for propagation. Papers Mich. Acad. Sci., Arts and Letters 21:587–97, 3 figs., 5 tables.

Cooper, Richard A. 1965. An unusually large menhaden, *Brevoortia tyrannus* (LaTrobe), from Rhode Island. Amer. Fish. Soc., Trans. 94(4):412, 1 fig.

Couch, Jonathan. 1869. A history of the fishes of the British Islands. Vol. IV. Groombridge and Son, London, iv + 439 p.

Crawford, D. R. 1923. The significance of food supply in the larval development of fishes. Ecology 4(2):147–53, 7 figs., 1 table.

Crossman, E. J. 1960. Variations in number and asymmetry in branchiostegal rays in the family Esocidae. Canadian J. Zool. 38(2):363–75, 2 figs., 7 tables.

———. 1962a. The redfin pickerel, *Esox a. americanus* in North Carolina. Copeia 1962(1):114–23, 6 figs., 3 tables.

———. 1962b. The grass pickerel, *Esox americanus vermiculatus* LeSueur in Canada. Life Sci. Div., Roy. Ontario Mus., Contrib. No. 55, iii + 29 p., 10 figs. 7 tables.

———. 1966. A taxonomic study of *Esox americanus* and its subspecies in eastern North America. Copeia 1966(1):1–20, 5 figs., 3 tables.

———, Keen Buss. 1965. Hybridization in the family Esocidae. J. Fish. Res. Bd. Canada 22(5):1261–92, 3 figs., 14 tables.

Cunningham, J. T. 1888. Eggs and larvae of teleosteans. Roy. Soc. Edinburgh, Trans. 33(1):97–136, 2 figs., 7 pls.

———. 1889. Studies on the reproduction and development of teleostean fishes occurring in the neighborhood of Plymouth. J. Mar. Biol. Ass. U. K. 1:10–54.

———. 1910. On the marine fishes and invertebrates of St. Helena. Zool. Soc. London, Proc. (1910):86–131, 6 figs., 4 pls.

Das, N., and S. N. Tibbo. 1962. On the feeding and growth of young herring (*Clupea harengus* L.) in captivity. J. Fish. Res. Bd. Canada 19:981:3.

Davis, Jackson. 1959. Management of channel catfish in Kansas. State Biol. Surv. and Forestry, Fish and Game Comm., Univ. Kansas, Mus. Nat. Hist., Misc. Publ. No. 21, 56 p., 8 figs.

Davis, James T., and Lloyd E. Posey, Jr. 1959. Length at maturity of channel catfish (*Ictalurus lacustris*) in Louisiana. Southeastern Ass. Game and Fish Comm., Proc. 12th Ann. Conf. (1958):72–4, 2 tables.

Davis, William S. 1957. Ova production of American shad in Atlantic coast rivers. U. S. Fish and Wildl. Serv., Res. Rep. No. 49, ii + 5 p., 3 tables.

Day, L. R. 1957a. Vertebral numbers and first year growth of Canadian Atlantic herring (*Clupea harengus* L.) in relation to water temperature. Fish. Res. Bd. Canada, Bull. 3:165–75, 2 figs., 4 tables.

———. 1957b. Populations of herring in the southern Gulf of St. Lawrence. Ibid. p. 121–37, 5 figs., 10 tables.

———. 1957c. Populations of herring in the northern Gulf of St. Lawrence. Ibid. p. 103–19, 5 figs., 10 tables.

Dean, Bashford. 1893a. Note on the spawning conditions of the sturgeons. Zool. Anz. 16(436):473–5.

———. 1893b. "Recent experiments in sturgeon hatching on the Delaware." N. Y. Acad. Sci., Trans. 13:69–74,

———. 1894. Recent experiments in sturgeon hatching on the Delaware. U. S. Fish. Comm., Bull. (1893) 13:335–9, 1 fig.

———. 1895a. The early development of gar-pike and sturgeon. J. Morphol. 11(1):1–62, 4 pls., 4 figs.

———. 1895b. Fishes, living and fossil. An outline of their forms and probable relationships. Columbia Univ., Biol. Ser. 3. Macmillan and Co., N. Y., 300 p., 344 figs.

———. 1895c. The early development of *Amia*. Quart. J. Microscop. Sci. 38(4):413–44, 13 figs., 3 pls.

———. 1896. On the larval development of *Amia calva*. Zool. Jahrb. (Abth. Syst.) 9(5):639–72, 11 pls.

———. 1899. On the dogfish (*Amia calva*), its habits and breeding. Comm. Fisheries, Game and Forest, New York, 4th Ann. Rep. (1898):246–56, 8 figs., 1 pl.

deBeer, G. R. 1924. The prootic somites of *Heterodontus* and *Amia*. Quart. J. Microscop. Sci. 68(1):17–38, 16 figs.

DeBruine, Harvey. 1937. The embryology of the spleen in *Amia calva*. Papers Mich. Acad. Sci., Arts and Letters 22:573–92, 3 pls.

Dees, Lola T. 1961. Sturgeons. U. S. Fish and Wildl. Serv., Fishery Leaflet No. 536, 8 p., 2 figs.

DeJean, James Allen. 1951. Some factors affecting the reproduction of the chain pickerel, *Esox niger* LeSueur, in ponds. MS Thesis, Alabama Polytechnic Inst., 52 p., 3 pls., 15 tables.

Delaval, A. 1899. Elevage de poissons télescopes de la Chine et du Japon à Saint-Max-Lez-Nancy. Soc. Acclim. Paris, Bull. 46:345–8.

Delsman, H. C. 1926. Fish eggs and larvae from the Java Sea. Treubia 8(3/4):389–412, 17 figs.

Dence, W. A. 1937. Part II. Preliminary reconnaissance of the waters of the Archer and Anna Huntington Wild Life Forest Station and their fish inhabitants. Roosevelt Wild Life Bull. 6(4):610–71, Fig. 301–18.

———. 1940. Part III. Progress report on a study of the dwarf sucker (*Catostomus commersoni utawana*) Ibid. 7(3):221–33, Fig. 60–3.

———. 1948. Life history, ecology and habits of the dwarf sucker, *Catostomus comersonnii utawana* Mather, at the Huntington Wildlife Station. Ibid. 8(4):81–150, Fig. 15–25, 16 tables.

Desrochers, J. E. 1904. Poisson-castor (*Amia ocellicaudata*). Natur. Canad. 31:38–9.

deSylva, Donald P., and W. P. Davis. 1963. White marlin, *Tetrapturus albidus*, in the Middle Atlantic Bight, with observations on the hydrography of the fishing grounds. Copeia 1963(1):81–99, 23 figs., 5 tables.

———, Frederick A. Kalber, Jr., and Carl N. Shuster, Jr. 1962. Fishes and ecological conditions in the shore zone of the Delaware River estuary, with notes on other species collected in deeper water. Univ. Del. Mar. Lab., Info. Ser., Pub. No. 5, ii + 164 p., 41 figs., 50 tables.

Dick, Myvanwy M. 1964. Suborder Esocoidea. p. 550–60, Fig. 145–9. *In* Fishes of the western North Atlantic. Sears Found. for Mar. Res., Mem. 1(Part 4).

Dill, William A. 1944. The fishery of the lower Colorado River. Calif. Fish and Game 30(3):109–211, Fig. 45–82.

Dmitrieva, E. N. 1957. Morpho-ecological analysis of two species of goldfish, p. 102–70, 9 fig., 17 tables. *In* C. V. Emelianov (Editor), Works on the early development of bony fishes (In Russian). Stud. A. N. Severtsova Inst. Anim. Morphol., Soviet Acad. Sci., No. 16.

Doan, Kenneth H. 1938. Observations on dogfish (*Amia calva*) and their young. Copeia 1938(4):204.

Dobie, John, O. Lloyd Meehean, S. F. Snieszko, and George N. Washburn. 1956. Raising bait fishes. U. S. Fish and Wildl. Serv., Circ. 35, iii + 124 p.

———, ———, and G. N. Washburn. 1948. Propagation of minnows and other bait species. Ibid. 12, 113 p.

Dovel, William L., Alice Jane Mansueti, and Eben H. Oldmixon. 1956. Notes on the identification of five species of juvenile herring, with a new artificial key to the species. Ches. Biol. Lab., Solomons, Md., Ref. 65–101, 13 p., 10 figs.

Doze, J. B. 1925a. The barbed trout of Kansas. Amer. Fish. Soc., Trans. 55:167–83.

———. 1925b. Barbed trout of Kansas or propagating the spotted channel catfish in Kansas ponds. Kan. Fish and Game Dept., Bull. No. 8, 22 p.

Duge, F. 1903. Heringseier im Magen der Schellfische. Mitt. Deutsch. Seefischerei Ver., Berlin 19:416.

Dunn, Horace D. 1897. On the occurrence of large numbers of larval herring at the surface. J. Mar. Biol. Ass. U. K. 5:184–5.

Dymond, J. R. 1964. A history of ichthyology in Canada. Copeia 1964(1):2–33.

Eddy, Samuel. 1957. How to know the freshwater fishes. Wm. C. Brown Co., Dubuque, Iowa, vi + 253 p., 615 figs.

———, and Thaddeus Surber. 1947. Northern fishes with special reference to the upper Mississippi Valley. Revised (2nd) edition. Univ. Minn. Press, Minneapolis, Minn. xii + 276 p., 57 figs.

———, and ———. 1960. Northern fishes with special reference to the upper Mississippi Valley. Revised Edition. Charles T. Bradford Co., Newton Centre, Mass. xii + 276 p., 57 figs.

Edsall, Thomas A. 1964. Feeding by three species of fishes on the eggs of spawning alewives. Copeia 1964(1):226–7.

Edwards, Linder A. 1964. The origin of pharyngeal teeth of the carp (*Cyprinus carpio* Linnaeus). PhD Thesis, Ohio State Univ., 85 p., 7 pls.

Ehrenbaum, E. 1904. Eier und larven von fischen der Deutschen Bucht. III. Fische mit festsitzenden Eiern. Wiss. meeresuntorsuch. Kiel (Abt. Helgoland) n.s., 6(2):127–200, Pl. 3–16, 1 fig.

————. 1909. Eier und larven von Fischen. Part 2. Nordisches Plankton. Kiel und Leipzig, Verlag von Lipsius und Tischer. pp. 217–413, figs. 83–148.

Eigenmann, Carl H. 1890. On the egg membrane and micropyle of some osseus fishes. Mus. Comp. Zool., Bull. 19(2):129–54, 3 pls.

Ellis, Robert W. 1956. Tarpon cooperative research and program, progress report, 56–20. Marine Lab., Univ. Miami, 13 p. (mimeo).

Ellison, W. A., Jr. 1951. The menhaden. pp. 85–107. In Survey of marine fisheries of North Carolina. Univ. North Carolina Press, Chapel Hill.

Elser, H. J., and R. J. Mansueti. 1961. Notes on the chain pickerel in Maryland. Md. Dept. Res. and Educ., Chesapeake Biol. Lab., Rep. No. 61–14, 13 p.

Embody, G. C. 1918. Artificial hybrids between pike and pickerel. J. Heredity 9(6):253–6, 2 pls.

English, Thomas S. 1952. Growth of the carp, Cyprinus carpio Linnaeus, in Clear Lake, Iowa. Iowa St. College, J. Sci. 24(4):537–40.

Erdman, Donald S. 1960a. Notes on the biology of the bonefish and its sport fishery in Puerto Rico. Paper prepared for 5th International Game Fish Conf., Miami Beach, Florida. Multilith.

————. 1960b. Larvae of tarpon, Megalops atlantica, from the Añasco River, Puerto Rico. Copeia 1960(2):146.

Erkkila, Leo F., James W. Moffett, Oliver B. Cope, Bernard R. Smith, and Reed S. Nielson. 1950. Sacramento-San Joaquin Delta fishery resources: Effect of Tracy Pumping Plant and Delta Cross Channel. Spec. Sci. Rep.—Fish. No. 56, iii + 109 p., 12 figs., 27 tables.

Evermann, Barton Warren, and Howard Walton Clark. 1920. Lake Maxinkuckee: A physical and biological survey. Vol. I. Dept. Conserv., State of Indiana, Pub. 7, 660 p.

————, and Millard C. March. 1902. The fishes of Puerto Rico. U. S. Fish. Comm., Bull. (1900) 20:51–350, 52 pls., 112 figs.

Ewart, James Cossar. 1883. The early history of the herring. Nature 29:105–7.

————. 1884a. Natural history of the herring. Fish. Bd. Scot., 2nd Ann. Rep. (1883), Appendix F:61–73, 6 pls.

————. 1884b. Note on deserted spawning grounds of the herring. Roy. Soc. Edinburgh, Proc. (1884):270–3.

————. 1884c. On the natural and artificial fertilization of herring ova. Roy. Soc. London, Proc. 36:450–61; also U. S. Fish. Comm. Bull. 4:193–7; and Nature 29:538–40.

————. 1886. Are herring ova likely to develop normally on the deep offshore fishing banks? Fish. Bd. Scot., 4th Ann. Rep. (1885), Appendix F (2):43–6.

————. 1888. On the hatching of herring ova in deep water. Roy. Soc. Edinburgh, Proc. 9:47–54.

Eycleshymer, Albert Chauncey. 1899. The cleavage of the egg of Lepidosteus osseus. Anat. Anz., Jena, 16:531–6.

————. 1901. Observations on the breeding habits of Ameiurus nebulosus. Amer. Nat. 35(419):911–8.

————. 1903. The early development of Lepidosteus osseus. Univ. Chicago, Decennial Pub. 10:261–75, 2 pls.

————, and B. M. Davis. 1897. The early development of the epiphysis and paraphysis in Amia. J. Comp. Neurol. 7(1): 45–70, 1 pl.

————, and J. M. Wilson. 1906. The gastrulation and embryo formation in Amia calva. Amer. J. Anat. 5(2):133–62, 4 pls.

Fage, Louis. 1920. Engraulidae, Clupeidae. Rep. Danish Oceanogr. Exped. 1908–1910, No. 6, 140 p., 50 figs.

Farran, G. P. 1938. On the size and number of ova in Irish herring. J. Cons. Int. Explor. Mer 13:91.

Farrin, A. E., L. W. Scattergood, and C. J. Sindermann. 1957. Maintenance of immature sea herring in captivity. Prog. Fish Cult. 19:188–9.

Ferguson, T. B., and P. W. Downes. 1876. Report of the Commissioners of Fisheries of Maryland to the General Assembly. J. F. Wiley, State Printer, Annapolis, 52 p., 7 figs.

Fearnow, E. C. 1925. Goldfish: Their care in small aquaria and ponds. U. S. Comm. Fish. Rep. for 1924 (Append. 7):445–58, 6 figs.

Fingerman, Sue Whitsell, and Royal D. Suttkus. 1961. Comparison of Hybognathus hayi Jordon and Hybognathus nuchalis Agassiz. Copeia 1961(4):462–7, 1 fig., 1 table.

Fish, Charles J., and Martin W. Johnson. 1937. The biology of the zooplankton population in the Bay of Fundy and Gulf of Maine with special reference to production and distribution. J. Biol. Bd. Canada 3(3):189–322.

Fish, Marie Poland. 1932. Contributions to the early life histories of sixty-two species of fishes from Lake Erie and its tributary waters. U. S. Bur. Fish., Bull. 47(10):293–398, 144 figs., 4 tables.

Fitch, John E. 1950. Life history notes on the early development of the bonefish, Albula vulpes (Linnaeus). Calif. Fish and Game 36(1):3–6, 2 figs.

Forbes, Stephen Alfred. 1878. Notes on the development of Amia. Amer. Ass. Adv. Sci., Proc. 27:296–8.

————, and Robert E. Richardson. 1908. The fishes of Illinois. Nat. Hist. Surv. Ill. No. 3, cxxxi + 357 p., 76 figs.

————, and ————. 1920. The fishes of Illinois. Ibid. 2nd Edition. cxxxvi + 357 p., 76 figs.

Ford, E. 1929. Herring investigations at Plymouth. VII. On the artificial fertilization and hatching of herring eggs under known conditions of salinity with some observations on the specific gravity of the larvae. J. Mar. Biol. Ass. U. K. 16:43–8.

————. 1930. Herring investigations at Plymouth. VIII. The transition from larva to adolescent. Ibid. 16:723–52, 12 figs., 7 tables.

Forney, John L. 1957. Bait fish production in New York ponds. New York Fish and Game J. 4(2):150–94.

Foster, Nathan W., and Charles G. Atkins. 1869. First Report—1867. Rep. Comm. of Fish., State of Maine (1867–1868):1–96.

Fowler, Edna. 1942. Embryology of the sea catfish, *Galeichthys felis* (Abstract). La. Acad. Sci., Proc. 6:81.

Fowler, Henry W. 1906. The fishes of New Jersey. New Jersey State Mus., Ann. Rep. (1905):34–477, 103 pls.

———. 1909. A synopsis of the Cyprinidae of Pennsylvania. Acad. Nat. Sci. Phila., Proc. (1908–9)60:517–53, 1 pl.

———. 1911. The fishes of Delaware. Ibid. 63:3–16.

———. 1912. Some features of ornamentation in fresh-water fishes. Amer. Nat. 46:470–6, 1 pl.

———. 1914. Notes on the fishes at Ocean City, Maryland. Copeia No. 2:2–3.

———. 1917a. Shufeldt's new mud minnow. Ibid. No. 50:94–6.

———. 1917b. Some notes on the breeding habits of local catfishes. Ibid. No. 42:32–6, 1 fig.

———. 1929. Notes on the fishes of New Jersey. Acad. Nat. Sci. Phila., Proc. 80:607–14.

———. 1931. Fishes obtained by the Barber Asphalt Co. in Trinidad and Venezuela in 1930. Ibid. 83:392, 1 fig.

———. 1935. Notes on South Carolina freshwater fishes. Charleston Mus. (South Carolina), Contrib. No. 7, 28 p., 54 figs.

———. 1945. A study of the fishes of the southern Piedmont and Coastal Plain. Acad. Nat. Sci. Phila., Monogr. 7, viii + 408 p., 313 figs.

———. 1948. A list of the fishes recorded from Pennsylvania. Revised edition. Bd. Fish. Comm., Commonwealth Penn., Bull. No. 7:3–26.

———. 1953. The shore fishes of the Colombian Caribbean. Caladasia 6(27):43–73, 3 figs.

———. 1956. Fishes of the Red Sea and Southern Arabia. Vol. I. Branchiostomida to Polynemida. The Weizman Science Press. Israel. iii + 240 p., 117 figs.

———. 1959. Fishes of Fiji. Gov. of Fiji, Suba, Fiji, vii + 670 p., 246 figs.

Franklin, Dwight. 1914. Some fish of the middle west. Amer. Mus. J. 14:37.

Frey, David G. 1951. The fishes of North Carolina's Bay Lakes and their intraspecific variation. J. Elisha Mitchell Sci. Soc. 67(1):1–44, 2 figs., 20 tables.

Fridriksson, Arni, and Olav Aasen. 1950. The Norwegian-Icelandic herring tagging experiments. Fiskeridrektoratets Skrifter, Serie Havundersketser (Rep. Norwegian Fish. and Mar. Invest.) 9(11):1–43,9 figs.

———, and G. Timmermann. 1951. Some remarks on the eggs of herring (*Clupea harengus* L.) and capelin (*Mallotus villosus* (O.F. Müll.)) in Icelandic waters. J. Cons. Int. Explor. Mer 17(3):261–3, 2 figs.

Fukuda, Hirowaza. 1935. The influence of light on the carp and the goldfish egg and their development [in Japanese]. Yôshoku Kaisha 5(3/4):55–8.

Fulleborn, F. 1894. Bericht über eine zur Utersuchung der Entwickelung von *Amia, Lepidosteus* und *Necturus* unternommene Reise nach Nord-America. Sitzungsberichte der Königlich Preussischen Akademie der Wissenschaften zu Berlin. 41:1055-70.

Galkov, A. A. 1958. Some data on the influence of the behavior of the Atlantic-Scandian herring on its catch by the pelagic trawl [in Russian]. Ryb. Khoz. 34(11):8–12, 4 figs.

Ganssle, David. 1966. Fishes and decopods of San Pablo and Suisun Bays, p. 64–94, 13 figs., 1 table. *In* D. W. Kelly (compiler), Ecological studies of the Sacramento-San Joaquin estuary. Part I. Zooplankton, zoobenthos, and fishes of San Pablo and Suisun Bays, zooplankton and zoobenthos of the Delta. State of Calif., Resources Agency, Dept. of Fish and Game. 133 p.

Gehringer, Jack W. 1959a. Early development and metamorphosis of the ten-pounder, *Elops saurus* Linnaeus. U. S. Fish. and Wildl. Serv., Bull. 59(155):619–47, 32 figs.

———. 1959b. Leptocephalus of the Atlantic tarpon, *Megalops atlanticus* Valenciennes, from offshore waters. Quart. J. Fla. Acad. Sci. (1958) 21(3):235–40, 1 fig.

Geibel, G. E., and P. J. Murray. 1961. Channel catfish culture in California. Prog. Fish Cult. 23(3):99–105, 1 pl.

Gerking, Shelby D. 1947. The use of minor post-glacial drainage connections by fishes in Indiana. Copeia 1947(2):89–91, 1 fig.

Gibbs, Robert H., Jr. 1959. A synopsis of the postlarvae of western Atlantic lizard-fishes (Synodontidae). Copeia 1959(3):232-6, 2 figs.

———. 1963. Cyprinid fishes of the subgenus *Cyprinella* of *Notropis*. The *Notropis whipplei-analostanus-chloristius* complex. Ibid. 1963(3):511–28 3 figs., 5 tables.

Gilbert, Carter R. 1961. *Notropis semperasper,* a new cyprinid fish from the upper James River system, Virginia. Copeia 1961(4):450–6, 1 fig., 4 tables.

Gill, Theodore. 1906. Le Fondule (*Fundula cyprinodonta*) of Carbonnier an *Umbra*. Science, n.s., 24(625):818–9.

———. 1907a. The family of Cyprinids and the carp as its type. Smith. Misc. Coll. 48:195–217, Pls. 45–58.

———. 1907b. Parental care among fresh-water fishes. Smith. Inst., Ann. Rep. (1905):403–531, 98 figs., 1 pl.

———. 1907c. The tarpon and lady-fish and their relatives. Smith. Misc. Coll. 48:31–46, 7 figs., 5 pls.

Gilpin, J. Bernard. 1863. On the food fishes of Nova Scotia. No. 1. On the common herring (*Clupea elongata*). Nova Scotian Inst. Nat. Sci., Trans. 1(1):4–11.

Goode, G. Brown. 1879. The natural and economic history of the American menhaden. U. S. Comm. Fish. and Fisheries, Rept. of the Comm. (1877) 5(Appendix A):xii + 530, 31 pl.

———. 1884. The food fishes of the United States, p. 163–682, 10 fig. *In* G. B. Goode and Associates. The fisheries and fishery industries of the United States. Section 1(Part 3), U. S. Comm. Fish and Fisheries, Washington, D. C.

Gopinath, K. 1946. Notes on the larval and postlarval stages of fishes found along the Trivandrum coast. Nat. Inst. Sci. India, Proc. 12(1):7–21, 7 figs.

Gordon, Malcolm S. 1948. A possible function of the urostyle in immature *Umbra pygmaea*. Copeia 1948(3):224.

Gosline, William A. 1948. Some possible uses of x-rays in ichthyology and fishery research. Copeia 1948(1):58-61.

Gowanloch, James N. 1933. Fishes and fishing in Louisiana. La. Dept. Conserv., Bull. 23:1–638.

Graham, J. J. 1956. Observations on the alewife, *Pomolobus pseudoharengus* (Wilson), in freshwater. Univ. Toronto, Biol. Ser. No. 62, 43 p., 20 figs., 5 tables.

———, and H. C. Boyar. 1966. Ecology of herring larvae in the coastal waters of Maine. Int. Comm. North Atlantic Fish., Spec. Pub. No. 6:625–34.

Graham, M. 1936. Investigations of the herring of Passamoquoddy and adjacent regions. J. Biol. Bd. Canada 2(2):94–140.

Graham, T. 1962. A relationship between growth, hatching and spawning in Canadian Atlantic herring (*Clupea harengus* L.). J. Fish. Res. Bd. Canada 19(5):985–7.

Gray, W. B. 1923. *Umbra pygmaeas.* Aquatic Life 7(6):67.

Greeley, J. R. 1928. Fishes of the Oswego watershed, p. 84–107, 12 pls., 1 table, *In* A biological survey of the Oswego River system. Suppl. To 17th Ann. Rep., Conserv. Dept., State of New York (1927).

———. 1929. Fishes of the Erie-Niagara watershed, p. 150–88, 8 pls. *In* A biological survey of the Erie-Niagara watershed. State of New York, Conserv. Dept., Supplement to 18th Ann. Rep. (1928).

———. 1930. Fishes of the Lake Champlain watershed, p. 44–87, 16 plates, *In* A biological survey of the Champlain watershed. Suppl. to 19th Ann. Rep., Conserv. Dept., State of New York.

———. 1935. Fishes of the watershed, with annotated list, p. 63–101, 4 pls. *In* A biological survey of the Mohawk-Hudson watershed. Suppl. to 24th Ann. Rep., Conserv. Dept., State of New York (1934).

———, and Sherman C. Bishop. 1932. Fishes of the area with annotated list. pp. 54–92, 3 figs., 19 pls., *In* A biological survey of the Oswegatchie and Black River systems. (Including also the lesser tributary streams of the upper St. Lawrence River and northeastern Lake Ontario). Suppl. to 21st Ann. Rep., Conserv. Dept., State of New York (1931).

———, and G. Willard Greene. 1931. Fishes of the area with annotated list, p. 44–95, 12 pls. *In* A biological survey of the St. Lawrence watershed (including the Grass, St. Regis, Salmon, Chateaugay systems and the St. Lawrence between Ogdensburg and the International boundary). State of New York, Conserv. Dept., Supplement to 20th Ann. Rept. (1930).

Green, S. 1874. Hatching of shad eggs. Amer. Fish. Soc., Trans. 18:75–6.

Greenback, John, and Melvin A. Munson. 1949. Size and maturity of channel catfish. Upper Mississippi River Conserv. Comm., Tech. Comm. Fish., Prog. Rep. 3, p. 28–31.

Grimm, Wilbur Winfield. 1937. The development of the fins of the goldfish (*Carassius auratus*). PhD Thesis, Ohio State Univ., 58 p., 5 pls., 2 tables.

Gross, R. W. 1953. Some observations on the landlocked alewife, *Pomolobus pseudoharengus* (Wilson), in New Jersey. New Jersey Dept. Conserv. and Econ. Dev., Fish. Surv., Rept. No. 2 (1951):157–64.

———. 1959. A study of the alewife *Alosa pseudoharengus* (Wilson) in some New Jersey Lakes, with special reference to Lake Hapatcong. MS Thesis, Rutgers Univ., New Brunswick, 52 p.

Gudger, E. W. 1916. The gaff-topsail (*Felichthys felis*). A sea catfish that carries its eggs in its mouth. Zoologica, New York, 11(5):125–48, Figs. 20–31.

———. 1918. Oral gestation in the gaff-topsail catfish, *Felichthys felis*. Carnegie Inst. Wash., Pub. No. 252:25–32, 4 pls.

———. 1919. The ovary of *Felichthys felis*, the gaff-topsail catfish: Its structure and function. Ibid. 281:111–28, 4 pls., 1 fig.

Gunter, Gordon. 1938a. Notes on invasion of freshwater of fishes of the Gulf of Mexico, with special reference to the Mississippi-Atchafalaya River system. Copeia 1938(2):69–72.

———. 1938b. Seasonal variations in abundance of certain estuarine and marine fishes in Louisiana, with particular reference to life histories. Ecol. Monogr. 8:313–46, 16 figs., 3 tables.

———. 1942. A list of the fishes of the mainland of North and Middle America recorded from both freshwater and sea water. Amer. Midl. Nat. 28(2):305-26, 4 tables.

———. 1945. Studies on marine fishes of Texas. Pub. Inst. Mar. Sci. 1(1):1–190, 11 figs., 75 tables.

———. 1947. Observations on breeding of the marine catfish, *Galeichthys felis* (Linnaeus). Copeia 1947(4):217–23, 1 fig.

———, and J. Y. Christmas. 1960. A review of literature on menhaden with special reference to the Gulf of Mexico menhaden, *Brevoortia patronus* Goode. U. S. Fish and Wildl. Serv., Spec. Sci. Rep.—Fish. No. 363, 31 p., 7 tables.

Halkett, Andrew. 1907. Note on the European carp. Ottawa Natur. 21:71.

Hamai, Ikusô. 1941. A study of the growth of the fish, *Cyprinus carpio* L. Sci. Rep. Tôholu Imp. Univ., 4th Ser. (Biol.) 16(1): 17–89, 13 figs., 36 tables.

Hammer, Ralph C. 1942. The homing instinct of the Chesapeake shad, *Alosa sapidissima* (Wilson), as revealed by a study of scales. MS Thesis, Univ. Md., 45 p., 8 figs.

———. 1943. Maryland commercial fish hatchery operations 1943. Dept. Res. and Educ., Chesapeake Biol. Lab., Solomons, Md., Pub. No. 60, 16 p.

Hankinson, Thomas L. 1908. Fish of Walnut Lake, p. 198–216. *In* T. L. Hankinson, C. A. Davis, and J. G. Needham, A biological survey of Walnut Lake, Michigan. State Bd. Geol. Surv. Michigan, Rep. (1907).

———. 1910. Ecological notes on the fishes of Walnut Lake, Michigan. Amer. Fish. Soc., Trans. 40:195–206.

———. 1919. Notes on life histories of Illinois fish. Ill. Acad. Sci., Trans. 12:132–50, 6 figs.

Harder, W. 1952. Zur postembryonalen Entwicklung des Darmes beim Hering (*Clupea harengus* L.). Zh. Anat. u. Entwgesch. 116:379–98.

———. 1953. Zum formwachstum des Herings (*Clupea harengus* L.). Zh. Morphol. Ökol. Tiere. 42:209–24.

———. 1954. Die Entwicklung der Respirationsorgare beim Hering (*Clupea harengus* L.). Zh. Anat. Entwgesch. 118: 102–23.

———. 1960. Vergleichende Untersuchunger zur Morphologie des Darmes bei Clupeoidae. Zh. Wiss. Zool. 163:65–167.

Hardy, A. C. 1924. The herring in relation to its animate environment. Part I. The food and feeding habits of the herring with special reference to the East Coast of England. Minst. of Agr. and Fish., London, Fish. Invest., Ser. 2, 7(3):1–53, 11 figs.

Harlan, James R., and Everett B. Speaker. 1956. Iowa fish and fishing. 3rd Ed. State Conserv. Comm., Iowa, 377 p.

Harrington, Robert W., Jr. 1947a. The early life history of the bridled shiner, *Notropis bifrenatus* (Cope). Copeia 1947(2): 97–102, 1 fig., 1 table.

————. 1947b. The breeding behavior of the bridled shiner, *Notropis bifrenatus*. Ibid. (3):186–92, 1 fig.

————. 1948. The life cycle and fertility of the bridled shiner, *Notropis bifrenatus* (Cope). Amer. Midl. Nat. 39(1)83–92, 3 figs., 5 tables.

————. 1950. Preseasonal breeding by the bridled shiner, *Notropis bifrenatus*, under light-temperature control. Copeia 1950(4):340–11, 1 fig.

————. 1957. Sexual photoperiodicity of the cyprinid fish, *Notropis bifrenatus* (Cope), in relation to the phases of its annual reproductive cycle. J. Exp. Zool. 135(3):529–55, 4 figs., 1 pl., 1 table.

————. 1958. Morphometry and ecology of small tarpon, *Megalops atlantica* Valenciennes from transitional stage through onset of scale formation. Copeia 1958(1):1–10, 5 figs., 2 pls., 3 tables.

————. 1959. Photoperiodism in fishes in relation to the annual sexual cycle, p. 651–67. *In* Photoperiodism and related phenomena in plants and animals. Amer. Ass. Advance. Sci., Washington, D. C.

————, and E. S. Harrington. 1960. Food of larval and young tarpon, *Megalops atlantica*. Copeia 1960(4):311–9.

Harrison, Harry M. 1954. Returns from tagged channel catfish in the Des Moines River, Iowa Acad. Sci., Proc. (1953)60: 636–44, 2 tables.

Hart, J. S. 1952. Geographical variations of some physiological and morphological characters in certain freshwater fish. Univ. Toronto Biol. Ser. No. 60, 79 p., 8 figs., 18 tables.

Hartshorne, H. 1872. Change of temperature in water containing recently fertilized shad eggs. Amer. Nat. 6:202.

Hay, O. P. 1895a. The lampreys and fishes of Indiana. Dept. Geol. and Nat. Res., Indiana, 19th Ann. Rep., p. 147–296.

————. 1895b. On the structure and development of the vertebral column of *Amia*. Field Columbia Mus., Zool. Ser. 1(1):1–54, 3 pls.

Heincke, F. 1898. Naturgeschichte des Herings. I. Die Lokalformen und die Wanderingen des Heringes in den europäischen Meeren. Abh. Deutsch. Seefischerei Ver., Berlin 2(Part 1):cxxxv + 128, 26 pls.

————. 1899 The natural history of the herring. Fish. Bd. Scot., 17th Ann. Rep. (1898) Part 3:274–87.

Hela, I., and T. Laevastu. 1962. Fisheries hydrography. Fishing News Books, Ltd. London. 137 p.

Hempel, G. 1953. Die Temperaturabhängigkeit der Myomerenzahl beim Hering (*Clupea harengus* L.). Naturwissenschaften 17:466–8.

————, and J. H. S. Blaxter. 1961. The experimental modification of meristic characters in herring (*Clupea harengus* L.). J. Cons. Int. Explor. Mer 26(3):336–46, 4 figs., 5 tables.

Henshall, James A. 1895. Notes on fishes collected in Florida in 1892. U. S. Bur. Fish., Bull. (1894)14:211–21.

————. 1920. Bass, pike, perch and other game fish of America. Stewart & Kidd Co., Cincinnati. xxi + 410 p.

Hentschel, E. 1950. Die Nahrung der Haringslarven. Helgol. Wiss. Meeresunt. 3:59–81.

Herman, Sidney Samuel. 1958. The plantonic fish eggs and larvae of Narragansett Bay. MS Thesis, Univ. Rhode Island, 65 p., 4 figs.

Heron, R. 1842. On the breeding of goldfishes in the author's menagerie. Ann. Mag. Nat. Hist. 8:533.

Heronimus, Ch. 1911. Die Entwickelung des Brustflossenkelettes bei *Amia calva*. Anat. Anz. 39(8):193–203, 8 figs.

Hesdörffer, Max. 1901. Der amerikanische Hundsfisch (*Amia calva*), ein neuer Aquarienfisch. Natur. U. Haus. 10:35–7.

Hessel, Rudolph. 1878. The carp, and its culture in rivers and lakes; and its introduction into America. U. S. Comm. Fish., Rep. (1875–76) 4 (Appendix C):865–99, 5 figs.

Hickling, C. F. 1940. The fecundity of the herring of the southern North Sea. J. Mar. Biol. Ass. U. K. 24:619–32.

Higham, Joseph R., and William R. Nicholson. 1964. Sexual maturation and spawning of the Atlantic menhaden. U. S. Fish and Wildl. Serv., Fish. Bull. 63(2):255–71, 8 figs., 8 tables.

Hikita, Toyoji. 1956. On the anatomy and development of the carp in Hokkaido. Sci. Rep. Hokkaido Fish Hatchery, Sapporo, Japan, No. 11, p. 65–95, 21 pls.

Hildebrand, Henry H. 1954. A study of the fauna of the brown shrimp (*Penaeus aztecus* Ives) grounds in the western Gulf of Mexico. Inst. Mar. Sci., Pub. 3(2):229–366, 7 figs., 30 tables.

————. 1955. A study of the fauna of the pink shrimp (*Penaeus duorarum* Burkenroad) grounds in the Gulf of Campeche. Inst. Mar. Sci., Pub. 4(1):169–232, 2 figs., 8 tables.

Hildebrand, Samuel F. 1934. The capture of a young tarpon, *Tarpon atlanticus*, at Beaufort, North Carolina. Copeia 1934 (1):45.

————. 1939. The Panama Canal as a passageway for fishes, with lists and remarks on the fishes and invertebrates observed. Zoologica, New York 24(3):15–45, 4 figs., 2 tables.

————. 1941. An annotated list of salt and brackish water fishes, with a new name for a menhaden, found in North Carolina since the publication of "The Fishes of North Carolina" by Hugh M. Smith in 1907. Copeia 1941(4):220–32.

————. 1943a. A review of the American anchovies (Family Engraulidae). Bull. Bingham Oceanog. Coll. 8(2):1–165, 72 figs., 24 tables.

————. 1943b. Notes on the affinity, anatomy and development of *Elops saurus* Linnaeus. J. Wash. Acad. Sci. 33(3):90–4, 3 figs., 2 tables.

————. 1948. A review of the American menhaden, genus *Brevoortia*, with a description of a new species. Smithsonian Misc. Coll. 107(18):1–39, 9 figs.

————. 1963a. Family Clupeidae, p. 257–385, 397–442, 452–4; Fig. 62–94, 98–115. *In* Fishes of the Western North Atlantic. Sears Found. Mar. Res., Mem. 1(3).

————. 1963b. Family Engraulidae. Ibid. p. 152–249, Fig. 25–59.

————. 1963c. Family Elopidae. Ibid. p. 111–31, Fig. 19–21.

————. 1963d. Family Albulidae. Ibid. p. 132–47, Fig. 22–4.

————, and Louella E. Cable. 1930. Development and life history of fourteen teleostean fishes at Beaufort, N. C. U. S. Bur. Fish., Bull. 46:383–488, 101 figs.

————, and ————. 1934. Reproduction and development of whitings or kingfishes, drums, spot, croaker, and weakfishes or sea trouts, Family Sciaenidae, of the Atlantic Coast of the United States. U. S. Bur. Fish., Bull. 48(16):41–117, 44 figs.

————, and ————. 1938. Further notes on the development and life history of some teleosts at Beaufort, N.C. U. S. Bur. Fish., Bull. 48(24):505–642, 159 figs.

————, and William C. Schroeder. 1928. Fishes of Chesapeake Bay. U. S. Bur. Fish., Bull. 43 (Part 1), 366 p., 211 figs.

————, and Irving L. Towers. 1929. Annotated list of fishes collected in vicinity of Greenwood, Miss., with descriptions of three new species. U. S. Bur. Fish., Bull. 43(2):105–36, 9 figs.

Hill, Donald R. 1959. Some uses of statistical analysis in classifying races of American shad (*Alosa sapidissima*). U. S. Fish and Wildl. Serv., Fish. Bull. 59(147):iv + 269–86, 13 tables.

Hinkelmann, Andreas. 1902. Ueber den Aufstieg und die Laichplätze des Herings in Kaiser Wilhelm-Kanal im Frühjahr 1902. Mitth. Deutsch. Seefischerei Ver. 18:362–7.

————. 1908. Die Treibnetzfischerei in der Ostsee mit besanderer Berücksichtigung des Laichplatzes fur Heringe bei Fehmarn. Mitth. Deutsch. Seefischerei Ver. 24:358–61, 2 figs.

Hjort, Johan. 1908. Some results of international ocean research. The Scot. Oceanogr. Lab., Edinburgh, 40 p., 18 figs.

Ho, Hsi J. 1933. Observations on the breeding habit of the goldfish. Sci. Soc. China, Trans. 7(1):67–8.

Hodder, V. M. 1966. Two further records of the American shad in Newfoundland waters. Amer. Fish. Soc., Trans 95(2): 228–9.

Hoek, Paulus Peronius Cato. 1903. The literature of the ten principal food fishes of the North Sea in the form of compendious monographs. Conseil Perm. Mer, Pub. Circonstance No. 3, 107 p., 10 pls.

Hoese, H. D. 1963. Salt tolerance of the eastern mudminnow, *Umbra pygmaea*. Copeia 1963(1):165–6.

Holbrook, John Edward. 1860. Ichthyology of South Carolina. Vol. I. Russell and Jones, Charleston, S. C., viii + 205 p., 28 pls.

Holliday, F. G. T. 1958. The spawning of the herring. Scot. Fish. Bull. No. 10, 11–13.

————, and J. H. S. Blaxter. 1960. The effect of salinity on the developing eggs and larvae of the herring. J. Mar. Biol. Ass. U. K., 39:591–603, 8 figs., 4 tables.

————, and ————. 1961. The effects of salinity on herring after metamorphosis. Ibid. 41:37–48, 7 figs.

————, ————, and R. Lasker. 1964. Oxygen uptake of developing eggs and larvae of the herring (*Clupea harengus*). Ibid. 44:711–23.

Hollis, Edgar H. 1948. The homing tendency of shad. Science 108(2804):332–3, 1 fig.

Hollister, Gloria. 1936a. Caudal skeleton of some Bermuda shallow water fishes. I. Order Isospodyli: Elopidae, Megalopidae, Albulidae, Clupeidae, Dussumieriidae, Engraulidae. Zoologica, New York, 21(23):257–90, 53 figs.

————. 1936b. A fish which grows by shrinking. Bull. New York Zool. Soc. 39(3):104–9.

————. 1937. Caudal skeleton of Bermuda shallow water fishes. III. Order Iniomi: Synodontidae. Zoologica, New York, 22 (28):385–99, 18 figs.

————. 1939. Young *Megalops cyprinoides* from Batavia, Dutch East India, including a study of the caudal skeleton and a comparison with the Atlantic species, *Tarpon atlanticus*. Ibid. 24(28):449–75, 21 figs.

Holloway, Ancil D. 1954. Notes on the life history and management of the shortnose and longnose gars in Florida waters. J. Wildl. Management 18(4):438–49, 3 figs., 4 tables.

Holstvoogd, C. 1957. The postembryonic development of the pronephros in *Clupea harengus* L. Arch. néerl. Zool. 12(3): 455–66, 7 figs.

Holt, Ernest W. L. 1889. Notes on the early life history of the herring. Ann. Mag. Nat. Hist. Ser. 4, 6:368–72.

Howarth, John N. 1961. Sampling for the young-of-the-year fishes with a 50-foot bag seine and surface trawl, p. 43–9, Fig. 11–15, Tables 27–30. *In* Richard R. Whitney (Project Leader), The Susquehanna fishery study 1957–60. A report of a study on the desirability and feasibility of passing fish at Conowingo Dam. Md. Dept. Res. and Educ., Solomons, Md., Contrib. No. 169.

Hubbs, Carl L. 1918. Geographic variation in *Notemigonus crysoleucas*—an American minnow. Ill. Acad. Sci., Trans. 11:147–51.

————. 1930. Materials for a revision of the catostomid fishes of eastern North America. Univ. Mich., Mus. Zool., Misc. Pub. No. 20, 47 p., 1 pl., 9 tables.

————. 1936. Fishes of the Yucatan Peninsula. Carnegie Inst. of Wash. Pub. No. 457, p. 157–287, 1 fig., 15 pls.

————. 1943. Terminology of early stages of fishes. Copeia 1943(4):260.

————. 1953. Identification and relationships of the anchovy described from California as *Anchovia scitula*. Ibid. 1953 (3):193–4.

————. 1958. *Dikellorhynchus* and *Kanazawaichthys*: Nominal fish genera interpreted as based on prejuveniles of *Malacanthus* and *Antennarius*, respectively. Ibid. 1958(4):282–5, 2 tables.

————, and Gerald P. Cooper. 1936. Minnows of Michigan. Cranbrook Inst. Sci., Bull. No. 8, 95 p., 2 figs., 10 pls.

————, and Charles W. Creaser. 1924. On the growth of young suckers and the propagation of trout. Ecology 5(4):372–8, 2 figs.

———, and Karl F. Lagler. 1947. Fishes of the Great Lakes Region. Cranbrook Inst. Sci., Bull. No. 26, xii + 186 p., 251 figs., 26 pls.

———, and ———. 1958. Fishes of the Great Lakes Region. Revised edition. Ibid., xiii + 213 p., 251 figs., 44 pls.

———, and Edward C. Raney. 1947. *Notropis alborus*, a new cyprinid fish from North Carolina and Virginia. Occ. Papers Mus. Zool., Univ. Mich. No. 498, 17 p., 3 figs., 1 pl., 2 tables.

Hunt, W. T. 1912. As to the carp. Amer. Fish. Soc., Trans. (1911):189–94.

Huntsman, A. G. 1918. The growth of scales in fishes. Roy. Canadian Inst., Toronto, Trans. 12:63–103, 17 figs., 12 tables.

———. 1919. Growth of the young herring (so-called sardine) of the Bay of Fundy. Canadian Fish. Exped. 1914–15, p. 165–71.

Hutchins, D. E. 1906. More about carp. Agr. J., Cape of Good Hope, 29:197–222, 3 figs.

Huxley, [Thomas Henry]. 1881. The herring. Nature 23 (April 28): 607–13.

Indian Council of Agricultural Research. 1951. Madras rural piscicultural scheme—Progress Report (Period: 1st April 1950 to 31st March 1951). Indian Council Agr. Res., 2 p.

Innes, William T. 1936. The complete aquarium book: The care and breeding of goldfish and tropical fish. 15th Edition. Halcyon House, New York. 317 p.

———. 1949. Goldfish varieties and water gardens. 2nd edition. Innes Pub. Co., Phila. 385 p.

International Game Fish Association. 1962. World record marine fishes. Miami. 16 p.

Jean, Yves. 1946. Two northern longnose gars, *Lepisosteus osseus oxyurus* Rafinesque, caught in the estuary of the St. Lawrence, Quebec. Copeia 1946(2):100.

———. 1956. A study of the spring and fall spawning herring (*Clupea harengus* L.) at Grande-Rivière, Bay of Chaleur, Quebec. Dept. of Fisheries, Province of Quebec, Contrib. No. 49, 76 p., 16 figs., 10 tables.

Jenkins, R. M., E. M. Leonard, and G. E. Hall. 1952. An investigation of the fisheries resources of the Illinois River and preimpoundment study of Tenkiller Reservoir, Oklahoma. Okla. Fish. Res. Lab. Rep. 26, 133 p.

Johansen, A. C. 1924. On the summer and autumn spawning herrings of the North Sea. Medd. Komm. Havunders. Kjobenhavn, Ser. Fisk. 7(5):1–118, 15 figs.

———. 1925. On the diurnal vertical movements of young of some fishes in Danish waters. Ibid. 8(2):1–28.

John, C. C. 1932. The origin of erythrocytes in herring (*Clupea harengus*). Roy. Soc. London, Proc., Ser. B, 110:112–9, 2 pls.

Jones, F. R. Harden. 1962. Further observations on the movements of herring (*Clupea harengus* L.) shoals in relation to tidal current. J. Cons. Int. Explor. Mer 27:52–76.

Jordon, David Starr. 1905a. A guide to the study of fishes. Vol. I. Henry Holt and Co., N. Y., 624 p., 393 figs.

———. 1905b. A guide to the study of fishes. Vol. II. Henry Holt and Co., N. Y., 599 p., 506 figs.

———, and Barton Warren Evermann. 1896. The fishes of North and Middle America: A descriptive catalogue of the species of fish-like vertebrates found in the waters of North America, north of the Isthmus of Panama. U. S. Nat. Mus., Bull. No. 47, part 1, lx + 1240 p.

———, and ———. 1900. The fishes of North and Middle America: A descriptive catalogue of the species of fish-like vertebrates found in the waters of North America, north of the Isthmus of Panama. Ibid. Part 4, p. cii + 3137–313, 392 pls.

———, and ———. 1902. American food and game fishes. A popular account of all the species found in America north of the equator, with keys for ready identification. Life histories and methods of capture. Doubleday, Page and Co., New York, xlx + 573 p.

June, Fred C. 1958. Variations in meristic characters of young Atlantic menhaden, *Brevoortia tyrannus*. Cons. Explor. Mer., Rapp. Proc.-Verb. 143(2):26–35, 2 figs., 5 tables.

———. 1961. The menhaden fishery of the United States. U. S. Fish and Wildl. Serv., Fish. Leaf. 521, 13 p., 10 figs.

———, and Lockwood Chamberlain. 1959. The role of the estuary in the life history and biology of Atlantic menhaden. Gulf and Carib. Fish. Inst., Proc. (1958):41–5.

Jungersen, Hector F. E. 1894. Die embryonalniere von *Amia calva*. Zool. Anz. 17(451):246–52, 5 figs.

Kajishima, Takao. 1958. Regional differences in pigment cell formation of the embryonic shield of the goldfish. Embryologica 4:133–47.

———. 1960. The normal developmental stages of the goldfish, *Carassius auratus*. Jap. J. Ichth. 8(1/2):20–8, 28 figs.

Kändler, R., and S. Dutt. 1958. Fecundity of Baltic herring. Cons. Int. Explor. Mer., Rapp. Proc.—Verb., 143(2):99–108, 6 figs.

Karvelis, Ernest G. 1964. The true pikes. U. S. Fish and Wildl. Serv., Fish. Leafl. 569, 11 p., 8 figs., 1 table.

Keene, J. H. 1879. Notes on the natural history of freshwater fishes. No. XI. The carps. Fishing Gazette n.s. 3:589, 600–1.

Keeton, D. 1963. Growth of fishes in the Des Moines River, with particular reference to water levels. Dissert. Abstr. 24(10): 3916.

Kendall, William Converse. 1904. Habits of some of the commercial catfishes. U. S. Fish Comm., Bull (1920)22:399–409.

———. 1910. American catfishes: Habits, culture, and commercial importance. U. S. Bur. Fish., Doc. No. 733, 39 p., 10 pls.

———. 1918. The Rangely Lakes, Maine; with special reference to the habits of the fishes, fish culture and angling. U. S. Bur. Fish., Bull. 35:485–594, 23 figs., 7 pls., 11 tables.

———. 1919. The pikes: Their geographical distribution, habits, culture, and commercial importance. U. S. Bur. Fish., Doc. 853, Rept. U. S. Comm. of Fish. (1917), Appendix 5, pp. 1–45, 6 figs., tables.

———, and W. A. Dence. 1929. The fishes of the Cranberry Lake Region. Roosevelt Wildl. Bull. 5(2):219–309, 92 figs., 3 tables.

———, and E. L. Goldsborough. 1908. The fishes of the Connecticut Lakes and neighboring waters, with notes on the plankton environment. U. S. Bur. Fisheries, Doc. 633:1–77, 5 figs., 12 plates, 2 tables.

Keup, Lewell, and Jack Bayless. 1964. Fish distribution at varying salinities in Neuse River basin, North Carolina. Chesapeake Sci. 5(3):119–23, 2 figs., 2 tables.

Khan, M. Hamid. 1929. Early stages in the development of the goldfish (Carassius auratus). J. Bombay Nat. Hist. Soc. 33: 614–7, 2 pls.

Kilby, John D. 1955. The fishes of two Gulf coastal marsh areas in Florida. Tulane Stud. Zool. 2(8):175–247, 10 figs., 9 tables.

Kirsch, Philip Henry, and Morton W. Fordice. 1890. A review of the sturgeons (Acipenseridae) of North America. Acad. Nat. Sci. Phila., Proc. (1889):245–7.

Kishita, Moriye. 1933. A new case of hermaphroditism in Carassius auratus (L.) J. Sci. Hiroshima Univ., Ser. B., Div. 2(12): 205–10.

Knox, Robert. 1834. Observations on the natural history of the salmon, herring and vendace. Roy. Soc. Edinburgh, Trans. 12:462–518.

Kostomarov, B. 1955. Rozmnožoráni A Plemenitba Ryb I. Československá Akademie Věd, Věda Mění Život, Sekce biologická. 158 p., 80 figs.

Kotthaus, A. 1939. Zuchtversuche mit Heringslarven (Clupea harengus L.). Helgoländ Wiss. Meeresunters. 1:349–58.

Kramer, Robert H., and Lloyd L. Smith, Jr. 1960. Utilization of nests of largemouth bass, Micropterus salmoides, by golden shiners, Notemigonus crysoleucas. Coepia 1960(1):73–4.

Krebs, Wilhelm. 1911. Geophysickalische, besonders klimatische Beziehungen des Auftretens der Heringsschwärme in der südösthchen Nordsee. Fischerbote 3:150–2.

Krevanovski, S. G. 1956a. Materials on the development of fish of the herring family (In Russian). Stud. A. N. Severtorva Inst. Anim. Morphol., Soviet Acad. Sci., No. 17:73–146.

———. 1956b. Development of Clupea harengus membras in water of high salinity. Voprosy Ikhtiologii (6)100–4.

Kubota, Saburoh. 1957. Development and morphological observations on the taste buds of Carassius auratus [in Japanese]. Dobutrugaku Zasshi 66(2/3):152.

Kuntz, Albert. 1914. The embryology and larval development of Bairdiella chrysura and Anchovia mitchilli. U. S. Bur. Fish., Bull (1913)33:1–19, 46 figs.

———, and Lewis Radcliffe. 1917. Notes on the embryology and larval development of twelve teleostean fishes. U. S. Bur. Fish., Bull. (1915–1916) 35:87–134, 126 figs.

Kupffer, C. 1878. Die Entwicklung des Herings im Ei. Wiss. meeresunters. Abt. Kiel. 3:175–226.

Laackmann, H. 1912a. Die Zucht der Goldfischaborten in Japan. Blätt. Aquar.-Terrar. Kunde 23:543–6, 2 figs.

———. 1912b. Die japanischen Abarten des Goldfisches. Ibid. 319–321, 335–7, 10 figs.

Lagler, Karl F., John E. Bardach, and Robert R. Miller. 1962. Ichthyology. John Wiley and Sons, Inc., N. Y., xiii + 545 p.

Landacre, Francis L. 1912. The epibranchial placodes of Lepidosteus osseus and their relation to the cerebral ganglia. J. Comp. Neurology 22(1):1–68, 10 pls.

———, and A. C. Conger. 1913. The origin of the lateral line primordia in Lepidosteus osseus. Ibid. 23(6):575–632, 8 pls.

Langlois, T. H. 1939. Ohio fish management progress report. Ohio Conserv. Bull. 3(1):16–19.

———. 1945. Ohio's fish program. Ohio Div. Conserv. and Nat. Res., 40 p.

———. 1954. The western end of Lake Erie and its ecology. J. W. Edwards, Inc., Ann Arbor, Mich., 479 p., 72 figs., 26 tables.

Lanman, C. 1874. The shad and gaspereau or alewife of New Brunswick and Nova Scotia. U. S. Fish Comm., Rep. (1872–1873)2:461–2.

Lanzi, Luigi. 1909. Richerche sui primi momenti di sviluppo degli olostei (od Euganoidi) Amia calva Bonap. e Lepidosteus osseus L. Con speciale riguardo al casi detto ispessimento prostomale. Arch. Ital. Anat. Embriol. 8:292–306, 13 figs.

La Rivers, Ira. 1962. Fishes and fisheries of Nevada. Nevada State Fish and Game Comm., 782 p., 270 figs.

Leach, G. C. 1919. The artificial propagation of the carp. U. S. Bur. Fish., Econ. Circ. 39, 19 p.

———. 1925a. Propagation and distribution of food fishes, fiscal year 1924. U. S. Comm. Fish., Rep. (1924):361–440, 2 figs.

———. 1925b. Artificial propagation of shad. U. S. Comm. Fish. (1924):459–86, 8 figs.

Lebour, Marie V. 1921. The larval and post-larval stages of the pilchard, sprat, and herring from the Plymouth District. J. Mar. Biol. Ass. U. K. 12(3):427–57, 12 figs.

Lee, Genevieve. 1931. Oral gestation in the marine six-whiskered catfish, Galeichthys felis. Anat. Record 51 (First Supplement): 60.

———. 1937. Oral gestation in the marine catfish, Galeichthys felis. Copeia 1937(1):49–56, 10 figs., 1 table.

Legendre, Vianney. 1954. Key to game and commercial fishes of the Province of Quebec. Vol. I. The freshwater fishes. Game and Fish. Dept., Province of Quebec, 180 p.

Lehman, B. A. 1953. Fecundity of Hudson River shad. U. S. Fish. and Wildl. Serv., Res. Rep. 33, 8 p., 4 figs., 2 tables.

Leim, A. H. 1924. The life history of the shad (Alosa sapidissima (Wilson)) with special reference to the factors limiting its abundance. Contrib. Canadian Biol. n.s. 2(11):161–284, 45 figs., 41 tables.

———. 1957a. Summary of results under the Atlantic herring investigation committee, p. 1–16, 8 figs. In Report of the Atlantic Herring Investigation Committee, Fish. Res. Bd. Canada, Bull. No. 111.

———. 1957b. Resume des travaux du comite des recherches sur le hareng de L'Atlantique. Ibid. pp. 17–33, 8 figs.

———, S. N. Tibbo, and L. R. Day. 1957. Explorations for herring in Canadian Atlantic waters, 1945–1950, p. 35–83, 54 figs. In Report of the Atlantic Herring Investigation Committee. Fish Res. Bd. Canada, Bull. No. 111.

Lennurt, J. T. 1883. Catch of spawning shad in the Potomac above Georgetown. U. S. Fish. Comm., Bull. 3:440.

Lenz, Gerhard. 1947a. Propagation of catfish. [reprint]. Progr. Fish Cult. 9(4):231–3.

————. 1947b. Propagation of catfish. Outdoor Nebraska 25(1): 4–6.

Leonhardt, E. E. 1912. Ontogenetisches und Anatomisches von Goldfisch. Blätt. Aquar.-Terrar. Kunde 23:528–31, 3 figs.

Lewis, Robert M. 1965. The effect of minimum temperature on the survival of larval Atlantic menhaden, *Brevoortia tyrannus*. Amer. Fish. Soc., Trans. 94(4):409–12, 1 table.

Lewis, William M. 1961. Mortality of fingerling shiners resulting from becoming entangled in the algae *Hydrodictyon*. Ecology 42(4):835–6, 1 fig.

Liamin, K. A. 1959. Investigation into the life-cycle of summer-spawning herring of Iceland, p. 166–202, 12 figs., 21 tables. *In* Leslie W. Scattergood (Editor), Herring of the North European basin and adjacent seas. Transl. from Russian. U. S. Fish and Wildl. Serv., Spec. Sci. Rep.-Fish. No. 327.

Livingstone, D. A. 1951. The freshwater fishes of Nova Scotia. Nova Scotian Inst. Sci., Proc. 23(1):1–90, 36 figs.

Lockley, Arthur S. 1957. Adrenal cortical hormones and osmotic stress in three species of fishes. Copeia 1957(3):241–2, 1 table.

Longley, William H., and Samuel F. Hildebrand. 1941. Systematic catalogue of the fishes of Tortugas, Florida with observations on color, habits, and local distribution. Carnegie Inst. Wash., Pub. No. 535, xiv + 331 p., 34 pls.

Louder, Darrell E. 1962. An annotated checklist of the North Carolina Bay Lake fishes. J. Elisha Mitchell Sci. Soc. 78: 68–73, 1 table.

Luce, Wilber M. 1933. A survey of the fishery of the Kaskaskia River. Ill. Nat. Hist. Surv., Bull. 20:v + 112, 12 figs.

MacCoy, Clinton V. 1931. Fishes. *In* Museum notes. Boston Soc. Nat. Hist., Bull. 61–21.

Maejima, Masanao. 1952. Observation on the hatching of *Cyprinus carpio* (L.) eggs [In Japanese]. Collecting and Breeding (Tokyo) 14(3):89–91, 6 figs.

Magnin, Etienne, and Gerard Beaulieu. 1960. Deplacements des esturgeons (*Acipenser fulvescens* et *A. oxyrhynchus*) du fleuve Saint-Laurent d'apres les donnes du Marquage. Natur. Canadien 87(11):237–52, 4 figs., 6 tables.

Maier, H. N., and L. Scheuring. 1923. Entwickelung der Schwimmblase und ihre Beziehungen zum statischen Organ und der Kloake bei. Clupeiden spez. beim Hering. Wiss. Meersunters. Abt. Helgoland 15(6):1–22.

Maison, Emile. 1897a. Le nid de l'*Amia calva*. Etangs and Riviéres 10(235):234–85.

————. 1897b. Note sur le nid d'*Amia*. Ibid. (233):241–7.

Mansueti, Alice J., and Romeo J. Mansueti. 1955. Eggs, larvae and juveniles of chain pickerel reared successfully. Md. Tidewater News 12(6):1–2, 2 figs.

Mansueti, Romeo J. 1950. Tentative key to the adult freshwater fishes and fishlike vertebrates of Maryland and the District of Columbia. Univ. of Md., Dept. Zool., 45 p., 1 fig. (mimeo).

————. 1954. A partial bibliography of fish eggs, larvae and juveniles, with particular reference to migratory and estuarine species of the Atlantic coast and supplemented by a check list and references to the early development of the fishes and fish-like chordates of Maryland waters. Md. Dept. Res. and Educ., Chesapeake Biol. Lab., Solomons, Md., 55 p. (mimeo).

————. 1955. Natural history of the American shad in Maryland waters. Md. Tidewater News 11 (Suppl. 4):1–2.

————. 1956. Alewife herring eggs and larvae reared successfully in lab. Md. Tidewater News 13(1):2–3, 1 fig.

————. 1957. Revised key to Maryland freshwater fishes. Maryland Dept. Res. and Educ., Chesapeake Biol. Lab., Ref. No. 57–22, 26 p.

————. 1958. The hickory shad unmasked. Nat. Mag. 51(7): 351–4, 386, 4 figs.

————. 1962a. Checklist of fishes of the Patuxent River drainage and of Chesapeake Bay off Calvert County, Maryland. Nat. Res. Inst., Univ. of Md., Ref. No. 62–36, 5 p.

————. 1962b. Eggs, larvae, and young of the hickory shad, *Alosa mediocris*, with comments on its ecology in the estuary. Chesapeake Sci. 3(3):173–205, 12 figs., 8 tables.

————, and Haven Kolb. 1953. A historical review of the shad fisheries of North America. Md. Dept. Res. and Educ., Pub. No. 97, vi + 293 p., 33 figs.

————, and R. S. Scheltema. 1953. Summary of fish collections made in the Chesapeake Bay area of Maryland and Virginia during October, 1953. Maryland Dept. Res. and Educ., Chesapeake Biol. Lab., Field Summary 1, 25 p.

Marak, Robert R., and John B. Colton, Jr. 1961. Distribution of fish eggs and larvae, temperature and salinity in the Georges Bank—Gulf of Maine area, 1963. U. S. Fish and Wildl. Serv., Spec. Sci. Rept.—Fish. No. 398, iii + 61 p.

————, ————, and Donald B. Foster. 1962. Distribution of fish eggs and larvae, temperature, and salinity in the Georges Bank—Gulf of Maine area, 1955. U. S. Fish and Wildl. Serv., Spec. Sci. Rept.—Fish. No. 411, iv + 66 p.

————, ————, ————, and David Miller. 1962. Distribution of fish eggs and larvae, and salinity in the Georges Bank—Gulf of Maine area, 1956. U. S. Fish and Wildl. Serv., Spec. Sci. Rept.—Fish. No. 412, iv + 95 p., 21 tables.

Mark, E. L. 1890. Studies on *Lepisosteus*. Part I. Mus. Comp. Zool., Bull. 19(1):1–127, 9 pls., 2 figs.

Marshall, Nelson. 1947. Studies on the life history and ecology of *Notropis chalybaeus* (Cope). Quart. J. Florida Acad. Sci. 9(3/4):163–88, 5 figs., 1 table.

Marshall, S. M., A. G. Nicholls, and A. P. Orr. 1937. On the growth and feeding of the larval and post-larval stages of the Clyde herring. J. Mar. Biol. Ass. U. K. 22(1):245–67, 4 figs., 6 tables.

Marshall, Tom C. 1965. Fishes of the Great Barrier Reef and coastal waters of Queensland. Livingston Publ. Co., Australia. xvi + 566 p., 71 pls.

Marty, Yu Yu. 1959. The fundamental stages of the life cycle of Atlantic-Scandinavian herring, p. 5–68, 13 figs., 8 tables. *In* Leslie W. Scattergood (Editor), Herring of the North European basin and adjacent seas. Transl. from Russian, U. S. Fish and Wildl. Serv., Spec. Sci. Rept.—Fisheries No. 327.

Marzolf, Richard C. 1957. The reproduction of channel catfish in Missouri ponds. J. Wildl. Manag. 21(1):22–8, 1 table.

Massmann, William H. 1952. Characteristics of spawning areas of shad, *Alosa sapidissima* (Wilson) in some Virginia streams. Amer. Fish. Soc., Trans. 81 (1951): 79–93, 4 figs., 8 tables.

———. 1953. Relative abundance of young fish in Virginia estuaries. Trans. 18th N. Amer. Wildl. Conf., p. 439–49, 4 figs., 3 tables.

———. 1954. Marine fishes in fresh and brackish waters of Virginia rivers. Ecology 35(1):75–8, 1 fig.

———. 1957. New and recent records for fishes in Chesapeake Bay. Copeia 1957(2):156–7.

———. 1958. A checklist of fishes of the Virginia waters of Chesapeake Bay and its tidal tributaries. Va. Fish. Lab., Finfish Prog. Rep. 60, 14 p.

———. 1960. Additional records for new fishes in Chesapeake Bay. Copeia 1960(1):70.

———, E. C. Ladd, and H. N. McCutcheon. 1952. A biological survey of the Rappahannock River, Virginia. Virginia Fish. Lab., Spec. Sci. Rept. 6 (part 1), xi + 112 p., 23 figs.

———, ———, and ———. 1954. Postlarvae and young of the menhaden (*Brevoortia tyrannus*) in brackish and fresh waters of Virginia. Copeia 1954(1):19–23, 1 fig., 4 tables.

———, J. J. Norcross, and E. B. Joseph. 1962. Atlantic menhaden larvae in Virginia coastal waters. Chesapeake Sci. 3(1):42–5, 1 fig., 3 tables.

———, and Anthony L. Pacheco. 1957. Shad catches and water temperature in Virginia. J. Wildl. Manag. 21(3):351–2, 2 figs., 1 table.

Mast, S. O. 1916. Changes in shade, color and pattern in fishes and their bearing on the problems of adaptation and behavior, with especial reference to the flounders *Paralichthys* and *Ancylopetta*. U. S. Bur. Fish., Bull. (1914) 34:173–238, 19 pls., 3 figs.

Masterman, Arthur Thomas. 1896. Note on the rate of growth, larval and post-larval forms of the herring. Fish. Bd. Scot., 14 Ann. Rep., p. 294–302, 2 pls.

Matsubara, Shinnosuke. 1890. Notes on *Cyprinus carpio* and *Carassius auratus*. Zool. Mag. 2(26):540–2.

Matsui, Isao. 1957. The number of eggs discharged at its primary spawning in relation to the number of ovarian eggs in carp. J. Shimonoseki College Fish. 7(1):147–50, 1 fig., 4 tables.

Matthews, J. Duncan. 1886. Report as to variety among the herrings of the Scottish coasts. Part I. Fish. Bd. Scot., 4th Ann. Rep. (1885), Append. F:61–98, 22 tables.

McAtee, W. L., and A. C. Weed. 1915. First list of the fishes of the vicinity of Plummers Island, Maryland. Biol. Soc. Washington, Proc. 28:1–14, 2 figs.

McCabe, Britton C. 1958. *Esox niger* LeSueur. Tabular treatment of the life history and ecology of the chain pickerel. Committee on Handbook of Biological Data, Nat. Acad. Sci. 45 p. (mimeo).

McCammon, George W., and Charles M. Seeley. 1961. Survival, mortality and movements of white catfish and brown bullheads in Clear Lake, California. Calif. Fish and Game 47(3): 237–55, 5 figs., 4 tables.

McCann, James A. 1958. Life history of the spottail shiner (*Notropis hudsonius*), Clear Lake, Iowa. MS Thesis, Iowa State Univ., 63 p.

———. 1959. Life history studies of the spottail shiner of Clear Lake, Iowa, with particular reference to some sampling problems. Amer. Fish. Soc., Trans. 88(4):336–43, 8 tables.

McClellan, W. G. 1954. A study of the southern spotted channel catfish, *Ictalurus punctatus* (Rafinesque). MS Thesis, N. C. State College, v + 69 p.

McCormick, Lewis M. 1892. Descriptive list of fishes of Lorain County, Ohio. Oberlin College, Ohio, Lab. Bull. 2, 34 p., 14 pls.

McCutcheon, Henry Norman. 1953. Differential growth of the menhaden, *B. tyrannus* (LaTrobe), during early development. MS Thesis, College of William and Mary, v + 40 p., 14 figs., 2 tables.

McDonald, M. 1884. The shad and alewives, p. 579–88, 594–609. *In* George Brown Goode and Associates, The fisheries and fishery industries of the United States. Section 1. U. S. Comm. Fish and Fish., Washington, D. C.

McGovern, H. D. 1882. Habits and food of the German carp. Amer. Fish. Soc., Trans. (1881):11–2.

McHugh, J. L., and John E. Fitch. 1951. An annotated list of the clupeoid fishes of the Pacific Coast, from Alaska to Cape San Lucas, Baja California. Calif. Fish and Game 37(4): 491–5.

———, R. T. Oglesby, and A. L. Pacheco. 1959. Length, weight, and age composition of the menhaden catch in Virginia waters. Limnol. and Oceanogr. 4(2):145–62, 8 figs., 3 tables.

McKenzie, R. A. 1964. Observations on herring spawning off southwest Nova Scotia. J. Fish. Res. Bd. Canada 21(1):203–4, 2 figs.

———, and B. E. Skud. 1958. Herring migrations in the Passamaquoddy region. J. Fish. Res. Bd. Canada 15(6):1329–43, 7 figs., 5 tables.

Meehan, William E. 1907. Report of the Commissioner of Fisheries. Rept. Dept. Fish. Commonwealth Penn., Dec. 1, 1905 to Nov. 30, 1906. p. 11–109.

———, 1907. The shad work on the Delaware River in 1907 and its lessons. Amer. Fish. Soc., Trans. (1907):105–8.

Meek, Alexander. 1916. The migrations of fish. Edward Arnold, London. xx + 427 p.

Meek, S. E., and S. F. Hildebrand. 1910. A synoptic list of the fishes known to occur within fifty miles of Chicago. Field Mus. Nat. Hist., Zool. Ser. 7(9):223–338, 77 figs.

———, and ———. 1923. The marine fishes of Panama. Field Mus. Nat. Hist. Pub., Zool. Ser. 15 (part 1):xi + 330, 23 pls.

Menzel, R. Winston. 1945. The catfish fishery of Virginia. Amer. Fish. Soc., Trans 73:364–72, 1 fig., 4 tables.

Merriman, Daniel. 1940. Morphological and embryological studies on two species of marine catfish, *Bagre marinus* and *Galeichthys felis*. Zoologica, New York, 25(13):221–48, 9 figs., 5 pls.

———, and Ruth C. Sclar. 1952. The pelagic fish eggs and larvae of Block Island Sound. Bingham Oceanogr. Coll., Bull. 13(3): 165–219, 7 tables.

Meyer, Heinrich Adolph. 1878a. Biologische Beobachtungen bei Künstlicher Augzucht des Herings der westlichen Ostsee. Wiegandt, Hempel and Parey, Berlin, 189 p.

——. 1878b. Beobuchtungen über das Wachsthum des Herings in westlichen Theile der Ostsee. Jber. Comm. Wiss. Untersuch. dtsch. Meere Kiel. (4–6):229–50.

——. 1878c. Das wachsthum des Harings. Naturforscher 11: 346–7.

——. 1879. Influence of temperature on the development of herring eggs. Chicago Field 11:191.

——. 1880. Biological observations made during the artificial raising of herring in the western Baltic. U. S. Fish. Comm., Rep. (1878) 6:629–38.

Meyer, William H. 1962. Life history of three species of redhorse (*Moxostoma*) in the Des Moines River, Iowa. Amer. Fish. Soc., Trans. 91(4):412–9.

Mielck, W. 1925. Heringslarven, Eier und larven anderer Fische und Nahrung der larven in den westlichen Nordsee im Oktober 1922. Ber. dtsch. Komm. Meeresforsch. 1:209–46.

Migdalski, Edward C. 1958. Angler's guide to saltwater game fishes: Atlantic and Pacific. The Ronald Press Co., N. Y. x + 506 p.

——. 1962. Angler's guide to freshwater sport fishes of North America. The Ronald Press Co., N. Y. x + 431 p.

Mihursky, Joseph A. 1962. Fishes of the middle Lenapewihittuck (Delaware River) basin. PhD Thesis, Lehigh Univ., lx + 207 p.

Miller, Jack G. 1962. Occurrence of ripe chain pickerel in the fall. Amer. Fish. Soc., Trans. 91(3):323.

Miller, Robert Rush. 1950. A review of the American clupeid fishes of the genus *Dorosoma*. U. S. Nat. Mus., Proc. 100 (3267):387–410, 11 tables.

——. 1952. Bait fishes of the lower Colorado River from Lake Meade, Nevada, to Yuma, Arizona, with a key for their identification. Calif. Fish and Game 38(1):7–42, 32 figs.

——. 1957. Origin and dispersal of the alewife, *Alosa pseudoharengus*, and the gizzard shad, *Dorosoma cepedianum*, in the Great Lakes. Amer. Fish. Soc., Trans. 86:97–111, 3 tables.

——. 1960. Systematics and biology of the gizzard shad (*Dorosoma cepedianum*) and related fishes. U. S. Fish and Wildl. Serv., Fish. Bull. 60(173):iv + 371–92, 4 figs., 4 tables.

——. 1963. Genus *Dorosoma* Rafinesque 1820 gizzard shads, threadfin shad. p. 443–451, Figs. 116–7. *In* Fishes of the western North Atlantic. Sears Found. Mar. Res., Mem. 1 (Part 3).

Milner, James W. 1874. Report on the propagation of the shad (*Alosa sapidissima*) and its introduction into new waters by the U. S. Fish Commissioner in 1873. Rept. U. S. Fish Comm. (1872–73)2:419–51.

——. 1877. Shad fisheries. Amer. Fish. Soc., Trans. (1877): 70–2.

——. 1878. The work of shad-hatching on the headwaters of Chesapeake Bay. Amer. Fish. Soc., Trans. (1878):87–9.

——. 1880. The shad and alewife. Harper's Mag. 60:845.

Mitchell, John M. 1861. On the migration of the herring. Rept. Brit. Assoc. Adv. Sci. 31:149–51.

——. 1863a. On the natural history of the herring. Roy. Soc. Edinburgh, Proc. 4:171–2.

——. 1863b. Some statements in Cuvier's "Natural history of fishes," as to the herring, shown to be erroneous. Roy. Physical Soc. Edinburgh, Proc. 2:269–70.

——. 1864. The Herring: Its natural history and national importance. Edmonston and Douglas, Edinburgh, xii + 372 p.

Mohrhardt, David E. 1961. Sampling for eggs and larval fishes with plankton nets, p. 50–5, Fig. 16–22, Tables 31–3. *In* Richard R. Whitney (Project Leader), The Susquehanna fishery study, 1957–1960: A report of a study on the desirability and feasibility of passing fish at Conowingo Dam. Md. Dept. Res. Educ., Solomons, Maryland, Contrib. No. 169.

Moore, G. A. 1957. Fishes, p. 31–210, 112 figs., *In* Blair, W. F., et. al., Vertebrates of the United States. McGraw Hill Book Co., N. Y.

Moore, H. F. 1898. Observations on the herring and herring fisheries of the northeast coast, with special reference to the vicinity of Passamaquoddy Bay. U. S. Comm. Fish and Fisheries, Rep. (1896)22(Append. 9):387–442, 2 pls.

Morrow, James E. 1957. Shore and pelagic fishes from Peru, with new records and the description of a new species of *Spheorides*. Bingham Oceanog. Coll., Bull. 16(2):5–55, 12 figs.

Mottley, C. McC. 1938. Carp control studies with special reference to Chautaqua Lake, N. Y. Conserv. Dept. N. Y., Suppl. 27th Ann. Rep., p. 226–35, 2 figs.

Murphree, John M. 1940. Channel catfish propagation. Privately printed by T. J. Rennick. 24 p.

Murphy, Garth I. 1951. The fishery of Clear Lake, Lake County, California. Calif. Fish and Game 37(4):439–84, figs. 175–9, 31 tables.

Nair, R. Velappan. 1952. Studies on some post-larval fishes of the Madras plankton. Indian Acad. Sci., Proc. 35:225–44, Fig. 1–12.

Nash, Carroll Blue. 1950. Associations between fish species in tributaries and shore waters of western Lake Erie. Ecology 31(4):561–6, 3 tables.

Nash, C. W. 1908. Checklist of the vertebrates of Ontario and catalogue of specimens in the Biological Section of the Provincial Museum. Fishes. Dept. Educ., Toronto, 122 p.

Nature. 1876. A contribution to the natural history of the herring. Nature 14:352.

Naumov, V. M. 1959. The ovogenesis and ecology of the sexual cycle of the Murmansk herring (*Clupea harengus* L.) (Transl. from Russian). U. S. Fish and Wildl. Serv., Spec. Sci. Rep.— Fish. No. 327:203–62.

Needham, James G. 1920. Clean water for New York State. Cornell Rural School Leaflet 13(4):153–82.

Netsch, Norval F., and Arthur Witt, Jr. 1962. Contributions to the life history of the longnose gar, (*Lepisosteus osseus*) in Missouri. Amer. Fish. Soc., Trans. 91(3):251–62, 7 figs., 5 tables.

Nichols, John Treadwell. 1911. Notes on teleostean fishes from the eastern United States. Amer. Mus. Nat. Hist., Bull. 30 (Art. 11):275–8, 1 fig., 1 pl.

——, and C. M. Breder, Jr. 1927. The marine fishes of New York and southern New England. Zoologica, New York, 9(1):1–192, 261 figs.

Nichols, Paul R., and Robert V. Miller. 1966. American shad . . . A springtime delicacy. Marine Res. of the Atlantic Coast. Leaflet (7):1–4, figs.

Nikitinskaya, I. V. 1958. On the variability of the larvae of the Sakhalin herring. Nauch. Dokl. vyssk. Shk. biol. Nauk. No. 4.

Nikolsky, G. V. 1954. Special Ichthyology. 2nd Edition. Moscow, U. S. S. R. Transl. from Russian, Israel Program for Sci. Transl., Jerusalem. 538 p., 312 fig.

——. 1963. The ecology of fishes. Transl. from Russian, L. Birkett, Translator. Acad. Press, New York. xvi + 352 p., 140 figs.

——, A. V. Chepurnov, and M. I. Shatunovsky. 1963. Regularities in the variability of features in certain forms of North Atlantic herring. Cons. Explor. Mer, Rapp. Proc.-Verb. 154: 41–3, 4 tables.

Nilsson, Sven. 1860. Aufenthalt, Lebensweise und Fortpflanzung des Herings. Zeitschr. Gesamt. Naturw. 16:1–15.

Norman, J. R. 1935. A revision of the lizard-fishes of genera Synodus, Trachinocephalus, and Surida. Zool. Soc. London, Proc. (1935):99–135, 18 figs.

——. 1949. A history of fishes. A. A. Wyn, Inc., N. Y., xv + 463 p. 148 figs.

Norris, T. 1868. American fish-culture; embracing all the details of artificial breeding and rearing of trout, the culture of salmon, shad and other fishes. H. T. Coates, Phila., xii + 304 p.

North Carolina Wildlife Resources Commission. 1962. Some North Carolina freshwater fishes. Raleigh, North Carolina. 46 p.

Nusbaum, Jozef. 1908. Entwickelungsgeschichte und morphologische Beurteilung der Occipitalregion des Schädels und der weberschen Knöchelchen bei den Knochenfischen (Cyprinus carpio L.). Anat. Anz. 32(21/22):514–32, 14 figs.

Nybelin, Orvar. 1960. A gular plate in Albula vulpes (L). Nature 188(4744): 78, 1 fig.

Odell, Theodore T. 1932. The depth distribution of certain species of fish in some of the lakes of New York. Amer. Fish. Soc., Trans. 62:331–5, 1 pl., 3 tables.

——. 1934. The life history and ecological relationships of the alewife (Pomolobus pseudoharengus (Wilson)) in Seneca Lake, New York. Ibid. 64:118–26, 9 figs., 4 tables.

Ogilby, J. Douglas. 1898. Some new genera and species of fishes. Linnean Soc. New South Wales, Proc. 22(86):245–51.

Okada, Yaichiro. 1959–1960. Studies on the freshwater fishes of Japan. Prefectural University of Mie Tsu, Mie Prefecture, Japan. xiv + 860 p., 133 figs., 135 tables.

Okonski, S., and H. Konkol. 1957. Daily migrations of herring shoals and their reaction to fishing gear [In Polish, English summary]. Prace Morsk. Inst. Rybackiego 6 dyni. 4:549–63.

Pacheco, Anthony L., and George C. Grant. 1965. Studies of the early life history of Atlantic menhaden in estuarine nurseries. Part I. Seasonal occurrence of juvenile menhaden and other small fishes in a tributary creek of Indian River, Delaware, 1957–58. U. S. Fish and Wildl. Serv., Spec. Sci. Rept.— Fish. No. 504, iv + 32 p.

Page, W. F. 1885. Effects of sunlight upon shad eggs. U. S. Fish Comm., Bull. 5:308.

Parker, W. K. 1882. On the development of the skull in Lepidosteus osseus. Roy. Soc. London, Proc. 33(217):107–12.

——. 1883. On the development of the skull in Lepidosteus osseus. Roy. Soc. London, Phil. Trans. 173(2):443–92, 10 pls.

Parrish, B. B., and A. Saville. 1965. The biology of the North-east Atlantic Herring populations. Oceanogra. Mar. Biol. Ann. Rev. 3:323–73, 11 figs., 4 tables.

——, ——, R. E. Craig, I. G. Baxter, and R. Priestley. 1959. Observations on herring spawning and larval distribution in the Firth of Clyde in 1958. J. Mar. Biol. Ass. U. K. 38(3): 445–53, 1 pl., 1 fig., 2 tables.

Pearson, Jay F. W., and E. Morton Miller. 1935. Aggregations of Ameiurus natalis erebennus Jordan, the Florida freshwater catfish. Ecology. 16(1):123–4.

Pearson, J. C. 1941. The young of some marine fishes taken in lower Chesapeake Bay, Virginia, with special reference to the gray sea trout, Cynoscion regalis (Bloch). U. S. Fish and Wildl. Serv., Fish. Bull. 50(36):79–102, 26 figs.

Peer, D. L. 1966. Relationship between size and maturity in the spottail shiner, Notropis hudsonius. J. Fish. Res. Bd. Canada 23(3):455–7, 1 table.

Pehrson, Torsten. 1922. Some points in the cranial development of teleostean fishes. Acta Zoologica Haft 1, Arg. 3, 63 p.

Perlmutter, A. 1939. An ecological survey of young fish and eggs identified from tow-net collections. New York Conserv. Dept., Suppl. 28th Ann. Rept. (1938):11–71, 8 figs., 34 tables.

Peterson, Carl Georg Johan. 1901. On the breeding grounds of the herring (In Danish). Danish Biol. Station, Rept. 10: 35–6.

Phelps, Jessie. 1900. The origin and development of the adhesive organ of Amia calva (Abstract). Mich. Acad. Sci., 1st Rep. (1894–99):137–9.

Pierson, Elaine C. 1953. The developmental morphology of Amia calva. PhD Thesis, Univ. Mich. 185 p., 10 pls.

Piper, H. 1902a. Die Entwicklung von Leber, Pankreas, Schwimmblase und milz bei Amia calva. Anat. gesellschaft, Jena. Verhandungen 16:18–25.

——. 1902b. Die Entwicklung von Magen, Duodenum, Schwimmblase, Leber, Pankreas, und milz bei Amia calva. Arch. Anad. und Physiol. (Anat. Abth.), Suppl. (1902):1–87, 4 pls., 55 figs.

——. 1903. Berichtigung zu meinen Aufsatz: Die Entwicklung von Magen, Duodenum, Schwimmblase, Leber, Pankreas und milz bei Amia calva. Ibid. (1903):27–8.

Plosila, Daniel S. 1961. Lower Susquehanna River sport fishery survey, 1958–1960, p. 55–76, fig. 23–7, tables 37–55. In Richard R. Whitney (Project Leader), The Susquehanna fishery study. 1957–1960. A report on the desirability and feasibility of passing fish at Conowingo Dam. Md. Dept. Res. and Educ., Solomons, Md., Contrib. No. 169.

Poll, Max. 1949. L'introduction en Belgique et l'acclimatation dans la nature d'un poisson Americain supplémentaire *Umbra pygmaea* (DeKay). Inst. Roy. Sci. Nat. Belgique, Bull. 25(35): 1–11, 1 pl.

———. 1953. Téleostéans malacopterygiens. Inst. Roy. Sci. Nat. de Belgique, Exped. Oceanogr. Belge Eaux Côtieres Afraicaines de L'Atlantique Sud (1948–1949). Resultats Sci. 4(2):1–258, 104 figs., 8 pls.

Prather, E. E. 1957. Experiments on the commercial production of golden shiners. Proc. 10th Ann. Conf., Southeastern Ass. Game and Fish Comm., p. 150–5.

Prather, J. M. 1900. The early stages in the development of the hypophysis of *Amia calva*. Biol. Bull. 1(2):57–80, 3 pls.

Prince, Edward E. 1907. The eggs and early life history of the herring, gaspereau, shad, and clupeoids. 39th Ann. Rept., Dept. of Mar. and Fish. Canada, Fisheries Branch, Sessional Paper 22:95–110, Pls. 8–10.

Putman, E. W. 1866. [Notes on young gar pike.] Boston Soc. Nat. Hist., Proc. (1864–66) 10:211.

Quast, Thomas. 1929. Goldfish industry. U. S. Bur. Fish., Econ. Circ. No. 68, 14 p., 5 figs., 2 tables.

Radcliffe, Lewis. 1914. The work of the U. S. Fisheries Marine Biological Station at Beaufort, N. C., during 1913. Science, n.s. 40(1029):413–7.

Radforth, Isobel. 1944. Some considerations on the distribution of fishes in Ontario. Roy. Ontario Mus. Zool., Contrib. 25: 5–116, 32 figs.

Ramanujam, S. G. M. 1929. The study of the development of the vertebral column in teleosts as shown in the life history of the herring. Zool. Soc. London, Proc. (1929):365–414, 28 figs.

Raney, Edward C. 1939. The breeding habits of the silvery minnow, *Hybognathus regius* Girard. Amer. Midl. Nat. 21 (3):674–80, 3 figs.

———. 1940. Nests under the water. New York Zool. Soc., Bull. 43(4):127–35, 8 figs.

———. 1942a. The summer food and habits of the chain pickerel (*Esox niger*) of a small New York pond. J. Wildl. Manag. 6(1):58–66, 6 tables.

———. 1942b. Propagation of the silvery minnow (*Hybognathus nuchalis regius* Girard) in ponds. Amer. Fish. Soc., Trans. 71:215–8, 1 fig.

———. 1943. Unusual spawning habitat for the common white sucker, *Catostomus c. commersonii*. Copeia 1943(4):256.

———. 1949. Nests under the water. Canadian Nature 11(3): 71–8.

———. 1950. Freshwater fishes, p. 151–94. *In* The James River Basin, past, present, and future. James River Proj. Comm., Va. Acad. Sci.

———. 1955. Natural hybrids between two species of pickerel (*Esox*) in Stearns Pond, Massachusetts. Supplement to fisheries report for some central, eastern, and western Massachusetts lakes, ponds and reservoirs, 1951–52. Commonwealth Mass., Div. Fish and Game, 15 p., 1 fig., 1 pl., 6 tables.

———, and W. H. Massmann. 1953. The fishes of the tidewater section of the Pamunkey River, Virginia. J. Wash. Acad. Sci. 43(12):424–32, 1 fig., 3 tables.

———, and Dwight A. Webster. 1942. The spring migration of the common white sucker, *Catostomus c. commersonii* (Lacépède), in Shaneateles Lake Inlet, New York. Copeia 1942(3):139–48, 3 figs., 5 tables.

———, and ———. 1952. Chain pickerel, p. 240–1. *In* The Wise fisherman's encyclopedia. Wm. H. Wise and Co., N. Y., 1336 p.

Rannak, L. A. 1959. Quantitative study of the Baltic herring eggs and larvae in the northern part of the Gulf of Riga and principal factors determining their survival. Transl. from Russian, Fish. Res. Bd. Canada, Transl. Ser. (238), 15 p.

Rasquin, Priscilla. 1946. On the reappearance of melanophores in blind goldfish. Copeia 1946(2):85–91, 1 table.

———. 1955. Observations on the metamorphosis of the bonefish, *Albula vulpes* (Linnaeus). J. Morphol. 97(1):77–118, 4 pls.

Regan, C. Tate. 1909. A revision of the fishes of the genus *Elops*. Ann. Mag. Nat. Hist. 3(8):37–40.

Reid, George K., Jr. 1954. An ecological study of the Gulf of Mexico fishes, in the vicinity of Cedar Key, Florida. Bull. Mar. Sci. Gulf and Carib. 4(1):1–94, 13 figs., 8 tables.

Reighard, Jacob. 1900. The breeding habits of the dogfish, *Amia calva*, (Abstract). Mich. Acad. Sci., 1st Rep. (1894–1899):133–7, 2 figs.

———. 1902a. Some further notes on the breeding habits of *Amia*. (Abstract). Mich. Acad. Sci., 3rd Rep. (1901):80–1.

———. 1902b. The breeding habits of certain fishes. Science, n.s., 15:380–1.

———. 1903. The natural history of *Amia calva* Linnaeus. Mark Anniversary Volume (Art. 4):57–109, 1 fig., 1 pl.

———. 1920. The breeding behavior of suckers and minnows. Biol. Bull. 38:1–32, 7 figs.

———, and S. O. Mast. 1908. Studies of ganoid fishes. II. The development of the hypophysis of *Amia*. J. Morphol. 19(2): 497–509, 1 pl.

———, and Jessie Phelps. 1908. The development of the adhesive organ and head mesoblast of *Amia*. J. Morphol. 19(2):469–96, 1 pl.

Reintjes, John W. 1961. Menhaden eggs and larvae from M/V Theodore N. Gill cruises, South Atlantic coast of the United States, 1953–54. U. S. Fish and Wildl. Serv., Spec. Sci. Rept.—Fish. No. 393, iv + 7 p., 1 fig., 3 tables.

———. 1964. The importance of the occurrence of menhaden in the coastal waters and estuaries of peninsular Florida. Gulf and Carib. Fish. Inst., Proc. 16th Ann. Session, p. 108–13.

Revoil, C. 1891. L'élevage du cyprin doré à Oldenburg. Soc. Centr. Aquicult. Peche, Bull. 3:5–10.

Rice, H. J. 1878. Notes upon the development of the shad, *Alosa sapidissima*. Rept. Comm. of Fish., State of Md., p. 95–106.

———. 1884. Experiments upon retarding the development of eggs of the shad, made in 1879, at the United States shad hatching station at Havre de Grace, Maryland. U. S. Fish Comm., Rep. (1881) 9:787–94.

Richards, Sarah W. 1959. Pelagic fish eggs and larvae of Long Island Sound. Bingham Oceanogr. Coll., Bull. 17(1):95–124, 3 Figs., 11 tables.

Richardson, R. E. 1913a. Observations on the breeding of the European carp in the vicinity of Havana, Illinois. Ill. State Lab. Nat. Hist., Bull. 9:387–404, 1 fig.

———. 1913b. Observations on the breeding habits of fishes at Havana, Illinois, 1910 and 1911. Ibid. p. 405–16.

Riggs, Carl D., and George A. Moore. 1960. Growth of young gar (Lepisosteus) in aquaria. Oklahoma Acad. Sci., Proc. 40:44–6, 1 fig.

———, and ———. 1963. A new record of Moxostoma macrolepidotum pisolabrum, and a range extension for Percina shumardi, in the Red River, Oklahoma and Texas. Copeia 1963(2):451–2.

Roach, Lee S. 1941. Long-nosed gar, Lepisosteus osseus. Ohio Conserv. Bull. 13(3):13.

Robeson, J. M., Jr. 1932. Hemopoiesis in Amia calva. Zeitschr. Zellfursch. mikr. Anat. 16:305–13.

Robinson, W. E. 1875. The western mud fish. Forest and Stream 5:83.

Roedel, Phil M. 1953. Common ocean fishes of the California coast. State of Calif., Dept. Fish and Game, Mar. Fish Branch, Fish Bull. No. 91, 184 p., 175 figs., 1 pl.

Rogalla, E. H., and D. Sahrhage. 1960. Heringsvorkommen und Wassertemperatur. Inform. Fischw. 7:135–8.

Ross, Robert D. 1958. Some taxonomic problems of Shenandoah River fishes. Virginia Agri. Exptl. Sta., Va. Polytechnic Inst., Tech. Bull. 137:10 p., 8 tables.

Rothschild, Brian James. 1962. The life history of the alewife, Alosa pseudoharengus (Wilson) in Cayuga Lake, New York. PhD thesis, Cornell Univ., 113 p.

Runnström, Sven. 1941. Quantitative investigations on herring spawning and its yearly fluctuations at the west coast of Norway. Fiskeridir. Skr. Havundersøk. (Rep. Norwegian Fish. and Mar. Invest.) 6(8):1–71, 26 figs., 9 tables.

Ryder, John A. 1882a. On the retardation of the development of the ova of the shad (Alosa sapidissima) with observations on the egg fungus and bacteria. U. S. Fish Comm., Bull. (1881) 1:177–90.

———. 1882b. Additional observations on the retardation of the development of the ova of the shad. Ibid. p. 422–4.

———. 1883. Preliminary notice of the development and breeding habits of the Potomac catfish, Amiurus albides (LeSueur) Gill. Ibid. (1883) 3:225–30.

———. 1884. On the retardation of the development of the ova of the shad (Alosa sapidissima) with observations on the egg fungus and bacteria. U. S. Fish. Comm., Rep. (1881) 9:795–811.

———. 1887. On the development of osseus fishes, including marine and freshwater forms. U. S. Fish. Comm., Rep. (1885) 13:489–604, 30 pls.

———. 1888. On the development of the common sturgeon. Amer. Nat. 22(259):659–60.

———. 1890. The sturgeons and sturgeon industries of the eastern coast of the United States, with an account of experiments bearing upon sturgeon culture. U. S. Fish. Comm., Bull. (1888) 8:231–326, Pl. 37–59.

———. 1894. The inheritance of modifications due to disturbances of the early stages of development, especially in the Japanese domestic races of gold-carp. Acad. Nat. Sci. Phila., Proc. (1893):75–94.

Ryzhenko, M. 1961. "Severyanka" in schools of herring and cod. Transl. from Russian, Dept. Agr. and Fish. for Scot., Mar. Lab., Aberdeen, Transl. 718, 2 p.

Saksena, Vishnu P., Kiichiro Yamamoto, and Carl D. Riggs. 1961. Early development of the channel catfish. Progr. Fish Cult. 23(4):156–61, 19 figs.

Sanders, Howard L. 1952. The herring (Clupea harengus) of Block Island Sound. Bingham Oceanogr. Coll., Bull. 14 (3): 220–37, 7 figs., 2 tables.

Sanderson, Albert Edward, Jr. 1950. An ecological survey of the fishes of the Severn River with reference to the eastern chain pickerel, Esox niger LeSueur and the yellow perch, Perca flavescens (Mitchill). MS Thesis, Univ. Maryland, 47 p., 6 figs., 4 tables.

Sato, Mitsuo. 1955. On the development of the neuromasts of the carp, Cyprinus carpio [In Japanese]. Jap. J. Ichth. 4(3): 105–12, 6 figs.

Saville, Alan. 1964. Clupeoidae. Con. Int. Expl. Mer, Identification sheets on fish eggs and larvae. Sheet 1, 5 p., 2 pls.

———, G. McPherson, and B. B. Parrish. 1965. Scottish Fisheries, 1963 [Herring]. Con. Int. Expl. Mer, Ann. Biol. 20: 175–87, Tables 35–57.

Scattergood, Leslie W. 1952. The maturity of the Maine herring (Clupea harengus). Dept. Sea and Shore Fish., State of Maine, Res. Bull. 7:1–11, 1 fig., 3 tables.

———. 1957. A bibliography of the herring (Clupea harengus and Clupea pallasii). Ibid. 26:1–108.

———, Carl J. Sindermann, and Bernard E. Skud. 1959. Spawning of the North Atlantic herring. Amer. Fish. Soc., Trans. 88:165–8, 1 fig., 1 table.

Schachs, H. 1939. Die Künstliche Aufzucht von Clupea harengus. Hologöländ Wiss. Meeresunters. 1:359–72.

Schaffman, R. J. 1955. Age and rate of growth of the yellow bullhead in Reelfoot Lake, Tennessee. J. Tenn. Acad. Sci. 30(1):4–7, 3 figs.

Schnakenbeck, W. 1929. Entwicklungsgeschichtliche und morphologische Untersuchungen am Hering. Berlin dtsch. Komm. Meeresforsch. 5:23–78.

Schreiner, K. E. 1902. Einige Ergebnisse über den Bau und die Entwicklung der Occipitalregion von Amia und Lepidosteus. Z. Wiss. Zool. 72(2/3):467–524, Pls. 28–9.

Schultz, Leonard P. 1927. Temperature-controlled variation in the golden shiner, Notemigonus crysoleucas. Papers Michigan Acad. Sci., Arts and Letters 7:417–32, 2 figs., 1 pls., 9 tables.

———. 1929. Description of a new type of mud-minnow from western Washington with notes on related species. Univ. Washington, College of Fish., Publ. in Fish. 2(6):73–82, 2 pls.

————. 1944. The catfishes of Venezuela, with descriptions of thirty-eight new forms. U. S. Nat. Mus., Proc. 94:173–338, 14 pls.

Schwartz, Frank J. 1960a. Recent additions to the upper Chesapeake Bay fish fauna. Chesapeake Sci. 1 (3/4):210–2.

————. 1960b. The pickerels. Maryland Conserv. 37(4):26–6.

————. 1961. Fishes of Chincoteague and Sinepuxent Bays. Amer. Midl. Nat. 65(2):384–409, 2 figs., 3 tables.

————. 1962a. The beaked fishes of Maryland. Maryland Conserv. 39(2):21–5.

————. 1962b. Know your Maryland fishes. Suckers. Ibid. (5):18–23.

————. 1963. The fresh-water minnows of Maryland. Ibid. 40(2):19–29.

————. 1964a. Fishes of the Isle of Wight and Assawoman Bays near Ocean City, Maryland. Chesapeake Sci. 5(4):172–93, 1 fig., 3 tables.

————. 1964b. Natural salinity tolerances of some freshwater fishes. Underwater Natur. 2(2):13–5, 1 tables.

Scott, Trevor D. 1962. The marine and fresh water fishes of South Australia. Handbook of the flora and fauna of South Australia. W. L. Hawes, Govt. Printing, Adelaide, Australia. 338 p.

Scott, W. B. 1954. Freshwater fishes of eastern Canada. Univ. Toronto Press. xvi + 128 p.

————, and E. J. Crossman. 1964. Fishes occurring in the freshwaters of insular Newfoundland. Roy. Ontario Mus., Univ. Ontario, Life Sci., Contrib. No. 58, ix + 124 p.

Senior, H. D. 1909. The development of the heart in shad (*Alosa sapidissima* Wilson) with a note on the classification of teleostean embryos from a morphological standpoint. Amer. J. Anat. 9:221–62.

Shapovalov, Leo, and William A. Dill. 1950. A checklist of the fresh-water and anadromous fishes of California. Calif. Fish and Game 36(4):382–91.

Shelford, Victor E. 1937. Animal communities in temperate America as illustrated in the Chicago region: A study of animal ecology. Geogr. Soc. Chicago, Bull. 5:xiii + 368 p., 306 figs., 58 tables.

Shields, James T. 1958. Experimental control of carp reproduction through water drawdowns in Fort Randelle Reservoir, South Dakota. Amer. Fish. Soc., Trans. 87:23–33, 2 figs., 2 tables.

Shira, Austin F. 1917a. Notes on the rearing, growth, and food of the channel catfish, *Ictalurus punctatus*. Amer. Fish. Soc., Trans. 46:77–88, 4 figs. 2 tables.

————. 1917b. Additional notes on rearing the channel catfish, *Ictalurus punctatus*. Ibid. 47:45–7.

Shlaifer, A. 1941. Additional social and physiological aspects of respiratory behavior in small tarpon. Zoologica, New York, 26(11):55–60.

Shoemaker, Myron E. 1945. Fresh water fishing: A fisherman's manual. Doubleday, Doran and Co., Garden City, N. Y. xvi + 218 p.

Shreves, Melvin L. 1959. Tarpon fishing in Virginia. Intern. Game Fish Conf., Proc. 4:1–5.

Shufeldt, R. W. 1885. The osteology of *Amia calva*, including certain special references to the skeleton of teleosteans. Govt. Print. Office, Washington, D. C. (Reprinted from U. S. Comm. Fish and Fisheries, Rep. for 1883, 11:747–878).

Sigler, William F. 1955. An ecological approach to understanding Utah's carp populations. Utah Acad. Sci., Proc. 32:95–104.

————. 1958. The ecology and use of the carp in Utah. Utah State Univ., Agri. Exp. Sta., Bull. 405, 63 p., 15 figs., 15 tables.

————, and Robert R. Miller. 1963. Fishes of Utah. Utah State Dept. of Fish and Game. 203 p.

Silliman, R. P. 1950. Thermal and diurnal changes in the vertical distribution of eggs and larvae. U. S. Fish and Wildl. Serv., Spec. Sci. Rep. 15:181–200.

Simmons, Ernest G. 1957. An ecological survey of the Upper Laguna Madre of Texas. Publ. Inst. Mar. Sci. 4(2):156–200, 13 figs., 9 tables.

Simpson, Donald G. 1954. Two small tarpon from Texas. Copeia 1954(1):71–2.

Simroth, Henrich Rudolf. 1910. Etwas vom Hering; ein Kapitel zur Natur- und Entstehungsgeschichte useres wichtigsten Fisches und der Knochenfische schlechthin. Aus der Natur, Stuttgart 5:641–51, 679–88, 717–29, 760–5.

Skud, B. E., and H. C. Boyar. 1958. Where the herring go. Maine Coast Fisherman 13(1):28.

Slastenenko, E. P. 1958. The freshwater fishes of Canada. Kiev Printers, Toronto. 388 p., 138 figs., 1 table.

Small, H. B. 1883. Fishes of the Ottawa district. Ottawa Field Natur. Club, Trans. 4:31–49.

Smallwood, W. M., and M. L. Smallwood. 1931. The development of the carp, *Cyprinus carpio*. I. The larval life of the carp, with special reference to the development of the intestinal tract. J. Morphol. 52(1):217–31, 7 figs.

————, and P. H. Struthers. 1928. Carp control studies in Oneida Lake. New York Conserv. Dep., Suppl. to 19th Ann. Rep. p. 67–83.

Smith, C. Lavett. 1954. Pleistocene fishes of the Berends fauna of Beaver County, Oklahoma. Copeia 1954(4):282–9, 7 figs.

Smith, Hugh M. 1903. Breeding habits of the yellow catfish (*Ameiurus nebulosus*). Science, n.s. 17(424):243–4.

————. 1907. The fishes of North Carolina. North Carolina Geol. and Econ. Surv. 2:xiv + 453 p., 21 pls., 187 figs.

————. 1909. Japanese goldfish, their varieties and cultivation, a practical guide to the Japanese method of goldfish culture for amateurs and professionals. W. F. Roberts Co., Washington, D. C. 112 p.

————, and Barton A. Bean. 1899. List of fishes known to inhabit the waters of the District of Colombia and vicinity. Bull. U. S. Fish Comm. (1898) 18:179–87.

————, and L. G. Harron. 1904. Breeding habits of the yellow cat-fish. U. S. Fish Comm., Bull. (1902) 22:151–4.

Sneed, Kermit E., and Howard P. Clemens. 1963. The morphology of the testes and accessory glands of the catfishes (Ictaluridae). Copeia 1963(4):606–11, 6 figs.

Snyder, Richard C. 1949. Vertebral counts in four species of suckers (Catostomidae). Copeia 1949(1):62–5, 2 tables.

Sobotta, J. 1896. Die gastrulation von *Amia calva*. Anat. Ges., Jena 10:108–11, 6 figs.

Soleim, P. A. 1942. "Arsaker til rike og fattige årganger av sild." Fiskeridir. Skr. Havundersøk. 7(2):1–39.

Solovyev, B. S., and A. A. Degtyarev. 1957. Diurnal vertical migrations of the Atlantic-Scandian herring during the pre-spawning and spawning season [in Russian]. Ryb. Khoz. 33(11):81–4.

Spillmann, J. 1959. Un petit poisson Américan *Umbra pygmaea* (DeKay), acclimaté depius 46 ans dans un etang du Bourbornais. Mus. Nat. Hist. Natur., Bull., Ser. 2, 31(5):401–2.

Spoor, William A. 1938. Age and growth of the sucker, *Catostomus commersonnii* (Lacépède), in Muskellunge Lake, Vilas County, Wisconsin. Wisconsin Acad. Sci., Arts and Letters, Trans. 31:457–505, 1 pl., 24 tables.

Sprenger, W. 1901. *Amia calva*, Schlammfisch. Blätt. Aquar.-Terrar. Kunde 12:190–3.

Springer, Victor G., and Kenneth D. Woodburn. 1960. An ecological study of the fishes of the Tampa Bay area. Florida State Bd. of Conserv., Mar. Lab., Prof. Paper Ser. No. 1, v + 140 p., 18 figs., 22 tables.

Stauffer, Jacob. 1879. *Amia calva*. Amer. Nat. 13:525.

Steele, J. H. 1961. The environment of a herring fishery. Mar. Res. Scot. No. 6, 19 p.

Sterba, Gunther. 1959. Susswasser Fische aus aller Welt. Urania-Verlag, Leipzig. 638 p., 1193 figs.

———. 1962. Freshwater fishes of the World. Vista Books, London. pp. 1–878, 1193 figs.

Stevenson, Charles H. 1899. The shad fisheries of the Atlantic Coast of the United States. U. S. Comm. Fish and Fisheries, Rep. (1898) 24:101–269.

Stevenson, R. A., Jr. 1958. A biology of the anchovies, *Anchoa mitchilli mitchilli* Cuvier and Valenciennes 1848 and *Anchoa hepsetus hepsetus* Linnaeus 1758. MS Thesis, Univ. Delaware, 56 p.

Stewart, Norman H. 1922. Fishes of the Upper Susquehanna basin. The Univ. Print Shop, Lewisburg, Pennsylvania. 12 p.

———. 1926. Development, growth, and food habits of the white sucker, *Catostomus commersonii* LeSueur. U. S. Bur. Fish., Bull. 42:147–84, 55 figs.

Stone, Udell Bennett. 1940. Studies on the biology of the satinfin minnows *Notropis analostanus* and *Notropis spilopterus*. PhD Thesis, Cornell Univ., 98 + vii p., 14 pls.

Storey, M., and L. M. Perry. 1933. A record of young tarpon at Sanibel Island, Lee County, Florida. Science 78(2022):284–5.

Stout, John F. 1959. The reproductive behavior and sound production of the satinfin shiner. (Abstract). Anat. Record 134(3):643–4.

———. 1963. The significance of sound production during the reproductive behavior of *Notropis analostanus* (family Cyprinidae). Animal Behavior 11(1):83–92, 6 tables.

———, and Howard E. Winn. 1958. The reproductive behavior and sound production of the satinfin shiner. Anat. Record 132(3):511.

Stranahan, J. J. 1910. Notes on the catfish and catfish culture at Cold Springs, Georgia, p. 27–30. *In* William C. Kendall, American catfishes: Habits, culture, and commercial importance. U. S. Bur. Fish., Doc. No. 733.

Stratton, H. 1833. Facts in the habits of the goldfish (*Cyprinus auratus* L.) and silverfish (*C. auratus* var.). Mag. Nat. Hist. 6:527–8.

Stromsten, F. A. 1931. The development of the gonads in the goldfish, *Carassius auratus* (L.). Univ. of Iowa Studies in Nat. Hist. 13(7):1–45, 11 pls.

Struthers, P. H. 1929. Carp control studies in Erie Canal. p. 208–19. *In* A biological survey of the Erie-Niagara System. New York Conserv. Dep., Suppl. to 18th Ann. Rep.

———. 1930. Carp control studies in the Cayuga and Oswego Lake basins. New York State Conservation Dept., Suppl. 19th Ann. Rep., p. 261–80.

———. 1931. Carp control in the Seneca, Canadaigua and Keuka Lake basins. pp. 217–29, 4 tables. *In* A biological survey of the St. Lawrence Watershed (including the Grass, St. Regis, Salmon, Chateaugay Systems and the St. Lawrence between Ogdensburg and the International Boundary). New York Conserv. Dept., Suppl. to 20th Ann. Rep.

Sturtevant, E. L. 1877. Supposed development of pickerel without fecundation. Amer. Nat. 11:494.

Surber, Eugene W., and Dorothy D. Friddle. 1946. Relative toxicity of suspension and oil formulations of native fishes in Back Creek, West Virginia. Amer. Fish. Soc., Trans. 76:315–21, 1 fig., 3 tables.

Surber, Thaddeus. 1920. A preliminary catalogue of the fishes and fish-like vertebrates of Minnesota. Minnesota Game and Fish Comm., Appendix to Biennial Rep. (1920), 92 p., 66 figs.

Susuki, Ryo. 1957. Studies on the artificial ovulation in cyprinid fishes. I. Artificial ovulation in the minnow, river-chub, goldfish, and Crusian carp. Aichi Gakugei Univ., Bull. (Nat. Sci.) 6:31–5, 5 tables.

Sutherland, Doyle F. 1963. Variations in vertebral numbers of juvenile Atlantic menhaden. U. S. Fish and Wildl. Serv., Spec. Sci. Rep.—Fish. No. 435, iii + 21 p., 3 figs., 4 pls.

Stuttkus, Royal D. 1963. Order Lepisostei, p. 61–88, Figs. 11–8. *In* Fishes of the Western North Atlantic. Sears Found. Mar. Res., Mem. 1 (Part 3).

Svetovidov, A. N. 1963. Fauna of the U. S. S. R., Fishes. Vol. 2, No. 1. Clupeidae. Inst. Acad. Sci. U. S. S. R., n.s. no. 48: iv + 428, 53 pls., 54 figs., 11 tables. Transl. from Russian, Israel Program For Scientific Translations. (From: Svetovidov, A. N. 1952. Fauna SSSR, Ryby. Sel'derye 2(1):1–323).

Swain, Joseph, and George B. Kalb. 1883. A review of the genus *Noturus*, with a description of one new species. U. S. Nat. Mus., Proc. 5:638–44, 1 table.

Swanson, Paul L. 1946. Tarpon in the Pacific. Copeia 1946(3):175.

Swingle, H. S. 1946. Experiments with combinations of large-mouth black bass, bluegills, and minnows in ponds. Amer. Fish. Soc., Trans. 76:46–62, 5 tables.

Sykes, James E., and Burton A. Lehman. 1957. Past and present Delaware River shad fishery and considerations for its future. U. S. Fish and Wildl. Serv., Res. Rep. 46, iv + 25 p., 10 figs.

Takahashi, Nisuke. 1955. On the influence of waste liquid drawn out of the alcohol factory upon the development of the eggs of *Cyprinus carpio* L. and *Plecoglossus altivelis* Temminck et Schlegel [in Japanese]. Jap. J. Ichth. 4(3):16–24, 8 tables.

Talbot, Gerald B., and James E. Sykes. 1958. Atlantic coasts migrations of American shad. U. S. Fish and Widl. Serv., Fishery Bull. 58(142):473–90, 6 figs.

Taylor, William R. 1956. A revision of the genus *Noturus* (Rafinesque), with a contribution to the classification of the North American catfish. PhD Thesis, Univ. of Mich. 192 p.

Thompson, W. Francis. 1919. Young of the ladyfish discovered. Calif. Fish and Game 5:158.

Threinen, C. W. 1958. Life history, ecology and management of the alewife, (*Pomolobus pseudoharengus* (Wilson)). Wis. Conserv. Dept., Pub. No. 223, 8 p.

Tibbo, S. N., 1956. Populations of the herring (*Clupea harengus* L.) in Newfoundland waters. J. Fish. Res. Bd. Canada 13(4):449–66.

———. 1957a. Herring of the Chaleur Bay area. Fish. Res. Bd. Canada, Bull. 3:85–102, 4 figs., 6 tables.

———. 1957b. Contribution to the biology of the Herring (*Clupea harengus* L.) on the Atlantic coast of Nova Scotia. Ibid. p. 139–151, 3 figs., 4 tables.

———, and J. E. Henri Legare. 1960. Further study of larval herring (*C. harengus*) in the Bay of Fundy and Gulf of Maine. J. Fish. Res. Bd. Canada 17(6):933–42, 2 figs., 3 tables.

———, ———, L. W. Scattergood, and R. F. Temple. 1958. On the occurrence and distribution of larval herring (*Clupea harengus* L.) in the Bay of Fundy and the Gulf of Maine. J. Fish. Res. Bd. Canada 15(6):1451–69, 9 figs., 4 tables.

———, D. J. Scarratt, and P. W. G. McMullan. 1963. An investigation of herring (*Clupea harengus* L.) spawning using free-diving techniques. J. Fish. Res. Bd. Canada 20(4):1067–79, 7 figs., 11 tables.

Titcomb, J. W. 1920. Some fish-cultural notes. Amer. Fish. Soc., Trans. 50:200–11.

Toole, Marion. 1951. Channel catfish culture in Texas: Helpful hints regarding propagation procedures. Progr. Fish Cult. 13(1):3–10, 11 figs.

Toom, M. M. 1962. Experiments in the incubation of Baltic herring eggs. Transl. from Russian, Israel Program for Sci. Transl., Jerusalem, 13 p.

Tracy, H. C. 1910. Annotated list of fishes known to inhabit the waters of Rhode Island. Rhode Island Comm. Inland Fish., 40th Ann. Rep. (1910):35–176.

Tramblay, Leon. 1962. Temperature de l'eau d'un lac et la migration de Frai du Catostome, *Catostomus c. commersoni*. Natur. Canadien 89(4):119–28, 3 figs., 1 table.

Trautman, M. B. 1948. A natural hybrid catfish, *Schilbeodes miurus* x *Shilbeodes mollis*. Copeia 1948(3):166–74, 1 pl., 1 table.

———. 1957. The fishes of Ohio. The Ohio State Univ. Press. xviii + 683 p., 172 figs., 7 pls.

Tremblay, F. J. 1930. The gar-pike of Lake Champlain, p. 139–45. *In* A biological survey of the Champlain watershed. New York Conserv. Dept., Suppl. to 19th Ann. Rep.

Truitt, Reginald V., B. A. Bean, and Henry W. Fowler. 1929. The fishes of Maryland. State of Maryland, Conserv. Bull. No. 3, 120 p., 62 figs.

Tung, Ti-Chow, and Yu-Fung-Yeh Tung. 1944. The development of egg-fragments, isolated blastomeres and fused eggs in the goldfish. Zool. Soc. London, Proc. 144:46–64, 20 figs.

Uchida, Keitaro. 1958. Leptocephalus stages of *Megalops cyprinoides* (Broussonet) (Megalopidae), *Elops machnata* (Forskal) (Elopidae) and *Albula vulpes* (Linné) (Albulidae). pp. 1–3, 1 pl. *In* Uchida, K., et al. Studies of the eggs, larvae and juveniles of Japanese fishes. Series I. Second Lab. of Fish. Biol., Fish. Dept., Fac. Agr., Kyushu Univ., Fukuoka, Japan.

Uhler, P. R., and Otto Lugger. 1876. List of fishes of Maryland. Md. Comm. Fish., Rep. (1876):67–176.

———, and ———. 1877. Additions to list of fishes of Maryland. Md. Comm. Fish., Rep. (1877):65–94.

Ulrey, Lorraine, Clifford Risk, and Will Scott. 1938. The number of eggs produced by some of our common fresh-water fishes, p. 74–7, 5 tables. *In* Investigations of Indiana lakes and streams. Indiana Dept. of Conserv., Div. of Fish and Game.

Underhill, A. Heaton. 1940. Estimations of a breeding population of club suckers. Trans. 5th N. Amer. Wildl. Conf. (1940):253–5, 2 figs.

———. 1948. Studies on the life history of the chain pickerel, *Esox niger* LeSueur. PhD Thesis, Cornell Univ., 177 p., 31 figs., 24 tables.

———. 1949. Studies on the development, growth and maturity of the chain pickerel, *Esox niger* (LeSueur). J. Wildl. Manage. 13(4):377–91, 3 figs., 1 pl., 10 tables.

Valenciennes, Achille. 1847. Histoire naturelle du hereng, comprenant la description zoologique et anatomique de cet important poisson et une histoire de'taillee de sa peche ancienne et moderne. Extrait du tome 20 de l'Histoire naturelle des Poissons, Paris. pp. 1–260, 3 pl.

Venicek, David. 1961. Life history of the quillback and highfin carpsuckers in the Des Moines River. Iowa Acad. Sci., Proc. 68:238–46, 2 figs., 5 tables.

Vessel, Matt F., and Samuel Eddy. 1941. A preliminary study of the egg production of certain Minnesota fishes. Minn. Bur. Fish. Res. Invest., Rep. 26, 26 p.

Virchow, H. 1896. Furchungsvilder von *Amia calva*. Ges. naturforsch. Freunde, Berlin (1896):31–42.

Vladykov, Vadim D. 1945. Trois poissons nouveaux pour la Province de Quebec. Natur. Canadien 72(1/2):27–39, 5 figs.

———. 1950. Movements of Quebec shad (*Alosa sapidissima*) as demonstrated by tagging. Quebec Dept. Fish., Contrib. 77(30):121–35, 4 figs.

———, and J. R. Greeley. 1963. Order Acipenseridae, p. 24–60, Figs. 7–10. *In* Fishes of the Western North Atlantic. Sears Found. Mar. Res., Mem. 1(Part 3).

———, and D. H. Wallace. 1937. Remarks on populations of shad (*Alosa sapidissima*) along the Atlantic coast region. Amer. Fish. Soc., Trans. 67:52–66.

Volodin, V. M. 1960. Embryonic development of the autumn Baltic herring and their oxygen requirements during the course of development. Transl. from Russian, Fish. Res. Bd. Canada, Transl. Ser. No. 252, 13 p. (Voprosy Ikhtiologii, 1956, (7):123–33).

Wade, Richard A. 1962. The biology of the tarpon, *Megalops atlanticus*, and the ox-eye, *Megalops cyprinoides*, with emphasis on larval development. Bull. Mar. Sci. Gulf and Carib. 12(4):545–622, 20 figs., 5 tables.

Wagner, Charles C., and Edwin L. Cooper. 1963. Population density, growth, and fecundity of creek chubsucker, *Erimyzon oblongus*. Copeia 1963(2):350–7, 2 figs., 4 tables.

Waite, Edgar R. 1904. New records or recurrences of rare fishes from eastern Australia. No. 3. Rec. Australian Mus. 5(4):231–44, 2 figs., 2 pls.

Walburg, Charles H. 1960. Abundance and life history of the shad, St. Johns River, Florida. U. S. Fish and Wildl. Serv., Fish. Bull. 60(177):487–501, 1 fig., 16 tables.

Wallen, I. Eugene. 1951. The direct effect of turbidity on fishes. Bull. Oklahoma Agr. and Mech. Coll., Arts and Sci. Studies, Biol. Ser. No. 2. 48(1):1–27, 5 figs., 4 tables.

Ward, J. W. 1957. The reproduction and early development of the sea catfish, *Galeichthys felis*, in the Biloxi (Mississippi) Bay. Copeia 1957(4):295–8, 1 table.

Warner, Edward N. 1940. Studies on the embryology and early life history of the gizzard shad, *Dorosoma cepedianum* Le Sueur. PhD Thesis, Ohio State Univ., 28 p., 1 figs., 4 pls.

Warren, Robert. 1906. Remarkable change in habits of the herrings visiting Killala Bay, County Mayo. Zoologist, 4th Ser., 10:105–7.

Watase, S. 1887. On the caudal and anal fins of the goldfish. J. Coll. Sci. Imp. Univ. Tokyo 1(3):247–267, 3 pls.

Watson, John E. 1963. A method for tagging immature herring. U. S. Fish and Wildl. Serv., Spec. Sci. Rep.—Fish. No. 451, iii + 7 p., 3 figs., 2 tables.

———. 1964. Determining the age of young herring from their otoliths. Amer. Fish. Soc., Trans. 93(1):11–20, 7 figs.

Watson, J. M. 1939. The development of the Weberian ossicles and anterior vertebrae in the goldfish. Roy. Soc. London, Proc., Ser. B, 123(849): 452–72, 8 figs.

Weber, Max, and L. F. deBeaufort. 1913. The fishes of the Indo-Australian Archipelago. Vol. 2. E. J. Brill, Ltd., Leiden. xx + 404 p., 151 figs.

Webster, Dwight A. 1942. The life history of some Connecticut fishes. p. 122–227, 60 figs. *In* A fishery survey of important Connecticut lakes. Bd. Fish. and Game, Lake and Pond Surv. Unit, Conn., Bull. No. 63.

Wells, F. R. 1923. On the morphology of the chondrocranium of the larval herring (*Clupea harengus*). Zool. Soc. London, Proc. (1922):1213–29, 11 figs.

Westman, J. R. 1952. Lakes, fish and fishing, p. 6–142. *In* New Jersey fisheries survey report no. 1 (1950). N. J. Dept. Conserv. and Econ. Development, Div. Fish and Game.

———, and R. F. Nigrelli. 1955. Preliminary studies of menhaden and their mass mortalities in Long Island and New Jersey waters. N. Y. Fish and Game J. 2(2):142–53.

Wheatland, Sarah B. 1956. Oceanography of Long Island Sound, 1952–1954. VII. Pelagic fish eggs and larvae. Bingham Oceanogr. Coll., Bull. 15:234–314, 2 figs., 27 tables.

Whitehead, P. J. P. 1962. The species of *Elops* (Pisces: Elopidae). Ann. Mag. Nat. Hist., Series 13, 5:321–9, 3 figs.

———. 1963. A revision of the recent round herrings (Pisces: Dussumieriidae). British Mus. Nat. Hist. (Zool.), Bull. 10(6):307–80, 33 figs., 3 tables.

———. 1965. The identity of *Clupea sadina* Mitchill, 1814. Copeia 1965(2):228–30.

Whitman, C. O., and A. C. Eycleshymer. 1897. The egg of *Amia* and its cleavage. J. Morphol. 12(2):309–54, 20 figs., 2 pls.

Whitney, Gilbert P. 1937. Studies in ichthyology. No. 10. Australian Mus. Rec. 20(1):3–24, 5 figs., 1 pl.

Whitney, Richard R. 1961. Report of planting and tagging operations, p. 18–43, Fig. 4–10, Tables 6–25. *In* Richard R. Whitney (Project Leader), The Susquehanna fishery study, 1957–1960. A report on the desirability and feasibility of passing fish at Conowingo Dam. Md. Dept. Res. Educ., Solomons, Md., Contrib. No. 169.

Wich, Kenneth. 1958. A compendium of the life history and ecology of the chain pickerel *Esox niger* (LeSueur). Mass. Div. Fish. and Game, Fish Bull.. 22, 23 p.

Wilder, Burt G. 1876. Notes on North America ganoids, *Amia, Lepidosteus, Acipenser*, and *Polyodon*. Amer. Ass. Advance. Sci., Proc. 24:151–96, 3 pls.

———. 1877a. Gar-pikes, old and young. Popular Sci. Monthly, 11:1–22, 10 figs., [Reprint].

———. 1877b. On the serrated appendages of the throat of *Amia*. Amer. Ass. Advance. Sci., Proc. 25:259–63.

———. 1877c. On the tail of *Amia*. Ibid. p. 264–7, 1 pl.

Williamson, Henry Charles. 1910a. Experiments to show the influence of cold in retarding the development of the eggs of the herring (*Clupea harengus*, L.), plaice (*Pleuronectes platessa*, L.) and haddock (*Gadus aeglefinus*, L). Fish. Bd. for Scot., 27th Ann. Rept. (1908) 3:100–28, 1 fig., 1 pl.

———. 1910b. On the herring of the Clyde and other districts. Ibid. p. 13–67.

———. 1911a. Experiments in retarding the development of the eggs of the herring. Fish. Bd. Scot., 28th Ann. Rept. 3:16–23, 1 pl.

———. 1911b. The retardation of the development of the ova of the herring. Fish. Bd. Scotland, Sci. Invest. (11):1–12, 1 pl.

Williamson, Richard F. 1951. A pre-historic killer: The longnose gar. Pennsylvania Angler 20(6):4–6.

Wilson, Alfred W. G. 1907. Chub's nest. Amer. Nat. 41(485):323–7, 3 figs.

Winn, Howard E., and John F. Stout. 1960. Sound production by the satinfin shiner, *Notropis analostanus*, and related fishes. Science 132(3421):222–3, 1 table.

Wolf, Herman T. 1908. Goldfish breeds and other aquarium fishes: Their care and propagation. Innes and Sons, Phila. 385 p., 234 figs.

Wood, Henry. 1960. The herring of the Clyde estuary. Scot. Home Dept., Mar. Res. No. 1, 24 p., 4 figs., 10 tables.

Worth, Stephen G. 1893. Observations on the spawning habits of the shad. U. S. Fish Comm., Bull. 11:201–6.

———. 1898. The shad, p. 133–58. *In* John J. Brice. A manual of fish culture, based on the methods of the United States Commission of Fish and Fisheries. U. S. Comm. Fish and Fisheries, Rep. (1897) 23 (Appendix).

———. 1900. The shad, p. 121–45. *In* Manual of fish-culture. (Revised Edition). U. S. Fish Comm., Washington, D. C.

Wright, A. H., and A. A. Allen. 1913. Field notebook of fishes, amphibians, reptiles and mammals. Copyrighted by the authors, Ithaca, New York. 88 p.

Wright, Edward Perceval. 1878. Die Entwicklung des Knochen-hechts und der Schollen. Kosmos 4:312–15.

———. 1879. On the development of the gar pike. Nature 19:100–101.

Wyman, J. 1856. On the development of the dorsal chord in the alewife. Bost. Soc. Nat. Hist., Proc. (1854–56)5:394–5.

Yamamoto, Takaharu. 1937a. The time required for hatching the eggs of Japanese killifish, *Oryzias latipes* (T. et. Sch.), and the Dutch-Lion-Head Gold-Fish, *Carassius auratus* (Linn.) [In Japanese]. Nihon Gakujitsu Kyôkai Kaihô 6(2):105–9, 6 figs., 4 tables.

———. 1937b. The influence on hatching of European Crucian carp by the changes of water temperature in the aquarium [In Japanese]. Jap. Soc. Sci. Fish., Bull. 5(5/6):326–32, 375–9.

———. 1954. Cortical changes in eggs of the goldfish (*Carassius auratus*) and the pond smelt (*Hypomesus olidus*) at the time of fertilization and activation. Jap. J. Ichth. 3:162–170.

Yamamoto, Toko-o. 1934. On the rhythmic movements of the eggs of goldfish. J. Fac. of Sci., Imp. Univ. Tokyo 3(3): 275–85, 6 figs.

Yarrow, H. C. 1874. Notes on the shad as observed at Beaufort Harbor, North Carolina and vicinity. U. S. Fish Comm., Rep. (1872–73) 2:452–6.

Yoshizaki, Masa. 1957. Morphological change of intestine in the larval stage of wild goldfish (*Carassius auratus*). I. Observations on variety "Gengôrobuna" [In Japanese]. Jap. J. Ichth. 5(3–6):78–82, 2 figs., 1 table.

INDEX TO COMMON AND SCIENTIFIC NAMES